SEMICONDUCTOR COUNTERS FOR NUCLEAR RADIATIONS

Series Editor

E. J. BURGE

Ph.D., M.A., F.Inst.P.

PLATE I A Variety of Silicon Radiation Detectors

Top row (left to right): a commercial surface-barrier detector (by courtesy of ORTEC, Oak Ridge); a commercial diffused junction detector (by courtesy of Ferranti Ltd., Manchester); a surface-barrier detector prepared in the laboratory.

2nd row (left to right): a large-area diffused junction counter; a 6-mm cube conduction counter (unmounted); a totally encapsulated silicon junction gamma-ray counter.

3rd row (left to right): a double proton-recoil fast neutron detector; a guard-ring surface-barrier detector; a 10-element multiple surface barrier detector.

Bottom row (left to right): a thin transmission detector for dE/dx measurements; a triple surface-barrier detector for polarization measurements; an annular detector for angular correlation studies.

Semiconductor Counters
for Nuclear Radiations

G. DEARNALEY M.A., Ph.D.

*Principal Scientific Officer, Nuclear Physics Division,
A.E.R.E., Harwell*

and

D. C. NORTHROP B.Sc., Ph.D., F.Inst.P.

*Senior Lecturer in Electrical Engineering,
Manchester College of Science & Technology*

Second Edition, revised and enlarged

1966

JOHN WILEY & SONS INC

605 THIRD AVENUE NEW YORK

First published 1963
Reprinted 1964
Second Edition 1966
© 1963, 1966 *Geoffrey Dearnaley and*
David Corell Northrop
Printed and bound in Great Britain
by Hazell Watson & Viney Ltd.,
Aylesbury, Bucks

PHYSICS

TO OUR WIVES

JEAN AND PAT

PREFACE TO THE SECOND EDITION

During the three years which have passed since the appearance of the first edition of this book there have been major advances in the field of semiconductor detectors. Accordingly we have taken the opportunity of a new edition to make extensive additions to the content of the book, most chapters of which have been completely revised in order to bring the treatment fully up to date.

The most striking development has certainly been in the preparation and use of lithium drifted germanium devices for gamma ray spectrometry. The excellent energy resolution these afford is opening a new phase in the study of gamma ray transitions, and as larger detectors are prepared it seems inevitable that semiconductor detectors will supersede sodium iodide scintillation counters in this area, just as they are at present almost universally preferred for charged particle detection. The chapter dealing with detector preparation now covers in detail techniques for the fabrication of germanium detectors whilst the section on the application of semiconductor detectors to gamma ray spectrometry has been entirely rewritten.

Lithium drifted silicon detectors have been developed further in a way which has again been reflected by a more detailed description of fabrication techniques and a revision of the section dealing with their applications to measurements of high energy charged particles.

The success of lithium drifted devices has taken away much of the early impetus of work on homogeneous conduction counters and the development of new materials, and although a gamma ray counter with a higher atomic number than germanium would have undoubted value there is so much that can be done with germanium counters that some of the urgency has gone from work on alternative devices. For this reason we have condensed the discussion of homogeneous counters so that it no longer forms a separate chapter.

Detector fabrication methods in general are described in more detail, and current theories of the physical processes involved in surface barrier formation are reviewed. This topic still retains obscurities which it is hoped that further research will clarify. Methods of encapsulation and edge protection have also advanced, adding to our understanding of semiconductor surfaces, and our treatment of this subject has been extended to include this new material.

The widespread application of semiconductor detectors has led to the intensive development of ancillary electronic instrumentation. Field effect transistor preamplifiers, equipment for fast pulse timing, new particle identification methods and data handling by "on-line" computers are new developments now dealt with in the chapter on instrumentation. It is essential that the experimenter be helped to keep abreast of such developments if he is to make best use of the performance of the detectors.

For the same reason the chapter on detector applications in nuclear physics has been extensively revised to include recent examples of experimental method. The aim here has been to review most of the capabilities of semiconductor counters throughout nuclear physics. Applications other than to nuclear physics have also been growing, though less spectacularly, and they now merit a separate chapter. They cover many widely differing topics, amongst which medical applications and space physics seem particularly important and exciting.

The coverage of radiation damage in semiconductor detectors has been extended to include recent data on the behaviour of lithium drifted devices while the treatment of the effects of radiation on semiconductor diodes in general has been revised in the light of new experiments.

Even the first chapter dealing with basic properties of nuclear radiation in solids has had to be revised to cover the behaviour of charged particles in single crystals. The phenomenon known as channelling has complicated our ideas of how ions lose energy in such media.

Since publication of the first edition two major conferences on the subject of semiconductor detectors have taken place; at Liège in September 1963 and at Washington D.C. in February 1964. The proceedings of these have been published in the *Mémoires de la Société Royale des Sciences de Liège*, Vol. 10, No. 2 and the *I.E.E.E. Transactions on Nuclear Science*, Vol. N.S.11, No. 3. The rate of publication in this field can be judged by the fact that we have selected a further two hundred references to add to the Bibliography.

We should again like to thank colleagues who have generously discussed their work with us and allowed us to make use of their results before publication. We have made every endeavour to acknowledge such help in the text.

September, 1965

G. D.
D. C. N.

PREFACE TO THE FIRST EDITION

Over the past three or four years the development of solid-state or semiconductor counters has revolutionized experimental work with charged nuclear particles, and recently such detectors have also been shown to have great potentialities for neutron and beta-particle detection. Besides their excellent characteristics as counters their compactness and simplicity of structure render them exceptionally versatile, and most of the types can be prepared from semiconductor crystals using techniques available in any well-equipped laboratory. We feel that it is important for designers and users of detection equipment that they should as far as possible be aware of the principles and potentialities of these recent developments, of which we hope this book will provide a useful account.

The problems of nuclear radiation detection are basic to all experimental nuclear science, to many of the technical applications of nuclear energy and the growing use of radioisotopes in industry. Military and Civil Defence requirements involve large numbers of compact and reliable radiation monitors. We have set out to cover all aspects of the subject in a logical sequence so that the book may be useful to many who are not specialists in the field.

In the case of semiconductor counters a comprehensive treatment is particularly necessary because the subject draws upon two diverse branches of physics—nuclear and solid-state—and there has been a considerable tendency towards specialization in one at the expense of the other. The combination of two branches of science generally benefits both fields of research, but in this case there seems to have been insufficient realization that nuclear radiation can be a powerful tool in the study of semiconductors, just as solid-state devices can be useful in nuclear physics. This book is therefore intended for both types of physicist and we have attempted to cover an adequate background to the relevant aspects of both nuclear radiation and semiconductors in order to reduce the need for reference elsewhere. Necessarily this implies that most physicists will find one chapter to be tediously familiar. The subject is presented at a level which should be suitable for research students and for specialists in neighbouring fields, such as instrument design, radiochemistry, radiobiology and health physics.

As may be judged from the bibliography, the literature on semiconductor counters has grown rapidly, yet as far as we are aware this is the first book to deal with the subject in its entirety. We hope that it will guide the reader through the multitude of specialized papers which have now appeared. Thus the discussion of semiconductor theory and the properties of counters is preceded by a summary of the various processes of energy loss by nuclear radiations in matter, with particular reference to silicon and germanium. In the survey of detection methods which follows we have stressed the features which are common to semiconductor detectors and other types. We feel that such a survey is helpful here since the design and usefulness of any new instrument are very much determined by the limitations of what is already available.

In the chapter on electronic instrumentation only the particular requirements for optimum performance of semiconductor counters are discussed, with some ideas on their implications for the future trends of nuclear instrumentation. We discuss at some length the numerous applications of the new detectors in a way which, it is hoped, may be of most value to the experimenter. Advantages and limitations of semiconductor counters are stressed in each case, with examples of results that best illustrate their capabilities. In the final chapter we have attempted the first survey of radiation damage effects in semiconductor counters, arising from all types of radiation.

Throughout the book the term 'semiconductor counter' has been used in preference to 'solid-state counter', a policy agreed at the conference on the subject held at Asheville, North Carolina, in 1960. The reason for this is that several other types of detector, including the solid scintillation counter, might be held to be solid-state devices, so that the alternative description is more specific. With regard to electrical units, the practical c.g.s. system has been employed.

We should like to acknowledge the help of Mr. V. R. W. Edwards, of King's College, London, for his comments on Chapter 7, and we are particularly indebted to Dr. E. J. Burge, who read the entire book in manuscript and made a number of most valuable suggestions. We should also like to express our gratitude to Mr. J. C. Lewis for his help in the preparation of the index. In addition to the customary acknowledgements in the text we should like to take this opportunity of thanking the many colleagues who have allowed us to make use of data from their work.

G. D.

D. C. N.

FURTHER ACKNOWLEDGEMENTS

We should like to thank the editors of the following journals for permission to reproduce a number of line diagrams:

The Royal Danish Academy of Sciences and Letters: *Mathematical & Physical Methods*, for Fig. 1.3; *Nucleonics*, for Figs. 1.5, 1.9, 10.5, and 10.14; *Helvetia Physica Acta*, for Fig. 2.2; *Nuclear Instruments & Methods*, for Figs. 2.6, 5.5, 6.5, 6.8, 7.3, 7.12, 7.17, 8.15, 8.33, 9.1 and 9.3; *The Proceedings of the Physical Society* (London), for Figs. 3.6, 3.7, 3.10; *The I.R.E. Transactions on Nuclear Science*, for Figs. 2.7, 6.16, 6.17, 7.2, 7.4, 7.5, 7.12, 7.13, 7.16, 8.1, 8.11, 8.21, 8.22, 8.34, 8.36, 8.41, 9.7, 10.8, 10.9, 10.11; *The I.E.E.E. Transactions on Nuclear Science*, for Figs. 1.4, 6.4, 6.10, 7.7, 7.8, 7.14, 10.15; *Health Physics*, for Fig. 9.2; *The Journal of Applied Physics*, for Figs. 10.3, 10.4; *The Proceedings of the Asheville Conference* (National Academy of Sciences-National Research Council Publication 871), for Figs. 7.10, 7.11, 8.7 and 8.8; *Review of Scientific Instruments*, for Figs. 6.9, 7.9, 8.2, 8.16; *Canadian Journal of Physics*, for Figs. 8.24, 8.25, 8.28, 8.30, 8.31 and 8.32; *Mémoires de la Société Royale des Sciences de Liège*, for Figs. 9.5 and 10.7; *Journal of Physics and Chemistry of Solids*, for Fig. 4.5; *Russian Journal of Physical Chemistry*, for Fig. 6.3; *Proceedings of the Paris Conference on Nuclear Instrumentation Nov.* 1963, for Fig. 9.4; *Physics in Medicine and Biology*, for Figs. 9.10, 9.11, 9.12.

We are also grateful to Oak Ridge Technical Enterprises Corporation for permission to reproduce Figs. 6.3, 7.15, 8.4, 9.13, 9.14, 9.15 from their *Semi-conductor Detector Technical Data Sheet*; to E. Fairstein of the Tennelec Instrument Company, Oak Ridge, Tennessee, for Fig. 7.4; to Prof. W. J. Price and the McGraw-Hill Publishing Co. for permission to adapt Figs. 2.4 and 2.5 from *Nuclear Radiation Detection*

(1958); to G. C. Phillips, J. B. Marion and J. R. Risser and Rice University for permission to reproduce Figs. 8.40 and 8.43 from *Progress in Fast Neutron Physics*; and, finally, to J. H. Crawford, Jr., J. W. Cleland and Messrs Heywood & Company, London, for permission to reproduce Fig. 10.7 from *Progress in Semiconductors*, 2, 1957.

We are indebted to the following colleagues who have allowed us to make use of their data in unpublished diagrams: D. L. Allan, of the Nuclear Physics Division, A.E.R.E., for Fig. 2.9; A. Poletti and M. Thomas, of the Clarendon Laboratory, for Fig. 8.3; J. E. Evans, of the Nuclear Physics Division, A.E.R.E., for Fig. 8.14; J. H. Aitken and W. R. Dixon of the National Research Council, Ottawa, for Fig. 8.42; B. C. Diven and others at Los Alamos Scientific Laboratory for Fig. 8.44; W. L. Hansen and B. V. Jarrett of Lawrence Radiation Laboratory, Berkeley, for Fig. 8.23; D. Holm and others at Los Alamos Scientific Laboratory for Figs. 8.26, 8.27, and 9.6; M. E. Lee and M. L. Awcock of Electronic Division, A.E.R.E., for Fig. 8.39; J. M. Palms of Los Alamos Scientific Laboratory and G. Dearnaley of Nuclear Physics Division, A.E.R.E., for Figs. 4.2, 4.3 and 6.6; J. M. Palms and R. B. Day of Los Alamos Scientific Laboratory for Fig. 8.29; Miss N. Blamires of Electronics Division, A.E.R.E., for Fig. 9.17; A. R. Sattler of Sandia Corporation, Albuquerque, for Fig. 1.10; and W. E. Stein of Los Alamos Scientific Laboratory, for Fig. 8.17.

September 1965   G. D.
D. C. N.

CONTENTS

PLATES

CHAPTER 1

PROPERTIES OF NUCLEAR RADIATION

1.1 Types of Radiation

One of the earliest experiments in the investigation of the phenomenon of radioactivity was a study of the interaction of the newly-discovered radiations with matter in the solid state. On the basis of this interaction the first classification of nuclear radiations was made. Rutherford[1] found, in 1899, that part of the ionizing radiation was easily absorbed by thin solid foils while another part had a considerably greater power of penetration, and he called these the alpha and beta rays respectively. Shortly afterwards Villard[2] discovered the still more penetrating gamma rays. Different factors are involved in the absorption processes of these radiations, and it is convenient to consider them separately. The same distinction which was drawn from the differing absorption in solid foils applies to the behaviour of the radiations in solid detectors. We shall therefore find this a very appropriate classification for the purpose of our discussion.

The alpha rays, which Rutherford[3] showed to be charged nuclei of He^4, are typical of the class we shall extend to include all charged nuclei from protons to the heaviest fission fragments. Such particles are generally called ions, and may carry any charge between e and Ze, where Z is the atomic number and e the electronic charge. With increasing Z it rapidly becomes more probable that only a small proportion of the orbital electrons are stripped from the ion. Alpha particles are emitted from many heavy elements by the process of natural radioactivity. Other light ions can be produced by electrical or thermal agitation of the atoms, and these ions can then be accelerated in one of a wide variety of particle accelerators. Various ions may result from the bombardment of a target with nuclear radiation. Fission is a special case of this method of production, generally induced by neutron bombardment of very heavy nuclei. Certain transuranic elements decay by spontaneous fission, breaking up into two fragments of comparable mass. The range in solids of ions is, in general, very small, and, for example, an alpha particle of 5 MeV energy will travel only about 0·001 of an inch in silicon, a distance about a thousand times smaller than its range in air at atmospheric pressure.

Beta rays are fast electrons which may be emitted in natural radioactivity or induced activity following a nuclear transmutation which is caused by another nuclear radiation. They may also be produced by the acceleration in an electric field of electrons emitted from a heated filament. In this class we also include positrons, which are particles of the same mass but a positive charge of the same magnitude as that of the electron. Positrons are produced in radioactive decay, either natural or induced, and the term 'beta decay' covers the emission of either electrons or positrons. Electrons and positrons are produced simultaneously during the interaction of high-energy gamma rays with matter. Electrons differ from heavy particles in that their paths in solids are not straight and their range is therefore rather indefinite. This is because their mass is the same as that of the electrons in the absorber so that as much as half the initial energy may be lost in a single collision. The deflections and the statistical straggling in range are therefore large, as has been revealed by cloud-chamber experiments in which the track of a single electron can be made visible. The high velocities often attained by electrons, quite commonly an appreciable fraction of the velocity of light, make it necessary to describe their motion relativistically.

Gamma rays and X-rays are both electromagnetic radiations differing only in that gamma rays are produced in nuclear processes while X-rays result from transitions between states of the orbital electrons. In general, gamma rays possess greater energy and are thus more penetrating. X-rays may also be produced by the deceleration of an electron beam, particularly when it strikes a target of high atomic number.

To these three types of ionizing radiation one must add a fourth type of radiation which is a flux of neutrons. The neutron, discovered by Chadwick in 1932, is a neutral particle of mass slightly greater than that of the proton. Since it has no charge it cannot directly cause ionization and its interaction with matter is almost entirely by nuclear processes. The range may be very long indeed in certain materials, and the particles may finally come into thermal equilibrium with the atoms of the absorber, following a sufficient number of collisions. Such slow neutrons, with energy of the order of an electron-volt or less, are called thermal neutrons, as opposed to the energetic particles emitted from nuclear reactions and fission; the latter are termed fast neutrons. The detection of neutrons almost always requires the transfer of some or all of the neutron energy to charged particles which are subsequently detected by the ionization they produce.

In order to clarify the requirements of detectors for these various types of radiation we shall consider in turn the absorption processes which are important in each case.

1.2 Energy loss processes in matter

(a) *Ions*

The principal mechanism for the energy loss of charged nuclear particles is ionization and excitation of the electrons of the absorber atoms owing to interaction with the electromagnetic field of the moving particle. Only for the case of completely ionized particles, such as protons, deuterons and doubly charged helium ions, has the rate of energy loss been fully calculated. For alpha particles the assumption of complete ionization ceases to be true below about 1 MeV and for fission fragments it is in practice never justified.

If the incident particle has mass M and energy E_p and collides with an electron of mass m, then the maximum energy which the electron can acquire is, by classical kinetics:

$$W_{\text{max}} = \{4mM/(m + M)^2\} E_p \qquad (1.1)$$

or approximately $W_{\text{max}} \simeq 4mE_p/M$ when $M \gg m$. For light particles of several MeV this energy is of the order 10 keV so that it is justifiable to neglect the electronic binding energy and consider the collisions to occur with free electrons. We shall not here be concerned with particles of such low energy that the collision should be treated as one with the atom as a whole. The more energetic recoiling electrons resulting from such collisions are often called 'delta rays', since their appearance in early cloud-chamber experiments led to the mistaken idea that they were a fourth type of radiation. Henneberg[4] has shown that a quantum mechanical calculation of the scattering process, taking into account the electron binding, allows the production of delta rays with energies greater than the classical maximum W_{max}, but with a very low intensity.

The transfer of energy at each collision is thus generally a small fraction, of the order 10^{-3} times the particle energy, so that the deflections from a straight-line path are small. The range, determined by a large number of events, is well defined. Calculations of the energy loss per unit path have been made by Livingston and Bethe[5] with a result expressed by

$$- \frac{\mathrm{d}E_p}{\mathrm{d}x} = \frac{4\pi e^4 z^2 ZN}{mv^2} \cdot B \qquad (1.2)$$

where e, m are the electronic charge and mass, ze and v are the particle charge and velocity, Z is the atomic number of the absorber and N the number of absorber atoms per cm^3. B, sometimes called the stopping number, is the logarithmic function

$$B = \log_e (2\,mv^2/I) - \log_e (1 - v^2/c^2) - v^2/c^2 \qquad (1.3)$$

Here I is the mean ionization potential of the absorber atoms and c is the velocity of light. The first term in this expression predominates up to 1000 MeV. B therefore varies rather slowly with particle energy, and approximately, from equation (1.2)

$$- \mathrm{d}E_p/\mathrm{d}x \propto z^2/v^2 \propto z^2/E_p \qquad (1.4)$$

This is to be expected since the slower the particle the greater is the time for which its Coulomb field acts upon the electron and the greater impulse imparted gives an increased probability of excitation.

Bloch[6] has shown that I varies almost linearly with Z, its value in electron-volts being approximately $10Z$. For different

absorbers, therefore, the main variation in dE_p/dx is given by
the variation of NZ in equation (1.2), for a given particle
velocity v. The energy loss per unit path is thus proportional
to the absorber electron density. Experimental results for the
energy loss in a number of absorbers as a function of energy
have been collected by Whaling,[7] and data for protons in
silicon and germanium are shown in Fig. 1.1. From equation

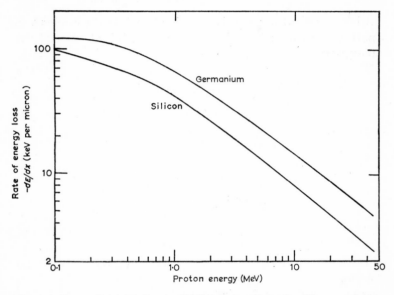

FIG. 1.1 Rate of energy loss, $-dE/dx$, for protons in silicon and germanium; from data given by WHALING[7]

(1.4) it can be seen that for different projectiles the energy
loss can be obtained quite simply from the data for protons.
In the case of a projectile of mass M the factor v^2 in equation
(1.4) is equal to that for protons of energy E/M; the energy
loss value so obtained must be multiplied by z^2 for $z > 1$.
Thus, to use Fig. 1.1 for $(He^3)^{++}$ ions, the energy scale must be
multiplied by 3, the vertical scale by 4. In fact, for heavy ions
and low velocities the calculations are complicated by the
possibility of capture and loss of electrons by the ion. Its
charge is then no longer constant. The approximations made
above, for instance, break down for alpha particles below a

few hundred keV. Experimental measurements have been made, however, of the energy loss of various ions under such circumstances. We shall return to this subject below to consider approximations for the case of fission fragments.

The range, R, of a particle is given by the integral

$$R = -\int_0^{E_p} \frac{dE}{dE/dx} = \frac{mM}{4\pi\, e^4 z^2 NZ} \int_0^{v_p} \frac{v^3 dv}{B(v)} \tag{1.5}$$

It is convenient to use this equation to relate the range of one particle to that of another of the same initial velocity. We may write

$$R(v) = M/z^2 . f(v) \tag{1.6}$$

where $f(v)$ involves only the particle velocity. Thus for the ranges of protons and deuterons ($z = 1$)

$$R_p(E_p) = \frac{M_p}{M_d}\, R_d\left(\frac{M_d}{M_p} \times E_p\right)$$

$$= 0.50\, R_d\, (2.0\, E_p)$$

For particles of different z there is a small correction term, C, owing to the different rate of capture and loss near the end of the range. Thus, for protons and alphas

$$R_p(E_p) = 1.007 R_\alpha(3.972 E_p) - C$$

where $C = 0.2$ cm in air, and 2 microns in silicon. Experimental ranges for protons in silicon and germanium are shown in Fig. 1.2.

Lithium ions, protons and alpha particles are often completely ionized and retain a constant charge over almost their whole range. For heavier ions, and especially fission fragments, this is no longer true. The charge on a fission fragment is typically 20 e at the beginning of the range and progressively decreases by the capture of electrons during the slowing-down process. Bohr[8] made the assumption that the fragment will shake off all those of its electrons with orbital speed in the atom smaller than the speed of the fragment itself. This leads to the approximate formula

$$z' = z^{\frac{1}{3}}\, \hbar v/e^2 \tag{1.7}$$

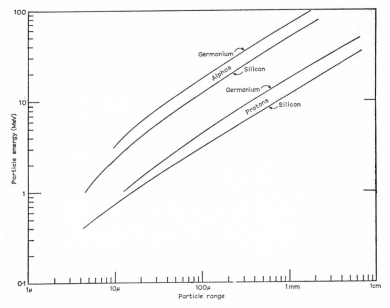

FIG. 1.2 The energies of protons and alpha particles in silicon and germanium as a function of particle range, computed from data for aluminium and copper given in *Nuclear Data Tables*, Part 3, ed. MARION J. B. (National Academy of Sciences, 1960)

where $z'e$ is the effective charge of a fragment of atomic number z moving with velocity v, and $\hbar$ is Planck's constant divided by 2π. Neglecting energy loss due to nuclear collisions Bohr obtained a useful relation between the range R_f of a fission fragment of mass number A and that of an alpha particle of the same initial velocity v

$$R_f/R_a \simeq 7A/(z')^2 \qquad (1.8)$$

At the end of the range collisions between the fission fragment and the nuclei of the absorber become more important than electronic excitations, and the ratio of the energy loss due to nuclear collisions to that due to electronic collisions is given approximately by the ratio Zmz^2/Mz'^2. Clearly this becomes large when z' falls to one or two. The expression (1.8) above is, however, in reasonable agreement with the experimental results of Katcoff, Miskel and Stanley,[9] in which the range for various fission products was measured by radiochemical methods. Curves showing the energy loss per unit path of light and heavy fission fragments along their range in argon at normal temperature and pressure are shown in Fig. 1.3 from the work of Lassen.[10] The rate of energy loss is greatest

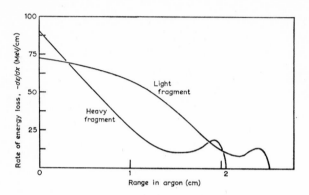

FIG. 1.3 Rate of energy loss for fission fragments in argon; from LASSEN[10]

at the beginning of the range, where the charge has its maximum value.

The total energy loss of an ion is shared between nuclear motion and electronic ionization and excitation. Lindhard and his collaborators[11] estimate that for a 6 MeV alpha particle slowing down in silicon only 12 keV of energy is given to nuclear recoils, while in the case of fission fragments the major fraction of the energy loss is by nuclear collisions. We shall see in later chapters that this fact is important in comparing the response of a detector to fission fragments and alpha particles.

So far we have omitted to consider the fact that the absorbing medium may have a crystalline structure. It is easily appreciated that anisotropic crystals possess different stopping powers for particles travelling along different directions in the lattice. Although it is less easy to understand, it has been found that even in isotropic cubic crystals such as silicon and germanium the stopping power is affected by correlations between the positions of the absorbing atoms. These effects are more marked when the ion trajectory lies along relatively open directions or lattice planes of the crystal. Then successive glancing collisions with atoms along the walls of such 'channels' are correlated and give a systematic tendency to return the ion towards the centre of the channel, which is a region of low electron density. Under such conditions the ion samples a lower mean electron density than in the normal trajectory and the stopping power is correspondingly reduced. Lindhard[12] points out that since half the energy loss takes place in close collisions and half in distant resonance collisions the stopping power may be reduced by at most a factor of two.

These effects were first observed at low energies by Nelson and Thompson[13], using protons and alpha particles of around

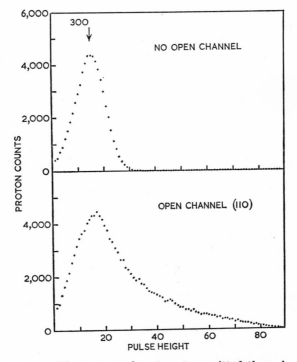

Fig. 1.4 The spectra of protons transmitted through single-crystal silicon, showing the effect of channelling.

50 keV. Dearnaley[14] and more recently Dearnaley and Sattler[15] have observed strong effects at ion energies of several MeV, and Gibson, Erginsoy and Wegner[16] have found the

phenomenon to be observable even for 30 MeV ions. Figure 1.4 shows the spectra of protons emerging from a thin crystal of silicon oriented in two different directions to the incident beam. When the protons travel along the $\langle 110 \rangle$ direction (a very wide channel) many of them emerge with a reduced energy loss, and the transmitted spectrum takes on a characteristic unsymmetrical distribution. We shall see in Chapter 8 that these results are important when thin single-crystal slices of semiconductor are used as 'dE/dx' detectors for particles which pass completely through them. The type of channelling here described is to be distinguished from that observed by Davies and others[17] and predicted by Robinson and Oen[18] for very slow, heavy ions in crystal lattices. There the pattern of nuclear collisions is the important factor rather than electron collisions and the phenomenon is unlikely to be important in practical applications of semiconductor detectors.

(b) Electrons

For electrons of up to 10 MeV the dominant modes of energy loss are excitation and ionization of the electrons of the absorber, just as in the case of heavy particles. The rate of energy loss is therefore given by the same formula, with $z = 1$:

$$-\frac{dE_\beta}{dx} = \frac{4\pi e^4 \, ZN}{mv^2}.B \qquad (1.9)$$

for $v \ll c$ the stopping number, B, is given by a formula due to Bethe[19]:

$$B = \log_e (0{\cdot}583 \, mv^2/I) \qquad (1.10)$$

This differs from the expression (1.3) owing to the impossibility of distinction between the two electrons which result from a collision; the one which retains the higher energy is defined to be the primary one for which the subsequent behaviour is followed.

At higher energies B increases more rapidly, in a manner given by Møller's[20] formula:

$$2B = \log_e[mv^2 \, E_\beta/2I^2 \, (1 - \beta^2)] -$$

$$(\log_e 2) \, (2 \, \sqrt{[1 - \beta^2]} - 1 + \beta^2) + 1 - \beta^2 \qquad (1.11)$$

in which β is equal to v divided by the velocity of light, c. The first term in this expression is the most important up to an electron energy of about 5 MeV. These calculations show that, as has been observed experimentally, the rate of energy loss passes through a broad minimum at about 1 MeV, above which it rises slowly and logarithmically with energy. In fact this behaviour is general for all charged particles and may be pictured physically as due to the relativistic contraction of the Coulomb field of the moving particle along its direction of motion. The resulting bunching of the lines of force increases the strength of the interaction with stationary electrons. In this way protons exhibit a region of 'minimum ionization' at about 1300 MeV, and μ-mesons at about 200 MeV energy.

Above 10 MeV electrons can also lose energy by the classical radiation of electromagnetic energy due to deceleration in matter. This mechanism is usually called *bremsstrahlung* or 'braking radiation' and the rate of loss of energy in this way is proportional to $Z^2 N E_\beta$ and therefore increases linearly with the electron energy.

The rate of energy loss of electrons in silicon is shown in Fig. 1.5, while Fig. 1.6 shows the range of electrons in silicon, at the lower energies. Because of appreciable straggling the range of electrons in matter is rather an indefinite quantity.

(c) Gamma rays

Gamma rays and X-rays interact with matter by one of three types of process, namely the photoelectric effect, Compton scattering and pair production. In the photoelectric effect the photon of energy E_γ interacts with a whole atom of the absorber, and the whole energy is used to eject an electron, usually from one of the inner electron orbits, with a kinetic energy

$$E_\beta = E_\gamma - E_b \qquad (1.12)$$

where E_b is the binding energy of the electron. The original gamma ray or X-ray disappears in this process, but the excited atom will subsequently emit one or more X-rays of total energy E_b.

The Compton scattering process may be considered as an

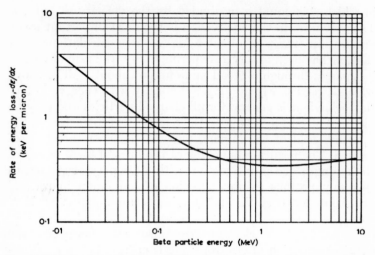

FIG. 1.5 Rate of energy loss, $-dE/dx$, for electrons in silicon as a function of energy; from WEISS, W. L. and WHATLEY, E. M., *Nucleonics*, **20**, 147 (1962)

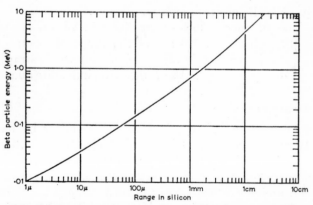

FIG. 1.6 Range of beta particles in silicon, reproduced by kind permission of ORTEC, from their 'Semiconductor Detector Technical Data Sheet'

elastic collision between a photon and an atomic electron, in which the electron binding energy is very small compared with the photon energy. The energy is shared between the scattered photon and the recoiling electron.

In pair production the photon disappears and an electron-positron pair is created with total kinetic energy equal to the photon energy less the rest-energy of the two particles.

In each of these processes photons are removed from a narrow beam by a single interaction process, unlike the case of the slowing-down of particle beams. The number of photons absorbed in a thickness dx of absorber is therefore proportional to dx and to the intensity of the beam at that point. This leads to the expression

$$I = I_0 \, e^{-\zeta x} \tag{1.13}$$

in which the beam intensity I, after passing through a thickness x of absorber, is related to the initial intensity by the absorption coefficient ζ. This may be subdivided into

$$\zeta = \zeta_{\text{phot}} + \zeta_{\text{Compt}} + \zeta_{\text{pair}} \tag{1.14}$$

Each of these coefficients depends differently on the gamma-ray energy and the nature of the absorber, in a manner summarized as follows.

THE PHOTOELECTRIC EFFECT

For energies above the K-shell binding energy, Heitler[21] has calculated an expression for the photoelectric absorption coefficient

$$\zeta_{\text{phot}} \simeq 10^{-33} \, NZ^5 \, E_\gamma^{-3.5} \text{ cm}^{-1} \tag{1.15}$$

This coefficient therefore increases very rapidly with the atomic number of the absorber, and decreases rapidly with the photon energy. In silicon, for example, the photoelectric effect is important only up to about 100 keV.

THE COMPTON EFFECT

If a photon of energy E_γ collides with an atomic electron it suffers a simple scattering process and is deflected through some angle θ to its original direction of motion. Assuming the electron binding energy to be negligible, Compton showed that the scattered photon energy, E_γ', is given by

$$E_\gamma' = E_\gamma / (1 + [1 - \cos \theta] \, E_\gamma / mc^2) \tag{1.16}$$

and the electron energy is $E_\beta = E_\gamma - E_\gamma'$. Recoil electrons may have any energy between zero and a maximum corresponding to a minimum value of E_γ' which occurs for a 'back-scattered' photon ($\theta = 180°$).

$$(E_\beta)_{max} = 2E_\gamma^2/(mc^2 + 2E_\gamma) \tag{1.17}$$

Every electron in the absorber can contribute independently to this process, so that the Compton absorption coefficient is proportional to the electron density NZ. Klein and Nishina[22] showed that at high energies ($E_\gamma > 1$ MeV) the absorption coefficient is given by

$$\zeta_{\text{Compt}} \simeq 1{\cdot}25. \; 10^{-25} NZ/E_\gamma. \; (\log_e [2\,E_\gamma/mc^2] + \tfrac{1}{2}) \, \text{cm}^{-1} \tag{1.18}$$

which approximates to an inverse dependence on E_γ. In silicon the Compton effect dominates the absorption between 50 keV and 15 MeV, that is over almost the whole region of practical interest in nuclear physics.

PAIR PRODUCTION

For pair production to occur the gamma-ray energy must exceed the rest-energy of the electron and positron, *i.e.* 1·02 MeV. In order that the momentum and mass-energy may both be conserved, the process can take place only in the field of a third particle. This is generally an atomic nucleus, although the effect can occur in the field of an electron. The excess energy appears as kinetic energy, E_{kin}, of the electron-positron pair, and a very small recoil energy is imparted to the nucleus.

$$E_{\text{kin}} = E_\gamma - 1{\cdot}02 \text{ MeV} \tag{1.19}$$

At energies near the threshold the absorption coefficient depends linearly upon the photon energy:

$$\zeta_{\text{pair}} \propto NZ^2 \, (E_\gamma - 2 \, mc^2) \tag{1.20}$$

while at higher energies the dependence becomes logarithmic

$$\zeta_{\text{pair}} \propto NZ^2 \log_e E_\gamma \tag{1.21}$$

Although pair production is not a significant mode of absorption in silicon below 15 MeV, the fact that $\zeta_{\text{pair}}/\zeta_{\text{Compt}}$ varies as Z causes pair production to dominate the absorption in lead above 5 MeV.

Figure 1.7 shows the variation with gamma-ray energy of

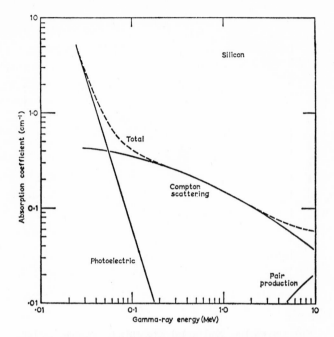

FIG. 1.7 Partial and total absorption coefficients for gamma rays in silicon, from data in GRODSTEIN, G. W., N.B.S. Circular **583** (1957)

the three partial absorption coefficients for silicon, while Fig. 1.8 shows the corresponding behaviour for germanium. It is noteworthy that the Compton absorption, increasing only linearly with Z, makes a relatively smaller contribution in the latter case.

(d) Neutrons

The interaction of neutrons with matter differs from all the cases we have so far considered because the neutron-electron interaction is essentially zero. Only nuclear forces, which play a negligible part in the absorption of charged particles and gamma rays, can bring about the absorption of neutrons. There is a large variety of nuclear reactions which may take place, with relative probabilities which differ very widely from one type of absorber to another, and the reaction probability in general varies in a complex manner with the neu-

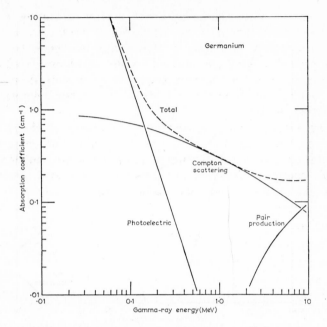

FIG. 1.8 Partial and total absorption coefficients for gamma rays in germanium, computed from data for copper in GRODSTEIN, G. W., N.B.S. Circular 583 (1957)

tron energy. We can therefore only summarize the possible interaction processes.

SCATTERING

It is always possible for a neutron to be scattered without transfer of potential energy to the struck nucleus. The scattering is then termed 'elastic', and the transfer of kinetic energy is obtainable by simple classical collision equations. A particularly important case for fast neutron detection purposes is the scattering of neutrons by hydrogen nuclei (protons). Since the proton and neutron masses are essentially equal the whole of the neutron energy is transferred to the proton in a head-on collision. Angles of scattering, θ, greater than zero result in a smaller energy transfer, according to

$$E_{\mathrm{p}} = E_{\mathrm{n}} \cos^2\theta \qquad (1.22)$$

It is easily shown that, assuming isotropic scattering in the centre-of-mass system of co-ordinates, all recoil-proton energies are equally probable, so that a monoenergetic neutron flux produces recoil protons with a flat spectrum extending from zero to the full neutron energy. Experiments show that the assumption made here is justified for neutron energies up to about 10 MeV.

Fast neutrons may transfer potential energy to the struck nucleus, which is left in an excited state. The energy of excitation may be lost by subsequent gamma-ray emission or, if the energy is sufficient, by emission of a second neutron. The latter process is described as an $(n, 2n)$ reaction.

CAPTURE

The Coulomb barrier does not inhibit the entry of neutrons into a nucleus, and on average, capture of a neutron by a nucleus is accompanied by the release of 7-8 MeV energy. The 'compound nucleus' produced by capture has the same charge but a mass number increased by one unit; it is therefore the adjacent isotope to the target nucleus. The excitation energy is usually released by gamma-ray emission, and the (n, γ) process is often the most probable reaction induced by slow neutrons. Owing to the phenomenon of resonance, the reaction probability rises sharply in the region of certain neutrons energies, characteristic of each particular isotope.

CHARGED PARTICLE EMISSION

If the excitation energy of the compound nucleus is sufficient, charged particles such as protons, deuterons, tritons or alpha particles may be emitted. Since the Coulomb barrier must be overcome, this process usually occurs only with fast neutrons and light- or medium-weight nuclei. There are a few (n, p) and (n, α) reactions which proceed with a release of energy, even for slow neutrons. Detection processes rely in almost all cases on ionization or excitation of the atoms of the detector medium, so that reactions which cause the transfer of energy from neutrons to charged particles are important in the detection of neutrons. We shall consider in more detail in Chapter 2 the methods which are employed.

FISSION

In this reaction the compound nucleus, after absorption of a neutron, divides into two fragments of comparable mass, and there are usually a few neutrons ejected also. The phenomenon is almost entirely limited to the heaviest nuclei. Since the fragments are charged and possess considerable energy, of the order 100 MeV, the process is useful in neutron detection.

CROSS-SECTIONS

Each of the neutron-absorption processes described above brings about the removal of neutrons from a narrow beam in a single interaction process. Just as in the case of gamma-ray absorption the neutron flux after passage through a thickness x of absorber is related to the incident flux by

$$I = I_0 \, e^{-\zeta x} \tag{1.23}$$

If N is the number of absorber nuclei/cm³, we may write

$$\zeta = N\sigma \text{ cm}^{-1} \tag{1.24}$$

Here σ is called the nuclear cross-section, as it has the dimensions of area, and its values are commonly expressed in units of 10^{-24} cm², which unit enjoys the name of 1 barn. The total cross-section is the sum of the individual cross-sections for the various reactions which can take place.

Since these cross-sections vary in a complex manner with neutron energy in a given isotope, and from one isotope to another, the accumulation of data on neutron cross-sections is obviously a considerable undertaking. It is also very important from the point of view of nuclear engineering. A comprehensive compilation of neutron cross-sections has been published by the U.S. Atomic Energy Commission.[23] Figure 1.9 shows the energy dependence of cross-sections for some processes which are important for neutron detection. The variation as $E^{-\frac{1}{2}}$, or $1/v$, with neutron energy E and velocity v, is common to many reaction cross-sections. It results from the time duration, proportional to $1/v$, for which the neutron is within the range of nuclear force of the target nucleus.

1.3 Energy loss and ionization

We have seen that charged particles lose energy in travelling through matter by transfer of energy to the atomic electrons of the absorber. Most of the electrons are ejected with a kinetic energy smaller than the ionization potential, I, but a few receive higher energies, up to the maximum $W_{max} \simeq 4m\ E_p/M$, as shown by equation (1.1). These energetic electrons are the delta rays referred to in Section 1.2(a). Such energetic electrons can themselves produce further

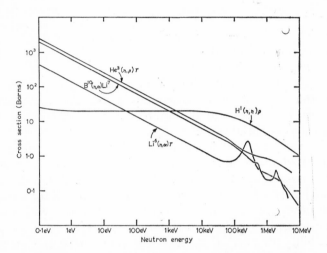

FIG. 1.9 Cross-sections of some neutron-induced processes which are important in neutron detection methods; from DEARNALEY, G. and FERGUSON, A. T. G., *Nucleonics*, 20, 84 (1962)

ionization so that the total ionization is the sum of primary ionization and the secondary ionization due to delta rays. With electrons of 1 MeV in hydrogen, Williams and Terroux[24] found that twice as many ions were produced by the secondary ionization process as by primary ionization.

A very important parameter for a detection medium is the mean energy per ion or electron produced, w, measured in electron-volts, for a given incident particle. There have been many studies of this in gases by means of proportional counters, and the results reveal the interesting facts that w is almost independent of particle energy and particle type in a given gas, and the values of w for different gases differ by less than a factor of two. The reasons for this have been considered by Fano.[25] Qualitatively the argument depends on the fact that the probability of formation of delta rays with kinetic energy greater than the ionization potential is very small, so that the energy is divided between excitation of atoms without ionization and emission of electrons with average energy, w_i. Since w is defined with respect to ionization events,

$$w\sigma_i \simeq w_{ex}\sigma_{ex} + w_i\sigma_i \qquad (1.25)$$

in which σ_i is the cross-section for ionization, and σ_{ex} is the cross-section for excitation to an average energy w_{ex}. The constancy of w with energy arises because the average energies w_{ex} and w_i do not change very rapidly with energy, nor does the *ratio* of the cross-sections σ_{ex}/σ_i. The fact that w remains much the same despite large differences in the ionization potential of different gases is explained as follows. In the inert gases which have high ionization potentials, I, the excited states all lie at energies close to I and the excitation cross-section σ_{ex} is small. Almost every collision leads to ionization and w is therefore not very much greater than I. With other gases, such as oxygen and ethylene, with much lower ionization potentials there is found to be a greater probability of excitation. A larger fraction of the energy, therefore, is lost in processes which do not give ionization, and w/I rises to 2·5 or even greater. Thus w does not vary over as wide a range as does I. Table 1.1 shows values of w for various common gases.

For β particles the available evidence leads to the conclusion that w is constant with respect to energy in any gas. For protons and heavier charged particles this no longer seems to be true. Cranshaw and Harvey[26] found, with alpha particles in argon, linearity of ionization with particle energy in the region 5 to 9 MeV, but the straight line through the experimental points made an intercept on the energy axis at 85 ± 10 keV. The ratio of the ionization produced in argon by the alpha particle and Li[7] nucleus which result from the $B^{10}(n, \alpha)$ Li[7] reaction has been studied in a number of experiments.

TABLE 1.1

Mean energy, w, absorbed per electron released in ionization

(a) *Gases*

Medium	*w for electrons*	*w for 5 MeV alphas*	*Mean ionization potential, I*
Hydrogen	36·9 eV	36·6 eV	15·4 eV
Helium	41·3	44·4	24·6
Nitrogen	34·9	36·3	15·5
Oxygen	31·3	32·1	12·2
Neon	35·9	36·8	21·6
Argon	26·3	26·3	15·8
Krypton	24·4	24·1	14·0
Xenon	22·1	21·9	12·1
Air	34·2	35·2	—
Carbon dioxide	32·7	34·1	13·7
Methane	28·1	29·1	13·1
Ethylene	26·4	—	10·6

Values from H. W. Fulbright, *Handbuch der Physik*, XLV, 1 (1958) (Springer-Verlag).

(b) *Solids*

Medium	*w*	*Type of radiation*	*Energy gap E_g*
Silicon	3·79 ± ·01 eV[1]	Electrons (365 KeV)	1·09 eV
	3·61 ± ·01[1]	5 MeV alphas	
Germanium	2·94 ± ·15[2]	several	0·75
Cadmium sulphide	7·3[3]	5 MeV alphas	2·5
Gallium arsenide	6·3	Electrons	1·35
Lead oxide	8·0[3]	Gamma rays	3·0
Indium antimonide	0·6[4]		0·16

[1] From C. Bussolati, A. Fiorentini and G. Fabri, *Phys. Rev.*, **136**A, 1756 (1964).

[2] From J. W. Mayer, *J. Appl. Phys.*, **30**, 1937 (1959).

[3] From F. Lappe, *Z. Physik*, **154**, 207 (1959).

[4] From J. Tauc, *J. Phys. Chem. Solids*, **8**, 219 (1959).

Milton, Rutledge and Lennox[27] have analysed these results and conclude that they are consistent with the hypothesis that both particles cease to ionize the argon atoms when the particle velocity is reduced to that of the outermost argon electrons. This is at about 48 keV for the Li^7 ion. This effect causes w to be slightly greater for heavy charged particles than for electrons. The results for 5 MeV alphas in various gases are shown in Table 1.1, the data being taken from the paper by Fulbright.[28] For fission fragments in gases the situation is complicated by the large amount of energy lost by nuclear collisions. Schmitt and Leachman[29] find an 'energy defect' due to this process of about 6 MeV, the value being somewhat greater for heavy than for light fragments.

In solids the electrons exist not in levels characteristic of an individual atom but rather in bands of many close levels, the positions of which are a property of the lattice arrangement of the crystal as a whole. The ionization process raises electrons to unoccupied levels in a higher band, after which there is a sharing of energy as the more energetic electrons make further collisions and transfer their energy. We reserve the detailed consideration of the processes involved until the band theory of the electron structure of semiconductors has been introduced in Chapter 3. Because of the proximity of the atoms the lowest energy for excitation of an electron is generally much lower in a solid than in a gas, and values of a few electron-volts are typical. This is important in a counting device because the lower the energy for ionization the greater is the number of ionization events produced by a particle of given energy. The signal is therefore greater and statistical fluctuations in signal amplitude are a smaller fraction of the mean.

In most solids the electrons which are released by ionization very soon drop into an unoccupied level of lower energy in which they are no longer able to move in an applied electric field. This process, which in its different forms is called 'trapping' or 'recombination', is much accelerated by the presence of impurity atoms or crystalline imperfections in the lattice. Very few solids have been prepared in a sufficiently pure and perfect crystalline form so that measurements can be made of the number of electrons liberated by the ionization process. Table 1.1 shows some of the more reliable results obtained for solids; the low value of w for germanium is noteworthy.

In considering the variation of w (the energy absorbed per electron released) in solids with the type and energy of the primary particle, it is important to distinguish between such a variation and an increase in the probability of recombination at very high densities of ionization. Until recently, many experiments with gamma rays, electrons, protons, alpha particles and some heavier ions showed no significant differences in w. However, careful measurements with electrons and alpha particles, after correction for recombination effects, have revealed a 5 per cent difference in the values of w (see Table 1.1). It is interesting to observe that this difference is opposite to that seen in gases, in which alpha particles as a rule ionize less efficiently than do electrons. It will be important to see whether a similar behaviour holds for germanium.

For a given primary particle there is some energy below which w ceases to be constant owing to a reduced probability of ionization and the increased importance of collisions with nuclei. Seitz[30] has given an approximate theoretical expression for this threshold energy, E_{th}

$$E_{th} \simeq ME_g/8\,m \qquad (1.26)$$

Here M is the mass of the moving particle, m is the electron mass and E_g is the lowest excitation energy of electrons in the solid. Schweinler[31] has made more detailed calculations in which he shows that the threshold may vary greatly from one solid to another. Thus, for a proton in silicon, it is only a few hundred electron-volts while in an alkali halide crystal the threshold is about a hundred times greater, *i.e.* 20 keV. Measurements of the ionization produced by silicon ions in silicon detectors were first made by Bilger, Baldinger and Czaja[32] by observing the pulses from recoiling silicon ions produced by fast-neutron irradiation of a silicon counter. Their results indicated the possibility of a much larger ionization threshold, around 200 keV. More recent measurement by Sattler[33] using the same method over a very extensive range of neutron energies show no evidence for any appreciable ionization threshold. Sattler's results are shown in Fig. 1.10, in which the ratio of the mean energy for electron-hole pair production in silicon by electrons w_e, to that for a production by silicon ions, w_{Si}, is plotted as a function of the particle energy. These results are in agreement with calculations of Lindhard and his collaborators[11], which predict an efficiency for ionization proportional to the square root of the particle energy, when the

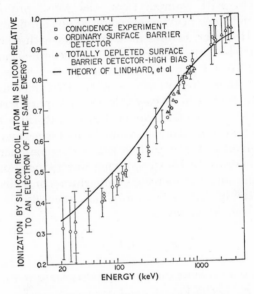

FIG. 1.10 The efficiency of ionization by a silicon ion coming to rest in silicon, relative to that due to an electron of the same energy.
From SATTLER[33]

energy is low. Sattler and Palms[34] are extending this work to germanium also, and preliminary results indicate that germanium ions ionize less efficiently in germanium than do silicon ions of the same energy in silicon. Since heavy ions and fission fragments lose much of their energy in producing nuclear recoils this work is important in considering the response of semiconductor detectors to such ions, (see Chapter 6).

1.4 Statistical fluctuations in ionization

Since the energy of a charged particle is often determined from the ionization produced over the whole or part of its range in the detection medium, the accuracy of the measurement may be governed by the fluctuation in the number of ionization events produced. In the simplest calculation the number of ionization events, n, is obtained by dividing the total energy loss in the medium by the mean energy per electron, w. Then, if the events are considered to be independent and n is large, the statistical fluctuation is $\sqrt{n}$, but these are not always justifiable assumptions. There are two cases to be considered, the first when the total ionization along the whole range is measured, the second when a small fraction of the total energy is expended in the detection medium.

Fano[25] showed that in the first case the ionization events should not be treated as completely independent, since the primary particle must lose the exact value of its initial energy in being brought to rest. In hydrogen, for instance, the assumption of random events leads to a mean square fluctuation which is about three times too large. The factor F, which is the actual mean square fluctuation divided by n, is often called the 'Fano factor'. The correct analysis considers the fluctuation in the division of energy loss between ionizing and non-ionizing collisions. If p_i is the probability of an ionizing collision, Fano showed that F is in general less than $1 - p_i$. For the inert gases p_i is quite large, in the region of 0·6, so that F must be small. Kirkwood, Pontecorvo and Hanna[35] have confirmed Fano's predictions for argon, and more recently Vorob'ev, Komar and Korolev[36] have found Fano factors as low as 0·09 in an ionization chamber gas mixture of Argon with 0·8 per cent acetylene. Using such a mixture these workers observed a line width of only 14 KeV for 5·68 MeV alpha particles.

In silicon detectors, measurements with electrons by Blankenship and Mruk[37], and Meyer[38], indicate Fano factors less than 0·5 and possibly as low as 0·2. Similar measurements[39] in germanium with gamma rays (see Section 8.10) show that the Fano factor cannot exceed 0·20. These results are important from the standpoint of the theory of ionization in semiconductors and from the practical point of view in defining the ultimate energy resolution of semiconductor detectors for electrons and gamma rays.

Recently, van Roosbroeck[45] has put forward a simple statistical model of the ionization process, in which the initial particle energy is divided as follows. The small energy for generation of a phonon is removed with probability r, the energy corresponding to the ionization threshold, E_i, is removed with probability $(1 - r)$ and a random partition of the remainder is made. The smaller or secondary part is then divided into a ratio corresponding to partition of energy between an electron and hole. The particle energies are divided again until none exceed E_i. At the end of the process many secondaries are incapable of ionizing, and this constraint largely determines the Fano factor. Under reasonable assumptions values of F as low as 0·1 can be understood.

In the case of ions, however, Lindhard and Nielsen[40] have drawn attention to another source of fluctuation in the number of electron-hole pairs produced. It arises from that part of the energy loss which is given up to low-energy, weakly ionizing nuclear recoils. Although this may represent only a small fraction of the total energy loss (about 0·2 per cent for 6 MeV alpha particles), this type of energy transfer involves only a small number of events and hence the fluctuations in its magnitude are large. Lindhard and Nielsen calculate that for 6 MeV alpha particles slowing down in a silicon detector this effect contributes a standard deviation of 0·04 per cent. This small, though observable fluctuation may often exceed the standard deviation in the number of electron ionization events if indeed the Fano factor is as low as 0·25. For ions heavier than alpha-particles the energy loss by nuclear recoils becomes greater and may exceed the loss by electronic processes. The fluctuation in the number of electron hole pairs produced will then be dominated by nuclear collision events.

In contrast with the beneficial reduction in fluctuation described by the Fano factor, the fluctuations in energy loss by ionization in a short element of the track of a particle are appreciably greater than the values obtained with the assumption of random fluctuation about a uniform rate of energy loss.

This is because in a single collision a large amount of energy may be transferred to a single electron, creating a so-called delta ray. Fluctuations in a small number of such collisions will markedly affect the distribution of energy losses in a thin absorber or detector. A treatment of this phenomenon was first given by Bohr,[41] and in a more quantitative form by Landau,[42] and Blunck and Leisegang.[43]

Two cases must be considered corresponding to whether an energy parameter ε, given by

$$\varepsilon = 2\pi \, e^4 \, z^2 \, NZ \, x/mv^2 \qquad (1.27)$$

is greater or less than W_{max}, the classical maximum energy transfer to an electron. Here x is the absorber thickness, and the other symbols are as defined in Section 1.2(a). For low values of ε, only one collision occurs on average, within the thickness x, with the transfer of energy greater than ε. Thus in a thin absorber the width of the distribution of energy losses is caused mainly by collisions in which an energy approaching ε is transferred. The distribution is then asymmetric, with a tail on the high energy side. Since ε is proportional to x the *relative* width of the distribution is nearly independent of x, and its full width at half maximum corresponds to about 30 per cent of the value of the most probable energy loss. Landau has calculated the shape of the distribution in terms of the most probable energy loss, $\widehat{\delta E}$, given by

$$\widehat{\delta E} = \varepsilon \, (\log_e [3.10^3 \, \varepsilon \, \beta^2/Z^2 \, (1 - \beta^2)] + 1 - \beta^2) \qquad (1.28)$$

in which β is the particle velocity, v, divided by the velocity of light, c. Studies have been made of the Landau effect in gases, in scintillation crystals, and in other solids by measurement of the residual energy after initially monoenergetic particles have traversed a thin sample. The breadth of the distributions of energy loss generally exceeds 35 per cent of the most probable energy loss, in closer agreement with the theory of Blunck and Leisegang than with that of Landau.

If the parameter ε exceeds W_{max}, higher energy transfers do not occur, and the distribution of energy losses is governed by a large number of collisions in which energies well below ε are transferred. The distribution then becomes Gaussian, and Cranshaw[44] shows how the full width at half maximum of the distribution relative to the most probable energy loss, $\widehat{\delta E}$, is given by

$$\text{Relative width} = 2 \cdot 6\ (W_{max}/\widehat{\delta E} \log_e [W_{max}/I])^{\frac{1}{2}} \quad (1.29)$$

where I is the atomic ionization potential, approximately equal to 10 Z, in electron-volts. This formula is useful in consideration of the accuracy of measurements with thin semiconductor counters.

REFERENCES

For this chapter

1. Rutherford, E., *Phil. Mag.*, ser. 5, **47**, 109 (1899).
2. Villard, P., *Compt. Rend.*, **130**, 1178 (1900).
3. Rutherford, E. and Royds, T., *Phil. Mag.*, **17**, 281 (1909).
4. Henneberg, W., *Z. Physik*, **86**, 592 (1933).
5. Bethe, H. A., *Z. Physik*, **76**, 293 (1938).
6. Bloch, F., *Z. Physik*, **81**, 363 (1933).
7. Whaling, W., *Handbuch der Physik*, **34**, 193, Julius Springer (Berlin, 1958).
8. Bohr, N., *Phys. Rev.*, **59**, 270 (1941).
9. Katcoff, S., Miskel, J. A. and Stanley, C. W., *Phys. Rev.*, **74**, 631 (1948).
10. Lassen, N. O., *Kgl. Dan. Vid. Selskab., Mat.-Fys. Medd.*, **25**, 11 (1949).
11. Lindhard, J., Nielsen, V., Scharff, M. and Thomsen, P. V., *Kgl. Dan. Vid. Selskab., Mat.-Fys. Medd.*, **33**, No. 10 (1963).
12. Lindhard, J., *Physics Letters.*, **12**, 126 (1964).
13. Nelson, R. S. and Thompson, M. W., *Phil. Mag.*, **8**, 1677 (1963).
14. Dearnaley, G., *I.E.E.E. Trans. Nucl. Sci.*, **NS-11**, No. 3, 249 (1964).
15. Dearnaley, G. and Sattler, A. R. , (*to be published*).
16. Erginsoy, C., Wegner, H. E. and Gibson, W. M., *Brookhaven National Laboratory Report*, BNL 8374 (1964).
17. Davies, J. A. and Sims, G. A., *Can. J. Chem.*, **39**, 601 (1961).
18. Robinson, M. T. and Oen, O. S., *Phys. Rev.*, **132**, 2385 (1963).
19. Bethe, H. A., *Handbuch der Physik*, vol. **24**, 273, Julius Springer (Berlin, 1933).
20. Møller, C., *Ann. Physik*, **14**, 531 (1932).
21. Heitler, W., *The Quantum Theory of Radiation*. Chap. 3, O.U.P. (London, 1944).
22. Klein, O. and Nishina, Y., *Z. Physik*, **52**, 853 (1929).
23. Hughes, D. J. and Schwartz, R. B., *Brookhaven National Laboratory report* **325** (1958), and supplements.

24. Williams, E. J. and Terroux, F. R., *Proc. Roy. Soc.*, A **126**, 289 (1930).
25. Fano, U., *Phys. Rev.*, **72**, 26 (1947).
26. Cranshaw, T. E. and Harvey, J. A., *Can. J. Res.*, A **26**, 243 (1948).
27. Milton, J. C. D., Rutledge, A. R. and Lennox, P. I. K., *Chalk River Report CRP-632* (1956).
28. Fulbright, H. W., *Handbuch der Physik*, vol. **45**, 1, Julius Springer (Berlin, 1958).
29. Schmitt, H. W. and Leachman, R. B., *Phys. Rev.*, **102**, 183 (1956).
30. Seitz, F., *Discussions, Faraday Soc.*, No. 5, 271 (1949).
31. Schweinler, H. C., *NAS-NRC Publication*, **871**, 91 (1961), Ed. Dabbs, J. W. T. and Walter, F. J.
32. Bilger, H., Baldinger, E. and Czaja, W., *Helv. Phys. Acta.*, **36**, 405 (1963).
33. Sattler, A. R., *Bull. Amer. Soc.*, **9**, 668 (1964).
34. Sattler, A. R. and Palms, J. M., *(to be published)*.
35. Kirkwood, D. H. W., Pontecorvo, B. and Hanna, G. C., *Phys. Rev.*, **74**, 497 (1948).
36. Vorob'ev, A. A., Komar, A. P. and Korolev, V. A., *J.E.T.P.*, **43**, 426 (1962). English translation in *Journ. Exp. Theor. Phys.*, **16**, 306, (1963).
37. Blankenship, J. L. and Mruk, W. F., *Bull. Amer. Phys. Soc.*, **9**, 49 (1964).
38. Meyer, O., *Private Communication*.
39. Mann, H. M. and Janarek, F. J., *Private Communication*.
40. Lindhard, J. and Nielsen, V., *Physics Letters*, **2**, 209 (1962).
41. Bohr, N., *Phil. Mag.*, **30**, 581 (1915).
42. Landau, L., *J. Phys. U.S.S.R.*, **8**, 201 (1944).
43. Blunck, O. and Leisegang, S., *Z. Physik*, **128**, 500 (1950).
44. Cranshaw, T. E., *Prog. in Nucl. Phys.*, **2**, 271 (1952).
45. van Roosbroeck, W., *Phys. Rev. (to be published)*.

For general reading

Bethe, H. A. and Ashkin, J., 'Passage of Radiations through Matter', in *Experimental Nuclear Physics*, **1**, ed. Segre, E., Wiley (New York, 1953).
Whaling, W., 'The Energy Loss of Charged Particles in Matter', in *Handbuch der Physik*, **34**, 193, Julius Springer (Berlin, 1958).
Rossi, B., *High-energy Particles*, Prentice-Hall (1952).
Bohr, N., 'The penetration of atomic particles through matter', *Klg. Dan. Vid. Selskab., Mat.-Fys. Medd.*, **18**, No. 8 (1948).

CHAPTER 2

AN OUTLINE OF DETECTION METHODS

2.1 Introduction

A number of factors are common to different methods of detection of nuclear radiations. Certain phenomena which occur in gaseous and scintillation detectors are closely related to processes which take place in the solid counters which are the subject of this book. The mode of operation of semiconductor counters can thus be clarified by outlining first the relevant aspects of more conventional methods of detection. The limitations of these various detectors can then be discussed and potential advantages of semiconductor counters may be more clearly borne in mind during their detailed description.

Detection methods are in general based on the processes of ionization or excitation of atoms in the detection medium by the passage of a charged particle. Neutral particles or electromagnetic radiation must first interact with the detection medium or with an adjoining converter in order to produce the charged particles required for ionization. The methods by which the ions, electrons or excited atoms are subsequently made apparent vary widely and have been adapted to many different types of system, solid, liquid and gaseous, both with and without an applied electric field.

In both gaseous and solid counters charged particles liberated by ionization can be collected at boundary electrodes under an applied electric field. In the other important type of solid detector, the scintillation counter, use is made of the emission of light by excited atoms, detected by conversion to a stream of electrons from the photosensitive cathode of a photomultiplier tube. In Čerenkov counters an electrodynamical phenomenon causes light to be emitted when a charged particle travels through a dispersive medium at a velocity greater than that of light in the medium. Ionization is the principal cause of activation by which the grains of silver halide in the nuclear emulsion are rendered developable. Ionization also creates centres for the condensation of droplets in the cloud-chamber, although the indirect process of local heating in a superheated fluid is thought to be responsible for the formation of a string of bubbles along the particle track in the bubble-chamber. In other instances the heating effect due to the absorption of nuclear radiation may be measured calorimetrically or the chemical dissociation induced by radiation may be determined. The use of the properties of semiconductors adds to an already extensive range of physical systems which can be applied to radiation detection.

In this chapter the detector is considered apart from its ancillary electronic equipment. This may in general comprise a high-voltage supply, an amplifier for the electrical signal pulses and means for distinguishing and recording output signals of differing amplitudes. It may also be required to detect the arrival of pulses from different detectors within a given short time interval in what is termed coincidence detection. An account of the electronic equipment for use with semiconductor detectors is reserved until Chapter 7.

Two types of detector arrangement are possible, depending on whether individual particles are to be distinguished or merely the mean level of a radiation flux is to be measured. Signals corresponding to individual events can always be integrated electronically to give a measure of the mean rate of arrival, but certain methods are suited only to the measurement of the total flux of radiation through the detector. An example of the latter case is the electroscope, widely used as a pocket dosimeter. Solid detectors of semiconducting materials have applications in both types of detection instrument.

2.2 Gas-filled counters

(a) The ionization chamber

The gold-leaf electroscope, consisting simply of a pair of insulated charged leaves held apart by electrostatic repulsion, was the first instrument in which ionization in a gas was used to indicate the presence of nuclear radiation. The flow of ions and electrons to the leaves reduces their charge, causing them to collapse at a rate proportional to the ionization between them. The gaseous ionization chamber is a development of this. An applied electric field sweeps the liberated charges to the electrodes, and a sensitive amplifier enables

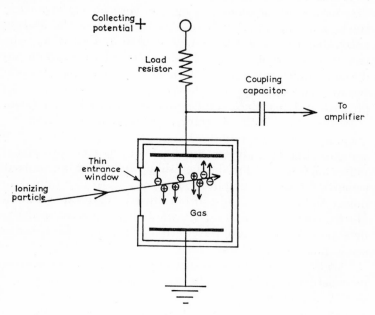

FIG. 2.1 Schematic diagram of a gaseous ionization chamber

the electrical pulse corresponding to the passage of a single nuclear particle to be detected.

The number of ion pairs resulting from direct ionization may be augmented by secondary processes following excitation of the gas atoms. Some of the electromagnetic radiation from excited atoms may be absorbed in the gas to produce further ion pairs. In the Auger effect an electronic transition in the excited atom may release sufficient energy for the ejection of a loosely-bound electron without accompanying radiation.

In about 10^{-7} sec after the passage of the nuclear particle the gas will contain ions and electrons with energies which have been reduced by collisions to below 10 eV. These begin to drift towards the electrodes at a rate dependent upon the electric field, the nature of the gas and its pressure and temperature. The electrons accelerate until they reach an energy at which they can first cause excitation of gas molecules in collisions. In argon this energy is about 10 eV, so the electrons may attain an effective temperature several hundred times the equilibrium value. The electron drift velocity is affected markedly by the addition of a small percentage of polyatomic gas, such as CO_2 or CH_4. These gases have lower energy levels for excitation so that the electron 'temperature' is kept lower. Under such conditions there is less randomization of the direction of electron drift by elastic collisions with gas molecules, and the net drift velocity is actually increased.

Certain electronegative gases such as oxygen, halogens and water-vapour capture electrons readily to form negative ions, the probability of capture being as much as one in a thousand for each collision with such a molecule. The inert gases, and nitrogen, hydrogen and methane, do not show this effect to any measurable degree, and such gases are therefore suitable for ionization chambers while even traces of electronegative gases must be strictly excluded.

Both positive and negative ions in a gas drift at a velocity, v, proportional to the electric field and inversely proportional to the pressure, p.

$$v \propto \mu E p_0 / p \qquad (2.1)$$

Here μ is the ion mobility and E the electric field strength. Ion mobilities in different gases vary between 1 and 10 in such units that E is in volts/cm and v is in cm/sec. A strong field is therefore required in order to collect these ions in a time less than 10^{-3} sec in a chamber of average dimensions. Equation (2.1) does not apply for electrons, for which the mobility is not a simple function of the pressure, and varies greatly with the composition of the gas mixture. Electron mobilities a thousand times that of the ions are not uncommon, however, in practical cases.

(b) Recombination

Electrons may collide with positive ions during the collection process and recombine with them. The rate at which this occurs is proportional to the density of both types of charge carrier.

$$\mathrm{d}n_-/\mathrm{d}t = a\, n_+\, n_- \qquad (2.2)$$

where n_+, n_- are the densities of positive ions and electrons respectively, and a is the recombination coefficient, which varies with the pressure, temperature and nature of the gas. The excess energy released in the recombination process may appear as radiation, or may be dissipated in a three-body collision. The latter process becomes important at higher pressures, for instance above 20 atm in helium.

The ions are not produced uniformly throughout the volume of the gas but lie initially along the track of the ionizing particle so that the ion density and therefore the recombination rate are much greater than in the case of a uniform distribution. This effect is termed columnar recombination and has been studied theoretically by Jaffé.[1] Another effect appears at high gas pressures, at which the electrons suffer many collisions and are brought to a low velocity while still only a short distance from the ionized track. The attraction between the positive ions and the surrounding electron sheath may be greater than the separating force due to the collecting field, so that recombination of ion pairs is enhanced until diffusion causes them to disperse. This effect appears as a pressure-dependence of the mean energy per ion-pair, w. We shall see in a later chapter that a similar form of recombination is observable in solids.

(c) Saturation

If the size of the output signal from an ionization chamber is measured for incident particles of a well-defined energy, it is found that the signal increases to a saturation value as the strength of the collecting field is increased. Figure 2.2 shows typical saturation curves in nitrogen obtained by Dick, Falk-Vairant and Rossel[2] at different pressures. Saturation is achieved when the field is sufficient to overcome the effect of recombination processes in the gas. Two factors account for the increase of saturation field with gas pressure. The first is the smaller drift velocity of both ions and electrons at higher pressures which allows a greater probability of recombination. The second is an enhanced recombination owing to greater attraction between the positive ions and the sheath of ejected electrons, since these are brought to rest closer to the ion track at higher gas pressures. A geometrical dependence

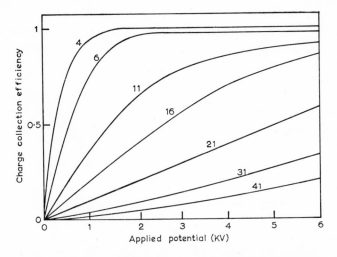

Fig. 2.2 Charge collection efficiency in nitrogen gas as a function of pressure and applied potential difference. The figure against each curve shows the pressure in kgm/cm^2; from DICK, FALK-VAIRANT and ROSSEL[2]

of the rate of columnar recombination on the angle between the field and the ionized track is also observed. The ion density remains greatest for collection parallel to the column of ions, while if the collecting field is at right angles to the track the ions are rapidly separated and the recombination rate is low.

The saturation field is higher if electronegative gases, such as oxygen, are present, since they may capture electrons to form negative ions. The mobility of these ions is much less than that of electrons so that the rate of separation of charge carriers is reduced and recombination becomes more probable.

(d) The shape of the pulse

Potential energy considerations show that the voltage induced at the collecting electrode by the motion of an ion is directly proportional to the potential difference through which it has moved. If recombination is neglected the rate of change of voltage at the electrode is therefore proportional to the velocity of the ion or electron towards that electrode. In gas counters this results in a fast and a slow component to the

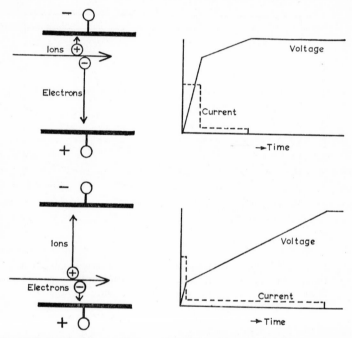

Fig. 2.3 Current and voltage pulse formation in a gaseous ionization chamber, illustrating the effect of different locations of the ionized track. For clarity, the ratio of electron to ion velocity is shown here as 8:1, in fact the ratio is of the order 1000:1.

rise of the voltage pulse due to collection of electrons and ions, respectively, since the electron velocity is of the order of a thousand times that of the ions. The relative magnitudes of the fast and slow components of the pulse depend on the relative distances of the two electrodes from the path of the ionizing particle. This is illustrated in Fig. 2.3. Fast pulse operation is generally desirable since the counter can then be used in a strong flux of particles. A partial solution to the problem is achieved in a cylindrical counter in which the anode is a thin wire along the axis. The potential drop is then concentrated near the anode and the major component of the pulse is due to fast collection of electrons through this potential drop. Another method was devised by Frisch.[3] A grid is introduced to separate the collector from the bulk of the chamber in which ionization occurs. Electrons are drawn through the grid, subsequently all moving through the same potential difference to the collector. Only a fast pulse proportional to the initial ionization appears between grid and collector.

(e) Energy resolution of ionization chambers

Ionization chambers, generally of the fast, gridded type, have been employed for many precision studies of charged particles from nuclear reactions initiated either inside or outside the chamber itself, or from a radioactive source. If the reaction takes place outside the chamber a thin window must be provided whereby particles can enter without appreciable straggling in energy. The amplitude of the output pulse height is subject to the fluctuations in the number of ionization events, as discussed in Section 1.4 of Chapter 1. There is, furthermore, a spread in the amplified pulse height due to electrical noise in the amplifier circuit. The standard deviation in pulse height due to this noise in the best present-day amplifiers corresponds to an input charge equivalent to the collection of about 300 ion pairs. This leads to a full width at half the maximum value of the pulse height distribution of over 20 keV. A 5 MeV alpha particle produces about 2.10^5 events if stopped within a chamber, so that, assuming a Fano factor of $\frac{1}{2}$, the standard deviation of pulse height is again about 300 ion pairs. These two factors account for the observed line widths, which have rarely been better than 30 keV. Recently, however, a remarkably low Fano factor of 0·09 has been achieved by Vorob'ev, Komar and Korolev[4] using a mixture of argon with 0·8 per cent of acetylene, which gave a line width for 5·68 MeV alpha particles of only 14 keV. This figure is close to the best (11 keV) which has been obtained with silicon detectors for alpha particles of this energy.

(f) The proportional counter

If the electric field in an ionization chamber is raised sufficiently electrons may gain sufficient energy between collisions
to cause ionization of the gas molecules. Electrons so produced
can themselves initiate further ionization so that an 'avalanche'
results. The charge collected at the electrodes then exceeds
that released in the initial ionization by a factor M, known
as the gas multiplication factor, which may under suitable
conditions be as high as 10^4. In order that the multiplication
factor should be as far as possible independent of the position
of the primary ionization in the chamber a cylindrical geometry is adopted. A fine wire anode produces a radial field
which is sufficient to produce multiplication only in a volume
very close to the wire so that M is the same for every pulse.

Fluctuations in pulse height occur due to any non-uniformity of the anode wire, and to smaller values of M in the
weaker field at the ends of the wire. Some form of guard-ring
is necessary to prevent field distortion here.

The output pulse rises to half amplitude in about 10^{-6} sec,
during which the electrons are collected. The slow component
of the pulse corresponding to ion collection takes much longer,
and the pulses are usually clipped short by an appropriate
coupling time-constant in the amplifier circuit. The counter
requires a time of about 100 μsec to recover completely after
a pulse, as the slowly-moving ion cloud modifies the collecting
field for this period.

Proportional counters are most valuable for the detection
of radiation which yields small amounts of ionization, for
instance X-rays and low-energy electrons. By making use of
gas amplification it has proved possible to obtain a standard
deviation of only 1 per cent in pulses due to 100 keV electrons, corresponding to a full line width at half maximum of only 2·5 keV.

(g) The Geiger counter

If the anode potential of a proportional counter is raised
sufficiently the output pulses fail to remain proportional to
the primary ionization and finally become of uniform amplitude, irrespective of the type or energy of the incident particle
or photon. The counter is then said to be operating in the
Geiger region.

The mechanism of operation depends upon emission of ultra-violet radiation from many atoms excited during the avalanche of electrons towards the anode wire. In the earlier forms of Geiger counter these photons eject photoelectrons from the metal walls of the counter. The photoelectrons are accelerated towards the anode, near which they produce further avalanches which spread in this manner along the entire length of the anode. The process ceases only when the space charge of slowly-moving positive ions reduces the electric field sufficiently to limit the number of electrons and excited atoms in the avalanche. When, eventually, positive ions reach the cathode they also may eject photoelectrons and so initiate a self-sustaining discharge in the counter. A number of electronic circuit arrangements have been devised to prevent this by reduction of the anode voltage for a time sufficient to prevent secondary pulses due to positive ion impacts. Such counters are now termed 'non-self-quenching'.

The other type of Geiger counter, called 'self-quenching', will operate without need for such a circuit. A small amount of polyatomic vapour such as alcohol or acetone is introduced into the gas filling. This causes photons from the electron avalanche to be strongly absorbed in the vapour, owing to its low ionization potential, and photoelectrons are produced close to the anode wire. The discharge spreads rapidly along the anode, at a speed of about 10^7 cm/sec. The polyatomic vapour plays a two-fold role since it also prevents positive ions from reaching the cathode. Collisions between positive ions and vapour molecules lead to neutralization of the ions because of the potential energy release on exchange of an electron. Positively charged polyatomic molecules thus arrive at the cathode, where, instead of ejecting secondary electrons, the molecules tend predominantly to dissociate so that the discharge terminates.

In both types of Geiger the recovery time is of the order of 200 μsec although the rise time of the output pulse may be only 1 μsec. The counters are useful in providing large signals which require little amplification, but they cannot be used to distinguish between different types of ionizing radiation nor do they give any measure of the energy of the incident particle or photon.

2.3 The scintillation counter

(a) Requirements of the scintillation counter

In this detector the scintillations emitted from atoms which are excited, directly or indirectly, by the passage of the radiation are converted to an electrical signal which is then amplified. Many early experiments were carried out, by Rutherford and others, in which scintillations from a screen coated with small crystals of zinc sulphide were observed and counted visually. The full possibilities of the method were not realized until the development of sensitive photomultiplier tubes.

The scintillator, or phosphor, may be solid, liquid or gaseous, the solid type being the most common. By comparison with

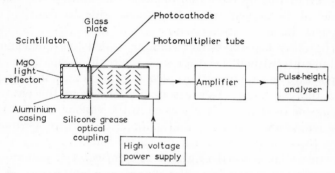

FIG. 2.4 A typical scintillation counter assembly (After PRICE, W. J., *Nuclear Radiation Detection* (McGraw-Hill, 1958))

gaseous ionization chambers, solid scintillation counters have the advantage of a detection medium of high electron density, in which particles and gamma rays have a short range. High efficiency for the detection of gammas is therefore obtained in a relatively small volume. Scintillation counters also give a fast output signal and are capable of relatively good energy resolution. With organic phosphors it is possible to distinguish between certain types of radiation by analysis of the pulse shape.

The arrangement of phosphor and photomultiplier is generally as shown in Fig. 2.4. Light received at the sensitive photocathode of the multiplier causes the emission of photoelectrons which are then accelerated through the structure of the tube. This is designed so that electrons collide with a number of plates, or dynodes, at which amplification by secondary electron emission occurs. If at each of n stages the secondary electron emission exceeds the incident pulse of electrons by a factor δ, the overall gain is δ^n, so that fast amplification with a gain of the order 10^6 can be easily achieved if n is 10 and δ about 4.

Two types of luminescent emission in the phosphor must be distinguished. Electrons which are raised into higher excited states by the Coulomb field of the nuclear particle can return to lower energy states either directly or via an intermediate state. If, while occupying this metastable state, the electron is raised back into its initial excited state by gaining thermal energy it may subsequently reach the ground state by emission of radiation corresponding in energy to the initial absorption. This delayed emission of radiation is called phosphorescence, the direct process being termed fluorescence. The intensity of phosphorescent emission increases with temperature, and whereas fluorescence takes place rapidly there is a time lag, generally of at least 10^{-8} sec, in the phosphorescent decay. Only those scintillators which have a short duration of phosphorescence are useful as detectors. Further requirements are that the scintillator should be transparent to its own luminescent radiation, and the spectral distribution of the radiation should match as far as possible the response curve of the multiplier photocathode.

Since the mechanism of operation is rather different in the cases of organic and inorganic scintillators it is necessary to consider these two types separately.

(b) Organic scintillators

Efficient fluorescence is obtained only when other modes of decay are minimized. Molecular dissociation and the radiationless transfer of energy to molecular vibrations should therefore be avoided. Aromatic hydrocarbons with linked benzene-ring structures, such as anthracene, stilbene and naphthalene satisfy such requirements and are transparent to optical radiation. Phosphorescence is only slight in pure crystals of these substances.

The fluorescence of such a molecule is best illustrated by a potential energy diagram (Fig. 2.5), in which the energy is shown as a function of interatomic distance. A series of closely-spaced vibrational states of the molecule is shown corresponding to each of the two electronic energy states concerned in the process. The nuclear radiation causes an electron to be excited $(A \rightarrow B)$ in a time which is short in comparison with

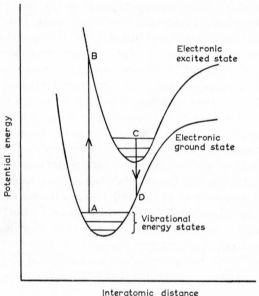

FIG. 2.5 Potential energy diagram for an organic scintillator; from PRICE, W. J., *Nuclear Radiation Detection* (McGraw-Hill, 1958)

the time of vibration of the molecule (the so-called Franck-Condon principle). The transition is therefore represented by a vertical line to the corresponding vibrational energy state. By successive collisions with other molecules the vibrational state C is reached, that potential energy which is lost appearing as heat. The fluorescent emission corresponds to the rapid transition $C \rightarrow D$ after which there may be further loss as heat until a lower vibrational state is reached. The energy of emitted radiation is thus lower than the absorbed energy and will generally be too low to excite electronic transitions in other molecules. Organic crystals can thus be transparent to their own fluorescent radiation. The fluorescent decay of organic scintillators is very fast; in anthracene, for example, Birks[5] finds a fluorescence lifetime of $3 \cdot 5 \times 10^{-9}$ sec.

If a small amount of some other hydrocarbon is present in solid solution the fluorescent emission is reduced and the emission spectrum will often contain a high proportion of radiation characteristic of the impurity. Thus a molar concentration of $0 \cdot 01$ per cent naphthacene in anthracene gives an emission spectrum in which 70 per cent of the radiation is characteristic of naphthacene. An efficient transfer of energy from the excited molecules to the impurity centres therefore occurs, and it has been shown probable that this takes place by the migration of what are termed 'excitons'. Each molecule is coupled in resonance with its neighbours, and in such a system excitation energy may be transferred from molecule to molecule through the crystal. It is convenient to picture the process as the migration of an exciton with a definite energy. Excited molecules may therefore decay by fluorescence, by a radiationless transition, or by exciton emission. Excitons move through the crystal and may encounter an impurity molecule for which there may be a high probability of fluorescent decay. Such a model for energy transfer is in good agreement with experimental measurements on the effect of different impurity concentrations.

(c) Inorganic scintillators

Inorganic crystals suitable as scintillators are transparent insulators, primarily the alkali halides, and in distinction from organic scintillators they are most efficient when containing small quantities of suitable impurities, known as 'activators'.

Excitons again play a major part in the mechanism of scintillation, on the basis of ideas put forward by Meyer and Murray.[6] Excitons migrate through the crystal until they encounter an impurity atom for which there is a high probability of exciation followed by radiative decay. This fluorescent radiation is generally too low in energy to excite electrons in the main constituent of the scintillator and as a result the crystal is transparent to the luminescent radiation. The activator may in addition be chosen to give an emission spectrum most suited to the photomultiplier response curve. Common activators are thallium in alkali halides and silver in zinc sulphide, used in concentrations of the order of 0·1 per cent, which corresponds to an activator site at intervals of about ten lattice sites.

The conversion of nuclear particle energy into light energy is much more efficient in these inorganic scintillators than in organic crystals. However, the decay time of the fluorescence is much longer, and in thallium-activated sodium iodide, for instance, the characteristic decay time is 0·25 μsec. The higher density of inorganic scintillators and in particular the high atomic number of the iodine constituent of the alkali iodides make them particularly suitable for gamma-ray detection.

(d) Variation of response with particle type and energy

The variation of light output with particle energy in a scintillation counter is slightly non-linear, particularly at low energies below about 0·5 MeV. Thus Engelkemeir[7] showed that the light output per unit energy of gamma rays in NaI(Tl) varied by as much as 20 per cent over the range 0 to 1 MeV. Figure 2.6 shows the results of measurements by Iredale[8] on this effect. The light output per unit energy also varies greatly with the type of radiation detected. Thus the pulse height in NaI(Tl) due to an electron of 5 MeV is approximately twice that of an alpha of the same energy, the ratio depending upon the temperature of the crystal and its method of preparation. The reasons for this behaviour have only recently become clear.

Again there are differences between organic and inorganic scintillators. In the former, Birks[9] has attributed the decrease in fluorescent light output with increasing rate of fluorescent emission to the presence of damaged molecules along the ion track. Clarke, Northrop and Simpson[10] have found, however, that such an explanation can, at most, account for 10 per cent of the observed effect. Instead they attribute the low conversion efficiency for excitation by heavily ionizing particles to an increase in the proportion of non-radiative transitions. Such transitions occur from states which are more readily

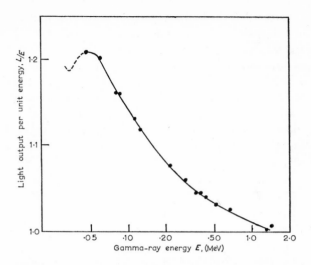

FIG. 2.6 Light output per unit energy as a function of gamma-ray energy for a $1\frac{1}{2}$ in. x 1 in. crystal of thallium-activated sodium iodide; from IREDALE[17]

excited by the low-energy electrons produced in the passage of a heavier particle.

It is also found that, besides the short-duration fluorescence, there is a tail corresponding to a decay time of the order 10^{-6} sec, and the relative amounts of light in the main pulse and in the delayed tail depend on the type of particle which excites the scintillation. This enhanced tail emission due to densely ionizing particles has enabled a useful method of discrimination between pulses due to gammas and heavy particles, by means of the difference in pulse shape (Brooks,[11] Owen[12]). Gibbons, Northrop and Simpson[13] have put forward the hypothesis that the slow component of the decay is due to interactions between pairs of excitons, the observed decay time being interpreted as that for a metastable complex of two excited molecules. The intensity of the scintillation tail is found to depend quadratically on the exciton lifetime, in accordance with this model.

In the inorganic scintillators, Meyer and Murray[6] account for the observed diminution of light output per unit energy with increasing density of ionization in terms of saturation of the activator sites near the ionized track. A diffusion equation relating the migration, decay and capture rates of excitons at activator atoms satisfactorily explains the observed effects, such as for instance the dip in light output[14] from CsI(Tl) around 100 keV for alphas, at which dE/dx is at a maximum (see Fig. 2.7). Some recent evidence from measurements with heavy ions has revealed differences in light output per unit energy loss for different ions at equal values of dE/dx. Murray and Meyer[15] explain this as due to different yields of fast electrons, or delta rays, which emerge from the saturation

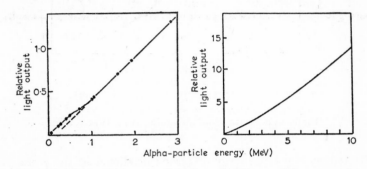

FIG. 2.7 Light output as a function of alpha particle energy in a thallium-activated caesium iodide scintillator; from GWIN and MURRAY[14]

column into regions in which scintillation can occur with greater efficiency (see Fig. 2.8).

(e) Efficiency and resolution of scintillation counters

The operation of a scintillation counter involves no less than five consecutive processes, and statistical fluctuations in the probability of each of these influence the overall energy resolution of the system. These are:

- (a) Excitation and ionization along the track of the nuclear radiation.
- (b) Conversion of energy of excitation into light energy by the process of fluorescence.
- (c) Transfer of the light through the crystal and on to the cathode of the photomultiplier tube.

(d) Absorption of light at the photocathode with emission of photoelectrons.

(e) Electron multiplication at successive dynodes of the photomultiplier.

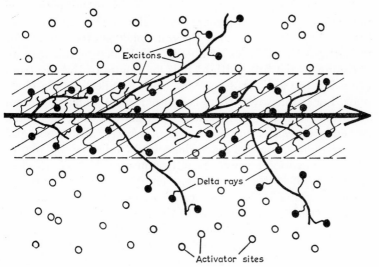

FIG. 2.8 Diagram to illustrate the Meyer and Murray scintillation model. The shaded area represents the approximate extent of the 'saturated column' in which almost all the activator sites are excited (shown black) by excitons migrating through the crystal from the track of the ionizing particle or the delta rays which it produces

Morton[16] calculates that a beta particle dissipates 30 to 50 eV in sodium iodide for each detectable photon produced, which represents a conversion efficiency from kinetic to light energy of about ten per cent. Other scintillators are less efficient. Despite choice of scintillator, activator and photo-cathode material to give a good match between the fluorescence spectrum and the photocathode response, the overall efficiency is low. Thus at best one photoelectron is released from the photocathode for each 300 eV of energy dissipated in a crystal of NaI(Tl), while in the organic scintillators the energy dissipation is between 1 and 5 keV per photoelectron. These values are to be compared with 3–4 eV per electron released in a semiconductor detector. It is clearly a more efficient process to collect all the charges liberated in ionization rather than to utilize the complex and inefficient processes by which charges migrate to an atom, causing it to emit light which is then reconverted to give a flux of electrons at a photocathode.

The energy resolution of a scintillation counter for charged particles is determined principally by fluctuations in the number of electrons produced at the multiplier photocathode. For monoenergetic particles of about 5 MeV energy this sets an optimum to the full width at half maximum of the spectrum of nearly 150 keV, or 3 per cent, with an alkali halide phosphor. For gamma rays there is another effect which causes an additional broadening. Iredale[17] has shown that, since the full energy peak is due both to photoelectric absorption and one or more Compton scattering events followed by photoelectric capture, the non-linear response of NaI(Tl) to electrons will affect the resolution. There is a further source of variance owing to the wide range of energies of delta rays produced in the slowing down of the electrons. Together these effects account for the results of Kelley *et al.*,[18] in which an intrinsic energy resolution of 6·6 per cent was found in a sodium iodide crystal, for 660 keV gammas. A small effect is to be expected even for heavy charged particles, owing to the non-linear response to delta rays of varying energy.

2.4 Nuclear emulsions

Photographic emulsions adapted for nuclear radiation detection consist of a high concentration of small silver halide crystals in a relatively thick gelatin film. When a charged particle passes through it activates the silver halide grains along its track, by excitation and ionization, in such a way that the whole grain can be converted to silver by subsequent development. The track of the particle can thus be made observable with the aid of a microscope, while the density of developed grains is related to the ionization density along the track.

It is interesting to compare this type of detector with other solid counters. The density of the emulsion is high, nearly 4 gm/cm³, and it has a high stopping power. The sensitive volume can be relatively large if many emulsions are stacked together, or if required it can be made very small and compact. The detector is continuously sensitive and can store a very large amount of information. The arrangement has no intrinsic time resolution, of course, and there is no means by which the properties of the detector itself can be altered during an observation. The emulsion can, however, give extremely precise information as to the spatial location and direction of motion of a nuclear particle, features which it is difficult to measure in other systems. Particle mass, charge and energy can be deduced from studies of track length, grain density and the magnitude of small-angle deflections along the track arising from Coulomb scattering. Most of the precision determinations of particle energies from nuclear transitions have been made with magnetic spectrographs, making use of the excellent spatial definition of the nuclear emulsion. Particles with a wide range of energies can be brought to a focus on a long strip of emulsion in a broad-range magnetic spectrograph, and instruments of this type allow discrimination between charged particle groups differing in energy by only 0·05 per cent.

2.5 Neutron detection methods

(a) *Introduction*

Neutrons produce no ionization directly but there are several processes by which the neutron energy can be transferred to one or more charged particles which are detected in the usual way. The most important of these processes are:

(1) Neutron-induced reactions in which protons, alpha particles or fission fragments are emitted. In certain light nuclei an (n, p) or (n, α) reaction may be accompanied by a considerable energy release, Q. The reaction products then consist of two fast ions with a total kinetic energy equal to the incident neutron energy together with the energy release, Q. The linear relation between the total kinetic energy and the neutron energy is important for fast neutron spectroscopy. Reactions commonly applied to this are:

$$B^{10} (n, \alpha) Li^7, Q = 2\cdot78 \text{ MeV}$$
$$Li^6 (n, \alpha) H^3, Q = 4\cdot77 \text{ MeV}$$
$$He^3 (n, p) H^3, Q = 0\cdot76 \text{ MeV}$$

Certain fission processes are induced only by neutrons which exceed a certain energy threshold so that a detector based on such a reaction can be made sensitive only to fast neutrons. Thus Np^{237} has a fission threshold of 0·75 MeV.

(2) Elastic scattering of a neutron by a very light target nucleus resulting in a charged recoiling ion. By far the most important case is that in which neutrons are scattered by hydrogen nuclei, since the recoil proton can receive energy up to 100 per cent of that of the incident neutron.

(3) Neutron-induced beta activity in a suitable sample. The amount of activity produced is a measure of the neutron flux to which the sample has been exposed. The half-life of the activity should be neither too long nor too short since in one case the counting time will be excessive and in the other the activity decays before the sample can be conveyed to the β-counting equipment. The radiation should consist of fairly

TABLE 2.1

Activation methods for neutron detection

(a) *Thermal Detectors*

Isotope	Thermal activation cross-section	Half-life of product	Principal induced activity
In^{115}	145 barns	54·1 min	β^-(1 MeV); γ (several energies)
Au^{197}	96	27 days	β^-(0·963 MeV); γ (0·41 MeV)
I^{127}	5·5	25 min	β^-(2·0 MeV)
Mn^{55}	13·4	2·58 hr	β^-(2·81 MeV); γ (0·82 MeV)

(b) *Threshold Detectors*

Reaction	Effective threshold	Half-life of product	Average cross-section for fission neutrons
P^{31} (n, p) Si^{31}	2·5 MeV	2·6 hrs	0·075 barns
S^{32} (n, p) P^{32}	2·9	14·3 days	0·30
Al^{27} (n, α) Na^{24}	8·6	15 hrs	0·11
Si^{28} (n, p) Al^{28}	6·1	2·3 min	0·19

(Adapted from tables in *Nuclear Radiation Detection* by W. J. Price (McGraw-Hill).)

high energy betas or associated gammas so that absorption within the sample is minimized. The neutron capture cross-section and its energy dependence are important in relation to the flux intensity and energy range to be studied. A few commonly employed isotopes for activation detectors are listed in Table 2.1.

(b) Neutron detector systems

Energy is transferred most efficiently from the converter isotope to the detector if the isotope can be dispersed throughout the detection medium itself, and this is accomplished in a number of useful detectors. A proportional counter containing BF_3 gas, enriched in B^{10}, has a high efficiency for the detection of slow neutrons by means of the B^{10} (n, α) reaction. The efficiency of this counter falls off rapidly with neutron energy, owing to the decrease in reaction cross-section, but Hanson and McKibben[19] have devised a system in which a number of long BF_3 counters are embedded in a carefully designed paraffin block. Neutrons entering at the end of this so-called 'long-counter' are partially slowed down or 'thermalized' and the counter efficiency remains moderately constant with neutron energy up to several MeV. Bollinger[20] has described a boron-loaded liquid scintillation counter while nuclear emulsions may also be impregnated with B^{10} or Li^6. Lithium iodide, activated with thallium, is a good scintillator and, being solid, the detector has a high efficiency. Thus a 2 cm thick Li^6 I(Tl) crystal is 90 per cent efficient for absorption of thermal neutrons. A more recent development is that of a Li^6-loaded glass scintillator. A He^3-filled proportional counter, operating by the He^3 (n, p) H^3 reaction can give an energy resolution better than 70 keV for fast neutrons, together with the relatively high detection efficiency of 0·2 per cent.

The fission process is often utilized in conjunction with gaseous counters since fission fragments have a sufficiently short range in a gas. Thus one electrode of an ionization chamber or proportional counter may be coated with fissile material for neutron detection.

The proton recoil method can be adapted for use with almost all detector methods. A proportional counter may be filled with methane or a mixture of hydrogen and argon, or alternatively the chamber may be lined with hydrogenous material such as polyethylene. Discrimination against pulses due to a high gamma-ray background can be achieved by operating a pair of ion chambers side by side, one filled with methane and the other with argon. The pressures in the two chambers are adjusted until the mean background due to gammas is equal in the two halves and then, for a mixed flux, subtraction of the spectra gives the true proton-recoil yield. Organic scintillators contain a high proportion of hydrogen in a dense medium and the scintillation counter is capable of a very fast response. It is therefore valuable in connection with time-of-flight methods for neutron velocity measurement. Since, as described in Section 2.3(d), a greater proportion of the luminescence occurs in the tail of the pulse for heavily ionizing recoil protons than for beta or gamma radiation, a useful discrimination between neutrons and gammas can be achieved by pulse shape analysis. The output pulse from organic scintillators is small, but a larger output can be obtained from a compound medium of about 15 per cent ZnS, activated with silver, dispersed in perspex, which provides the source of recoil protons. Such a device,[21] known as a 'Hornyak button', gives relatively good discrimination against gammas. Nuclear emulsions can be used for fast neutron detection by measurement of recoil proton tracks resulting from the hydrogen content of gelatin.

2.6 The spark chamber

This simple form of counter consists essentially of a pair of parallel conducting plates with gas between them. A high voltage is applied between the plates, not quite sufficient to cause electrical breakdown through the gas. When an ionizing particle crosses the gap between the plates sufficient ionization is produced to initiate a discharge in the form of a spark. It is generally necessary to pulse the potential difference on for short intervals of time so that sparking does not occur continuously. Between the pulses a small 'sweeping field' removes ions from the chamber. Besides providing a fast signal which can be used for recording the time of arrival of the particle, the spark counter can also give reasonably precise information regarding the spatial location of its track, if the spark is photographed.

A number of investigations of suitable gases, electrode materials and operating characteristics have now been published; see, for example, the paper by Burleson, Roberts and Romanowski.[22] Although most of the applications of such counters have been in high energy physics, supplementing

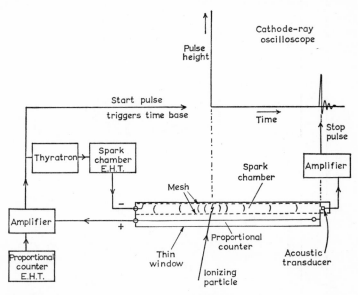

FIG. 2.9 Schematic diagram of the spark chamber with acoustic delay line used by D. L. ALLAN[25] with a broad-range magnetic spectrometer. The shallow proportional counter provides a signal which triggers on the spark chamber high tension

the bubble-chamber, some interesting applications have been made in the high-resolution spectrometry of low-energy charged particles. Fulbright[23] made the suggestion that an acoustic transducer might be used to measure the time delay in arrival of the sound wave at the end of a spark chamber by the interval following the electrical discharge. In this way the position of the spark has been located electronically[24, 25] to an accuracy of about 0·3 mm. Such a system can then be used in conjunction with magnetic analysis of charged particles in

TABLE 2.2

Type of Radiation	Application	Detector	Advantages	Disadvantages
Alphas (natural source) Charged particles (protons, deuterons, alphas) from nuclear reactions up to 50 MeV	Energy and flux measurement in nuclear physics	(*i*) Gridded ion chamber	High energy resolution Large area	For short range particles only Thin window required, or source must be mounted inside counter Slow response
		(*ii*) Magnetic analysis, with scintillation detector	High energy resolution. Can measure weak groups in the presence of other strong ones	Small solid angle Very bulky apparatus Counter affected by magnetic field
		(*iii*) Magnetic analysis, with nuclear emulsion	Highest possible energy resolution Can measure weak groups in the presence of other strong ones	Very small solid angle Very bulky apparatus Results not immediately available
		(*iv*) Magnetic analysis, with acoustic delay line	High energy resolution Can measure weak groups in the presence of other strong ones Results immediately available	Very small solid angle Very bulky apparatus Limited counting rate
		(*v*) CsI scintillation counter	Large detector area Fast response	Only moderate energy resolution Not very compact

Alphas and betas (Large area weak source)	Health physics	(*i*) Proportional counter	Large detector area Simple operation	Not very compact Requires high-voltage supply Thin alpha window is fragile
		(*ii*) CsI scintillation counter, as mean-level device	Fairly large detector area	Requires high-voltage supply Not very compact Fragile
Alphas and betas (Small weak source)	Wound probe Biological tracer studies	(*i*) Catheter-type Geiger counter	Small diameter. Robust	Low efficiency for betas Requires high-voltage supply
		(*ii*) Scintillation counter	Good energy resolution	Requires light guide Not very compact
Betas below 1 MeV	Energy and flux measurement in nuclear physics	(*i*) Anthracene or stilbene scintillation counter	Moderately large detector area Moderate energy resolution Fast signal	Not very compact Response non-linear with energy
Betas below 0·1 MeV	Energy and flux measurement in nuclear physics	(*i*) Proportional counter	Good energy resolution Large detector area	Limited to short-range betas Slow signal
Betas 0·1-5 MeV	Energy and flux measurement in nuclear physics	(*i*) Plastic scintillation counter	Large detector volume Fast signal	Not very compact Only moderate energy resolution
		(*ii*) Magnetic analysis with scintillation detector	Very good energy resolution	Bulky apparatus Small solid angle
X-rays and gammas below 100 keV	Energy and flux measurement in nuclear physics	Proportional counter	Good energy resolution	Low efficiency Slow signal

55

Type of radiation	Application	Detector	Advantages	Disadvantages
Gammas above 100 keV	Energy and flux measurement in nuclear physics	NaI (Tl) scintillation counter	Moderately good energy resolution Large detector volume Relatively high Z – good efficiency Fairly fast signal	Not very compact Subject to gain shift with counting rate in a high flux Affected by magnetic fields
Gammas above 100 keV	Health physics	Ionization chamber, as mean-level device	Simple in operation Robust	Requires high-voltage supply Small output
Thermal neutrons	Reactor control	B^{10} ion chamber	Discriminates neutrons from gammas Stable	
	Flux density mapping	(i) Activation foil	Compact	Result not immediately available
		(ii) Small B^{10} ionization chamber	Result immediately available Robust	Presence may affect flux Not very compact Low efficiency
	Health physics	B^{10} ion chamber	Good discrimination against gammas High efficiency	
	Flux measurement	Li^6 – glass scintillation counter		Not very compact
Fast neutrons	Energy and flux measurement in nuclear physics	(i) He^3 proportional counter	Good energy resolution High efficiency	Spectrum ambiguous due to He^3 recoils Slow signal
		(ii) Time-of-flight system with organic scintillation counter	Very good energy resolution	Requires pulsed source of neutrons Low efficiency

Radiation type	Application	Detector	Advantages	Disadvantages
	Health physics	(i) Tissue-equivalent proportional counter	Robust	Low efficiency
		(ii) Scintillation counter with pulse shape discrimination	High efficiency	Not very compact
	Flux measurement	Long counter	Good efficiency, stable	Requires calibration; Bulky apparatus—can affect the flux
Weakly interacting radiation (e.g. neutrinos)	Flux measurement	Large-volume liquid scintillator	Large detector volume	High cost
	Energy and flux measurement	(i) High density glass scintillator	High efficiency	Only moderate energy resolution
		(ii) Čerenkov counter	Can discriminate against low energy particles	Cannot be triggered
Very high energy particles	Rare events and complex processes	(i) Nuclear emulsion	Continuously sensitive; High electron density	Good spatial definition
		(ii) Cloud chamber	Can be triggered	Low electron density
		(iii) Bubble chamber	Can be triggered; Liquid can be used as target and counter	Low repetition rate; Low rate of operation
		(iv) Spark chamber	Can be triggered; Fast operation	Only moderate spatial definition

a similar way to the nuclear emulsion. By comparison, the poorer spatial resolution of the spark counter is often outweighed by the fact that the results are immediately available. Allan[25] has used a shallow proportional counter in front of the spark chamber in order to distinguish sparks not due to charged particles. Since the sound wave takes an appreciable time to travel across the chamber through what is effectively an acoustic delay line, the dead time of the system may be as much as a millisecond.

2.7 Advantages and limitations of earlier detectors

It is important to bear in mind, during the detailed discussion of the design of semiconductor counters, the limitations and useful features of previously existing types of counter. This is because the design of a detector depends greatly upon the purpose for which it is required. We shall see in subsequent chapters that semiconductor counters have a number of advantages in fields for which existing detectors had some limitation. Likewise, the future development of semiconductor counters is guided by requirements which are not at present satisfied by, for instance, the scintillation counter.

For reasons of brevity, these good and bad features of various types of counter are summarized in Table 2.2, under the headings of certain common applications. Typical inadequacies noted concern the energy resolution, range of operation, compactness, speed of response, robustness, and detection efficiency of the counter. These are therefore features which are to be examined closely in new types of detector.

In conclusion, a detector can only be discussed usefully in relation to the considerable armoury which has, mainly within the past two decades, become available to meet the ever-increasing demands of nuclear radiation measurement. The semiconductor counter has rapidly proved to be a most powerful and flexible instrument for such work.

REFERENCES

For this chapter

1. Jaffé, G. *Phys. Zeits.*, **30**, 849 (1929).
2. Dick, L., Falk-Vairant, P. and Rossel, J., *Helv. Phys. Acta*, **20**, 357 (1947).

3. Frisch, O. R., *British Atomic Energy Report BR 49* (1945).
4. Vorob'ev, A. A., Komar, A. P. and Korolev, V. A., *J.E.T.P.*, **43**, 426 (1962). English translation in *Journ. Exp. Theor. Phys.*, **16**, 306 (1963).
5. Birks, J. B., *Phys. Rev.*, **94**, 1567 (1954).
6. Meyer, A. and Murray, R. B., *Phys. Rev.*, **122**, 815 (1961).
7. Engelkemeir, D., *Rev. Sci. Instr.*, **27**, 589 (1956).
8. Iredale, P., *Nucl. Instr. & Methods*, **11**, 336 (1961).
9. Birks, J. B., *Phys. Rev.*, **84**, 364 (1951).
10. Clarke, H. B., Northrop, D. C., and Simpson, O., *Proc. Phys. Soc.*, **79**, 366 (1962).
11. Brooks, F. D., *Nucl. Instr. & Methods*, **4**, 151 (1959).
12. Owen, R. B., *I.R.E. Trans. Nucl. Sci.*, NS-9, No. 3, 285 (1962).
13. Gibbons, P. E., Northrop, D. C. and Simpson, O., *Proc. Phys. Soc.*, **79**, 373 (1962).
14. Gwin, R. and Murray, R. B., *I.R.E. Trans. Nucl. Sci.*, NS-9, No. 3, 28 (1962).
15. Murray, R. B. and Meyer, A., *I.R.E. Trans. Nucl. Sci.*, NS-9, No. 3, 33 (1962).
16. Morton, G. A., *Proc. 1st Geneva Conf.*, vol. **14**, 246, U.N.O. (New York, 1956).
17. Iredale, P., *Nucl. Instr. & Methods*, **11**, 340 (1961).
18. Kelley, G. G., Bell, P. R., Davis, R. C. and Lazer, N. A., *I.R.E. Trans. on Nucl. Sci.*, NS-3, No. 4, 57 (1956).
19. Hanson, A. O. and McKibben, J. L., *Phys. Rev.*, **72**, 673 (1947).
20. Bollinger, L. M., *Proc. 1st Geneva Conf.*, vol. **4**, 47, U.N.O. (New York, 1956).
21. Hornyak, W. F., *Rev. Sci. Instr.*, **23**, 264 (1952).
22. Burleson, G. R., Roberts, A., and Romanowski, T. A., *Proc. Symp. on Nucl. Instr.*, Harwell, 1961, 104 (Heywood & Co. London, 1962).
23. Fulbright, H. W. and Kohler, D., *Proc. Symp. on Nucl. Instr.*, Harwell, 1961, 142 (Heywood & Co. London, 1962).
24. Whitehead, C., *Proc. Conf. on Instrumentation for High Energy Physics*, CERN 1962 (to be published).
25. Allan, D. L., private communication.

For general reading

Handbuch der Physik, vols. **44** and **45**, ed. Flugge, S., Julius Springer (Berlin, 1958).
Birks, J. B., *Scintillation Counters*, Pergamon Press (London, 1953).

Curran, S. C. and Craggs, J. D., *Counting Tubes and Their Applications*, Butterworths (London, 1949).

Price, W. J., *Nuclear Radiation Detection*, McGraw-Hill (New York, 1958).

Sharpe, J., *Nuclear Radiation Detectors*, Methuen (London, 1955).

Staub, H. H., 'Principles of Nuclear Particle Detection', in *Experimental Nuclear Physics*, vol. 1, ed. Segrè, E., Wiley (New York, 1953).

Wilkinson, D. H., *Ionization Chambers and Counters* (Cambridge University Press, 1950).

CHAPTER 3

PHYSICAL PROPERTIES OF SOLID STATE COUNTERS

3.1 Introduction

All the solid state counters to be discussed are ionization chambers in which the charges released during the absorption of radiation constitute the signals by which the radiation is detected. The processes by which radiation is absorbed all involve the production of one or more secondary electrons by the primary radiation. The secondaries in turn produce further ionization and the cascade process continues until no electron has enough energy to cause further impact ionization. In most cases therefore the number of ion pairs produced will depend only on the energy deposited by the primary radiation, and will be independent of the type of radiation. This gives the ion chamber its characteristic linear relation between signal amplitude and energy deposited, for all particles above a certain low threshold energy.

Semiconducting solids have a number of advantages over gaseous ionization chambers. Firstly, their greater density and stopping power make it feasible to achieve complete absorption of long-range particles such as beta particles and high-energy protons; these might have ranges of a metre or more in air, but could be absorbed completely in a millimetre of silicon. At the same time solid counters can be made very thin, when necessary, so that they absorb only a small part of the energy of incident particles, giving a measure of the specific ionization dE/dx. Subsequent total absorption of the particle to measure its total energy E then allows the particle to be identified. Secondly, and far more important, the accuracy with which E can be measured is greater for the solid counter than for either the gaseous ionization chamber or the scintillation counter. This is because the average energy needed to produce an ion-pair by impact ionization in a semiconductor is low. It is 3·6 eV in silicon compared with an average figure of about 30 eV for gases, or 300 eV per photo-electron in a scintillator photomultiplier combination. The available signal is therefore about eight times as big in silicon as in the other counters and the statistical fluctuations expressed as a percentage of the signal will be reduced by a factor of at least $2\sqrt{2}$. There is some uncertainty about this figure because of doubts about the Fano factor for semiconductors. It is to be expected that there will be some correlation between the final ionization processes in any cascade, because of the requirement that the energy of the initial radiation must be absorbed *exactly*. However, it was long thought that in solids, where lattice vibrations can take up energy in almost arbitrary amounts the correlation would be small. The results of Tavendale[1] and others have now shown that this view is erroneous and that the Fano factor in germanium is much less than unity – perhaps as low as 0·1. These results will be described more fully in the section dealing with lithium-drifted germanium detectors. There is no complete treatment of Fano factor in particular semiconductors, although, as indicated in section 1.4, a general argument shows that it must be less than unity.

There are, of course, difficulties to be overcome before the potential performance of solid counters can be fully realized. They all have to do with the properties of the crystal lattice through which the ion pairs produced by radiation have to move to give a signal in an external circuit. Firstly, the lattice will have finite electrical conductivity, so that any field applied to a counter to detect pulses of ionization will cause a standing current through the device. Unless this is very small it will interfere with the performance of the counter, either by generating noise comparable with the signals, or by interfering with the collection of charge. In general, therefore, the semiconductor should contain comparatively few free charge carriers. Secondly, semiconductors contain traps and other localized sites at which free charges may be held up or completely lost in their journey across the counter, so reducing the size of the observed signal. These centres can be tolerated only to a very limited extent, so it is unfortunate that they tend to be most numerous in those materials with low enough conductivities to satisfy the first criterion. A third problem is that of crystal uniformity. Unless the counter is uniform as regards most of its basic semiconductor properties it is unlikely to behave in an ideal way.

Before dealing with the basic theory of semiconductor counters more fully it may be of value to introduce the relevant concepts and terminology of solid state physics. The next section, without maintaining a rigorous treatment, tries to give a brief account of the thermal equilibrium properties of a simple semiconductor, and the ways in which a disturbed equilibrium is restored.

3.2 Properties of semiconductors

(a) Energy bands

To understand semiconductor conduction counters it is necessary to grasp some of the simpler fundamentals of the band theory and charge transport theory as applied to these materials. A digression is therefore necessary at this point for the benefit of those not familiar with semiconductor theory. The energy bands in a semiconductor arise from the allowed energy levels of electrons in the individual atoms which make up the crystal. In an isolated atom the allowed energies are very sharply defined, as is shown by the narrowness of the emission and absorption spectral lines of atoms. When a collection of atoms is brought together to form a crystal, Pauli's principle states that no two electrons can have exactly the same set of quantum numbers. The atomic energy levels therefore change, to an extent dictated by the closeness of the atoms and the periodicity of the electric field due to the atomic nuclei, and the sharply-defined energy levels of the separate atoms are broadened into bands of levels, each of which is non-localized; a property of the whole crystal. In the simplest case each band contains one level for each atom in the crystal. Adjacent bands may or may not overlap in energy.

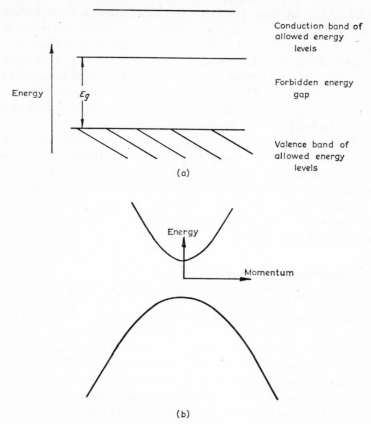

FIG. 3.1 Energy band diagrams of a semiconductor

Semiconductors and insulators have the property that, at the absolute zero of temperature, where the available electrons fill the lowest available energy levels, one or more energy bands are completely full, and the highest filled band is separated from the next higher band by an energy interval E_g in which there are no allowed levels. This is the basis for the familiar energy band diagram of Fig. 3.1(a) which shows the highest filled, or valence, band and the lowest empty, or conduction, band separated by an energy gap E_g.

Again, just as in an atom, the allowed energies are closely associated with allowed values of momentum, and an alternative method of depicting the valence and conduction bands is that shown in Fig. 3.1(b) which plots the allowed energies E as a function of the allowed momentum vectors $\mathbf{k}$. A very simple case is shown where the bands both have parabolic form with energy extrema at $\mathbf{k} = 0$. It is suitable for the present purpose, though things are not usually as simple as this.

At absolute zero no conduction can occur, because in this case there are no electrons in the conduction band, and the valence band being full means that no electron can have its momentum changed without there being an equal and opposite change in the momentum of another electron: the total momentum of the electrons in a full band is always zero. At any higher temperature there will be some thermal excitation of electrons from the valence band to the conduction band. In equilibrium these are balanced by electrons falling back into the vacant states in the valence band, resulting in a new population distribution between the two bands given by the Fermi function, which gives the occupation probability of a level at energy E as

$$f(E) = \frac{1}{1 + \exp{(E - \zeta)/kT}}$$

where k is Boltzmann's constant, T the absolute temperature, and ζ, the Fermi level, or Fermi energy, has the physical significance of that energy where the occupation probability of an allowed state would be $\frac{1}{2}$. It is symmetrical about the line $E = \zeta$ in the sense the probabilities of finding an electron at an energy ε above and below the Fermi level total unity. Figure 3.2(a) shows it for zero and high temperatures. To obtain the number of electrons in the conduction band (and the equal number of electrons missing from the valence band) the Fermi function has to be multiplied by the density of states function $N(E)$ shown schematically in Fig. 3.2(b). This is simply the number of allowed energy states per unit energy interval and is another property of the band structure of each semiconductor. In a pure (or intrinsic) semiconductor such as has been described here ζ is necessarily always in the centre of the forbidden energy gap, so that $(E - \zeta) = E_g/2$ for levels near the bottom of the conduction band. If, as is usually the case, $E_g \gg kT$ the Fermi function reduces to the simple

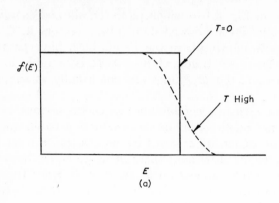

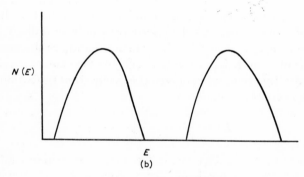

Fig. 3.2 (a) The Fermi function
(b) The density of states

exponential $\exp\left(-E_g/2kT\right)$ and the number of electrons in the conduction band is

$$n_i = N(E) \exp\left(-E_g/2kT\right) \tag{3.1}$$

The number of vacant states, p_i, in the valence band is equal to n_i.

An applied electric field can now produce net momentum changes in the electrons in the conduction band, and those in the valence band, giving two distinct contributions to the total current.

(b) Charge transport

Normally both the conduction band and the valence band will be partially filled, so that when an electric field is applied it can give energy and momentum to the electrons in each band. Usually the conduction band will be comparatively thinly populated with electrons which move essentially independently of one another. This automatically means that the valence band is almost full, and the collective motion of its electrons is more complicated, depending upon the vacant energy levels into which electrons can be accelerated by the field. In this situation, where energy and momentum are quantized in the way described by Fig. 3.1(b), the electron does not have its free space inertial mass as the constant relating its energy and momentum, but it has instead a quantum mechanical effective mass m^* given by the relation

$$\frac{1}{m^*} = \frac{4\pi^2}{h^2} \frac{\partial^2 E}{\partial \mathbf{k}^2} \qquad (3.2)$$

It will be seen by inspection of Fig. 3.1(b) that the effective mass of the electrons near the top of the valence band is negative. Rather than consider the collective motion of the electrons of negative effective mass in a nearly full band it is conventional to consider the vacant states as having positive mass and charge and calculating the valence band current by considering their motion as independent entities, holes. The total current density resulting from a field E is then

$$J = E\,e(n\mu_n + p\mu_p) \qquad (3.3)$$

where μ_n is the mobility of electrons in the conduction band, and μ_p that of holes in the valence band, n and p are the densities of electrons and holes in the respective bands, and e is the electronic charge.

In a pure semiconductor n and p would be equal, and given by equation (3.1). The mobilities have the same significance as those of electrons and ions in a gas discharge, i.e. the average drift velocity in the direction of a unit electric field, when on average the energy taken from the electric field is lost by scattering mechanisms to the lattice. Fortunately it will not be necessary to consider the various scattering processes, which can arise from interactions with the lattice vibrations or impurity molecules, or with the Coulomb fields due to charged impurities and other electrons and holes. These are rather complex topics, and it is often not clear which

scattering mechanism will predominate in a particular semiconductor at any given temperature. Two things should be
noted, however, for future reference; firstly, the semiconductors with sharply curving $E - \mathbf{k}$ plots will have low
effective masses and hence higher mobilities for a given set of
scattering conditions. Secondly, note that there is a limit to
the energy which any scattering event can absorb from a
moving charge carrier, so that at high fields the mobility is not
a constant, but is a function of field. The carriers are then no
longer in thermal equilibrium with the lattice, and are said to
be hot.

(c) Impurities and lattice defects

So far only intrinsic semiconductors have been discussed,
in which the numbers of holes and electrons are equal. Impurities or departures from perfect lattice structure modify
this simple picture by introducing localized energy levels,
usually in the forbidden energy gap. Localized centres may
become ionized either by donating an electron to the conduction band (donors) or accepting one from the valence band
(acceptors), and the energy needed for these processes will be
less than the energy gap E_g. Either of these processes will give
only one free charge carrier in one of the bands, so that the
equality between the numbers of electrons and holes is broken,
and the semiconductor is said to be extrinsic. The number of
free charges at any temperature now depends on the numbers
of impurities and their activation energy; for example, N_D
donor levels at an energy E_D would result in an electron
concentration

$$n = N_D \frac{1}{1 + \exp{(E_D - \zeta)/kT}} \qquad (3.4)$$

It can be shown that in an extrinsic semiconductor $np = n_i^2$
where n_i is the intrinsic carrier density, so that the equation
for the current density is simplified by having only one type
of carrier to consider.

Localized centres are important not only for adding to the
numbers of charge carriers, but also, in other circumstances,
for reducing them. They can act as traps at which holes or
electrons become localized for some period of time, subse-

quently returning to the band where they again contribute to the conductivity. Centres of this kind also act as sites where electrons and holes recombine in pairs, annihilating one another as far as their conductivity is concerned.

These localized levels may be either impurity atoms, introduced substitutionally or interstitially into the lattice, or lattice defects of various forms, of which missing atoms, or extra interstitial atoms are the simplest. In considering semiconductor counters it is important always to bear in mind that the incident radiation may produce localized centres by nuclear transmutations, or ballistic processes, causing the device to deteriorate in a number of possible ways.

(d) Relaxation processes

In thermal equilibrium a semiconductor is characterized by a certain number of electrons and holes, each with a velocity distribution characteristic of the lattice temperature, and by an overall electrical neutrality. It is necessary now to ask how equilibrium is restored if it is once disturbed in any of these respects. When a number of excess charge carriers is introduced, for example, by light absorbed in the material, or by ionizing particles, these will recombine with charges of the opposite sign to give an exponential decay towards the equilibrium numbers. Thus if an extra number of electrons Δn_0 is created at time $t = 0$ the number at a time t later may be written

$$\Delta n = \Delta n_0 \exp\left(-t/\tau_r\right) \tag{3.5}$$

where τ_r is the recombination time for electrons and is a characteristic property of the semiconductor. The law derives from a simple theory of recombination at localized centres, of which there are assumed to be a large number compared with Δn_0, so that it holds only for comparatively small departures from equilibrium. It is also usually true that electrons and holes have the same recombination times, but again this rule may break down when large signals are encountered, or where one type of carrier is trapped at a second kind of centre, to be released after a time greater than τ_r. These processes illustrate more fully the importance of localized centres and show the complex ways in which they can affect the electrical properties of semiconductors.

The second relaxation process involves the scattering of electrons which have greater than normal velocities and need not concern us, as it takes place in very short times ($\sim 10^{-13}$ sec) and may be regarded as instantaneous in the present context.

Reversion to electrical neutrality also occurs exponentially with a time constant called the dielectric relaxation time τ_0. This has the value

$$\tau_0 = \frac{\rho\varkappa}{4\pi} \tag{3.6}$$

where ρ is the resistivity and $\varkappa$ the dielectric constant of the semiconductor. It can be regarded as the resistance-capacity time constant of a block of material, the resistance being $\rho d/A$, and the capacity $\varkappa A/4\pi d$ where d is the electrode separation, and A the cross-sectional area. In high-resistance semiconductors this time can be as long as a millisecond.

3.3 Ionization and charge collection

To describe the physical processes taking place in a semiconductor counter, and in the next chapter to discuss noise and energy resolution, it is convenient to assume that the counter is a homogeneous block of material and that the electric field is constant throughout its volume. This implies that the electrodes are ideal in the sense that they do not disturb the field or the charge carrier concentrations anywhere in the material. Clearly ideal counters are unlikely to exist in practice, but consideration of the departures from ideal behaviour, or of the non-uniform field which must exist in a junction counter merely complicate the analysis without adding anything fundamental to an understanding of the physical principles involved. The system shown schematically in Fig. 3.3 will be considered throughout this and the next chapter as representing an ideal conduction counter. The electrode separation is d, and the electric field E is everywhere equal to V/d, where V is the potential difference between the electrodes. A charged particle of energy W is incident in a direction normal to the electric field and generates N ion pairs at a distance x from the negative electrode.

The particle is brought to rest almost instantaneously, in most cases in a time between 10^{-12} and 10^{-11} sec, losing almost all its energy in the production of low-energy electrons by impact ionization. Gamma rays do not quite fit this pattern, but at each interaction they produce an energetic electron either by the photoelectric or Compton process which may then be considered in the same way as a primary bombarding particle, though it will not originate at the surface of the counter. The secondary electrons in turn lose their energy very rapidly by further impact ionization until their remaining kinetic energy is insufficient to excite an electron-hole pair. These ionization events are quite accurately represented

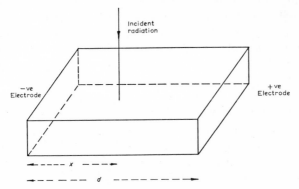

FIG. 3.3 Schematic diagram of conduction counter

as ballistic 'billiard ball' interactions in which both momentum and energy are conserved. Therefore, although the threshold for a photon to create an electron hole pair is E_g, the energy gap, the threshold for impact ionization will be higher, and is normally about 1·5 E_g when the electron and hole masses are equal. When they are unequal it will be rather more. As the energy of an electron approaches this threshold it can also lose energy by interacting with the crystal lattice to create optical phonons (*i.e.* lattice vibrations in which oppositely charged atoms vibrate out of phase with one another). Shockley[2, 3] has calculated the magnitude of this competing energy loss process in silicon and the effect that it has in making the average energy deposited in the crystal per ion pair generated higher than the threshold energy for impact ionization. The average will also be higher than the threshold because of the total kinetic energy which all the secondary electrons have after their final ionizing collision when their energy is reduced below the threshold. It is easy to see that in the simplest case where all energies from zero to the threshold are equally likely the average would be 1·5 times the threshold. The problem is quite an involved one, and it is necessary to make some assumption about when the electrons have enough energy to be free, and when they exist in quantized energy states of the lattice. Shockley arrives at the answer that in silicon the mean energy required to generate an electron-hole pair is 3·6 eV, the energy gap being 1·1 eV at room temperature. As will be discussed below the agreement between this figure and the (identical) one obtained experimentally for the mean energy per electron-hole pair collected at the electrodes of the counter may be somewhat fortuitous.

The track of a heavy charged particle will be essentially straight so that it creates a narrow cylinder of ionization in which the charge carriers will rapidly lose their excess kinetic energy in the generation of optical phonons. A rough estimate of the time taken for this is

$$\frac{\tau E_g}{h\nu_0} = 10^{-12} \text{ sec for silicon} \tag{3.7}$$

where τ is the relaxation time for lattice scattering by the optical modes and $h\nu_0$ is the energy of an optical phonon. Within this time the carriers released by the ionizing particle take up a Boltzmann velocity distribution characteristic of the lattice temperature, and these extra carriers are indistinguishable from those present before the incidence of the ionizing particle. The generation and thermalization of carriers is thus complete by the time the primary particle is brought to rest. For beta and gamma rays the tracks will be folded up on themselves in a complex manner, but the same time scales will apply.

The signal by which the particle will be detected and its energy measured is due to the separation of the electron-hole pairs around the particle track and their collection at the counter electrodes. At first the applied field will begin to separate the positive and negative charges, but as the column of ionization becomes polarized an opposing space charge field develops which may completely counteract the applied field at the centre of the column. Separation then continues by normal ambipolar diffusion near the centre of the column, and by the applied field continuing to operate on those charges near the edge. Eventually diffusion will so enlarge the diameter of the ionized column that the applied field can again penetrate it, at which stage separation is considered complete and charge collection can begin, with each carrier attracted towards its relevant electrode by the full applied field. The time taken for complete separation by diffusion is shown by a simple calculation to be approximately $\rho^2/\varkappa^2 E^2 D$, and has been called the plasma time, where ρ is the linear density of charge, $\varkappa$ is the dielectric constant of the medium and D the ambipolar diffusion constant given by

$$D = \frac{D_n \, D_p}{D_n + D_p}$$

where D_p and D_n are the hole and electron diffusion constants. When the ionizing particle is a 10 MeV proton and the applied field 1000 volts cm^{-1} this time falls between 10^{-9} and 10^{-8} seconds in silicon. This is an upper limit for the charge separation process, and observed charge collection times are often much shorter. In these cases the whittling down of the ionized column by the applied field acting on its edges could well be faster than the diffusion process.

If the stated carrier lifetime of the material is 10^{-6} seconds or more it appears at first sight that the amount of carrier recombination occurring during the separation process should be extremely small, and for most purposes negligible, but this is not necessarily so. The recombination time is measured for the small signal situation where the equilibrium number of charge carriers is only slightly perturbed. The charge densities around charged particle tracks can easily be an order of magnitude higher than the equilibrium number and may be as high as 10^{19} cm^{-3} for fission fragments so that the same considerations do not necessarily apply. Gibson and Miller[4] have made a detailed analysis of the various ways in which the charge collection efficiency could be reduced by charge trapping and recombination in the case where the localized charge densities are much greater than the equilibrium carrier densities. The carrier lifetime is not a useful quantity in this case, since it depends on the concentration of electrons and holes, and the density and capture cross-sections of the recombination centres. Their analysis is algebraically complicated, but the conclusions are quite clear. The most important process is recombination within the plasma at localized impurity centers, which may be the residual impurities in the high resistivity semiconductor. Charge collection efficiency will be lowest for densely ionizing radiation such as alpha particles and fission fragments, and this can lead to a deterioration in energy resolution due to fluctuations in the numbers of recombination centres in the plasma region. This again will be most significant for densely ionizing particles, and for inhomogeneous trap distributions, and, since diffused junctions and other devices which have to be heated may contain unwanted impurities, diffused into the counter in an uncontrolled way, they are likely to have worse energy resolution than surface barrier counters made with good quality materials. The theory predicts an accurate value for the lost charge (about 5 per cent) in silicon junctions counting alpha particles, and predicts qualitatively that resolution will be poorer for densely ionizing particles, and for diffused junction counters, particularly heavily compensated lithium ion drift devices.

In addition to the loss of carriers by recombination Lindhard and Nielson[5] have pointed out another effect which occurs mainly with heavy ions and fission fragments and which reduces the initial ionization. An appreciable fraction of the energy of a heavy ion is lost in direct nuclear collisions, and the slower moving recoil ions so produced have reduced efficiency for producing electron-hole pairs (see Fig. 1.10). In the case of fission fragments in silicon this energy loss may result in a reduction of the equivalent of 5 MeV from the total ionization.

There are thus two effects which are important for heavy ions resulting in the total charge collected being less than expected. One is a reduction in the number of ionizing events, and the other a loss of electron-hole pairs due to recombination in the plasma. Baldinger, Czaja and Gutman[6] have predicted that plasma losses can be reduced by increasing the collecting field, thereby reducing the time available for recombination. They show that $1/Q$ should be proportional to $1/E$, where Q is the charge collected and E is the collecting field. These two effects have been demonstrated by Shirato,[7] who investigated the signals due to fission fragments in silicon surface barrier detectors by examining the so-called 'pulse-height defect'. This is defined as

$$\text{P.H.D.} = \frac{W}{w} - N$$

where W is the energy of the fission fragment, w is the mean energy per electron-hole pair and N is the number of electron-hole pairs comprising the signal. It is the difference between the expected and observed signals. He found that the pulse height defect consists of two parts, one of which is field dependent as predicted by Baldinger et al,[6] and the other field independent. The field dependent part is larger for the heavier fission fragments, as would be expected for recombination in the plasma.

For an understanding of the way in which the signal in an external circuit builds up as the electrons and holes are swept towards the electrodes it is necessary to consider the displacement currents due to the movements of individual charges. The same concepts are also used in deriving the current noise superimposed on the signal by those carriers present before the ionization event. Each electron contributes a current $e\bar{v}/d$ when moving with a velocity $\bar{v}$ in a counter with electrode separation d, and induces an identical current in the external circuit. This current ends abruptly when the electron is trapped or reaches an electrode. The signal is made up of square current pulses from both electrons and holes, and any electron causes a charge to flow in the external circuit $\int \frac{e\bar{v}}{d}\, dt$ integrated over the total path of the carrier. If the carrier traverses the counter completely in however many stages, the limits of integration are zero and $d/\bar{v}$, so that the integral reduces to e. But if the carrier drift length λ is less than the specimen dimension then the charge flowing in the external circuit is reduced proportionately to $e\lambda/d$. It is easy to see that this

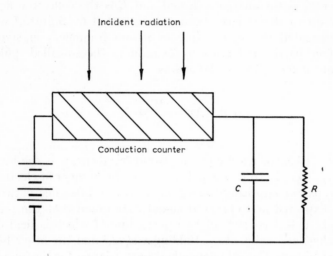

Incident radiation

Conduction counter

C R

FIG. 3.4 A simple counter circuit

should be so by considering the simple circuit of Fig. 3.4 in which the transit time for carriers τ_c, given by

$$\tau_0 = d/\mu E \tag{3.8}$$

where μ is the mobility appropriate to the carrier considered, is much shorter than the circuit integration time CR. Then each electron hole pair completely collected will put charges $\pm\,e$ on the two plates of the capacitor C. This charge will be reduced in the case of incomplete charge collection by the ratio of the work done by the applied field, namely λ/d. This problem has been discussed fully by Gunn[8] who gives a rigorous proof of the results quoted here.

The proton which generates a total of N ion pairs at a distance x from the negative electrode will give a total charge Ne flowing through the external circuit, if there is no trapping or recombination, of which the holes will contribute a charge

$$q_h = \frac{Nex}{d}$$

in a time

$$\tau_c = \frac{x}{\mu_p E}$$

and the electrons

$$q_e = Ne\left(\frac{d - x}{d}\right)$$

in a time

$$\tau_c = \frac{d - x}{\mu_n E}$$

(3.9)

If the counter were a perfect dielectric the magnitude of the total charge Ne could be observed in a circuit of infinitely long integration time. In practice the situation is more complicated because the resistivity ρ is not infinite and the dielectric relaxation time τ_0 will be finite. For example, in highly compensated silicon at $90°K$, where $\rho = 10^8\ \Omega$ cm it is 10^{-4} sec. This is the time taken to re-establish electrical neutrality everywhere in the counter by the movement of charge carriers generated thermally in the material. It is necessary that the collection time for the N ion pairs produced by the ionizing particle should be substantially less than τ_0 if the size of the signal is not to be affected by these movements of thermally generated carriers. Further, all real crystals will contain lattice imperfections which can act as electron traps, hole traps, or recombination centres, and a great many effects are due to these, depending on the relative magnitudes of the mean time before trapping, the mean time spent in traps, the mean time before recombination, the charge collection time and the dielectric relaxation time. The charge collection efficiency and the shape of the pulse observed in the external circuit depend in an intricate way on all these parameters and on the circuit time constants. The problem is further complicated by not being one of dynamic equilibrium, so that the usual kinetics of trapping and recombination which are adequate for small signal photoconductivity theory do not apply and mathematical formulation is difficult. Fortunately the solution of the general case is not necessary for an understanding of the physical principles involved. It is possible to distinguish four types of behaviour, each of which may apply to either type of carrier. They are:

 (i) Complete collection – all the charge carriers of one sign are completely and promptly collected without trapping or recombination.

 (ii) Short-term trapping – the carriers spend some time in traps but are eventually collected in less than the dielectric relaxation time.

(iii) Partial recombination – some pairs of carriers recombine without completing their journey to the electrodes.

(iv) Long-term trapping – the time spent in traps by some carriers exceeds the dielectric relaxation time.

In the interests of clarity an arbitrary distinction is made between trapping and recombination by taking extreme examples of each. Short-term trapping as defined above changes the shape of the current pulse by increasing the charge collection time. But the total charge collected is unchanged. Recombination is the loss of charge before complete collection occurs, and involves pairs of carriers of opposite sign. It will reduce both the electron and hole contributions to the signal whether one or both the recombining carriers originated in the ionization pulse due to the particle. This follows from the way in which the signal is built up from displacement currents due to all the individual charge carriers.

In practice what matters is the relation between the trapping times and the integration time of the measuring circuit. It may be worthwhile to look ahead towards more practical things and point out that where trapping is followed by recombination after a time longer than the integration time only one component will be lost from the signal. In this case, and a number of others, there is no clear distinction between trapping and recombination.

The fourth category in which charges are trapped for a long time without recombining is a special one which has some practical importance.

3.4 The signal pulse

Most cases of physical interest can be described by considering four cases in turn. In each case one carrier is in the first category, *i.e.* it is promptly and completely collected. The other carrier belongs successively to the four categories. Which category a carrier belongs to may depend on the electric field and to some extent on the dimensions of the counter, so that counters made from a given material may well be able to function in more than one of the modes described.

Figure 3.5 shows the arrangement assumed in this discussion, R_d and C_d being the resistance and capacitance of the detector, R_L the load resistor and C_s the stray capacitance,

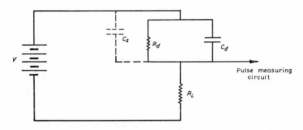

FIG. 3.5 The effective circuit of a counter

shown for simplicity as being all in parallel with the counter. The actual distribution of stray capacitance does not affect the argument. The integrating time constant of the circuit is given by

$$\tau = CR$$

where $\qquad \dfrac{1}{R} = \dfrac{1}{R_d} + \dfrac{1}{R_L}$ and $C = C_d + C_s$ $\qquad\qquad$ (3.10)

For the purposes of this discussion τ is taken to be longer than τ_c, the charge collection time for carriers in category (i) but shorter than the carrier trapping times in categories (ii) and (iv). It is much shorter than the dielectric relaxation time τ_0. This is emphatically not the circuit condition to get the best performance out of the counter; it is intended to aid the discussion of what is happening inside the counter.

Case I: both carriers in category (i).

This is the most straightforward case, and the most favourable from the point of view of counter operation. The rising edge of the observed pulse will be short, never exceeding the charge collection time τ_c for the carrier of lowest mobility, and decaying with the circuit time constant τ. The current pulse is completely defined by equations (3.9) which give the amplitude and the rise time of the two components of the signal due to holes and electrons. Each is a function of x, the position of the ionization, but the main characteristic of this case is that the total charge integrated on the condenser C and hence the pulse height observed are independent of x. Therefore the characteristic signal for the case is that shown in Fig. 3.6 where no distinction is made between the two components.

Case II: one carrier in category (i), the other in (ii).

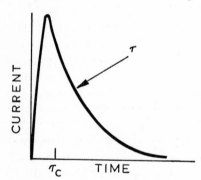

FIG. 3.6 Current pulse with complete charge collection (After NORTHROP and SIMPSON[9])

One component, due to the carrier in category (i), will be the same as in case I, with rapid rise and decay time τ, with its pulse height a function of x. The second carrier is delayed by trapping. When the drift length before trapping is short compared with the counter dimension d the carriers may be trapped and released many times before reaching the electrodes. If the mean time before trapping is τ_1 and the mean time spent in traps is τ_2 then the apparent mobility of the carrier is reduced to

$$\mu' = \mu \frac{\tau_1}{\tau_1 + \tau_2}$$

and the charge collection time is increased to

$$\tau_c' = \tau_c \cdot \frac{\tau_1 + \tau_2}{\tau_1} \tag{3.11}$$

The charge collection time $\tau_c{}'$ remains a function of x, just as τ_c is. The signal shape will now depend on the value of x and can vary widely. If the electron moves freely and the hole is the carrier which suffers trapping, then when $x = 0$ the hole contribution to the signal is zero, and the electron contribution is a total charge Ne with a collection time $d/\mu_n E$. At the other extreme when $x = d$ the electron contribution is zero and the holes contribute a charge Ne, but in the much longer time $d/\mu_p E \cdot \dfrac{\tau_1 + \tau_2}{\tau_1}$. Taking the circuit time constant shorter than the trapping time has the effect of reducing the pulse height in this case, but the area under the curve remains the same. At any intermediate value of x both electrons and holes will contribute amounts of charge proportional to $(d - x)$ and x respectively. At $x = d/2$ each will contribute $Ne/2$ with their different time constants $d/2\mu_n E$ and $d/2\mu_p E \cdot \dfrac{\tau_1 + \tau_2}{\tau_1}$. These three examples give the current waveforms shown in Fig. 3.7; (a), (b) and (c) being for $x = 0$, $d/2$ and d respectively. The waveform for any other value of x could easily be deduced in the same way as the above examples. In practice it would obviously be desirable to lengthen the circuit time constant to a value greater than $\tau_c{}'$, so that all particles of energy W generate a signal of the same size in the external circuit but this can only be done at the expense of increasing the noise entering the measuring system. A counter with trapping can never be as good, therefore, as the equivalent one without traps.

Case III: one carrier in category (i), the other in category (iii).

The carrier in category (i) is again promptly collected and contributes to the signal an amount of charge proportional to the fraction of the counter traversed. For the second carrier there is no trapping in the sense used in case *II*, but rather the carriers are lost completely. Eventually they must recombine with other carriers of the opposite sign, but this does not necessarily happen immediately. Recombination is most likely to occur at localized centres, not very different from the traps already discussed, which capture first one carrier,

and then another one. The two capture rates may be very different, and it is possible that the second carrier might be captured
to bring about recombination after a time much longer than

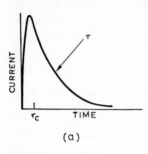

either the collection time for the first
carrier or the circuit time constant.
Again there are many possible cases
which could be discussed, all having
in common the feature that the total
charge constituting the signal in the
external circuit is less than Ne. This
is often expressed by saying that the
charge collection efficiency is less
than unity. It is worth restating that
there is a difference in principle
between trapping and recombination as defined here. If charges are
trapped they will eventually reach
the counter electrodes, they are
merely delayed in transit. Carriers
which are localized at recombination
centres will remain there until they
recombine with carriers of the opposite sign. They inevitably reduce
the signal, whatever the integration
time of the circuit.

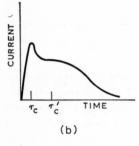

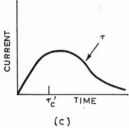

These are convenient definitions
for the purpose of this discussion,
but to put things in perspective two
practical points need to be made.
Firstly, localized centres in a semiconductor are rarely either traps or
recombination centres exclusively. A
more realistic description would be
that a centre first has a certain
capture cross-section for a particular

Fig. 3.7 Current pulses
when one carrier is
trapped (After NORTH-
ROP and SIMPSON[9])

sign of carrier, say an electron. Having captured an electron
it then has relative probabilities α and β that it will either lose
its electron to the conduction band by thermal excitation, or
will capture a hole and so bring about recombination. When α
is greater than β the centre is loosely labelled a trap, but if β

is the larger it is a recombination centre. It is generally true that a level near the centre of the energy gap is more likely to be a recombination centre than a trap.

Secondly, there is a point concerned with the practicalities of the measuring circuit. It will not generally be possible to make the integrating time indefinitely long in order to wait for trapped charge to be collected. Charge which is trapped longer than the integrating time τ will not in fact contribute to the signal, although in principle it could do so.

These two considerations mean that in practice the distinction between trapping and recombination, and their effects on the performance of a counter, may be vague in the mind of the user. Nevertheless, the definitions adopted here are valid.

Finally, as a specific example Fig. 3.8 illustrates what would happen for $x = d/2$ when the recombination of the trapped carrier occurs (a) in a time shorter than the collection time of

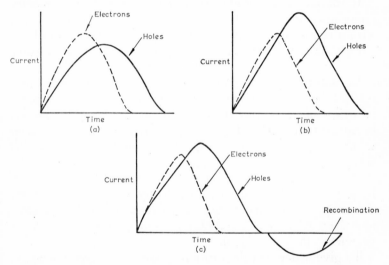

FIG. 3.8 Effect of recombination on charge collection efficiency

the other carrier, and (b) in a time longer than τ_c. For clarity the hole and electron components are shown separately, and it is assumed that the electron is captured first. In the first case both holes and electrons will be lost in the recombination process in equal numbers, so that the two components are equal, but both less than $Ne/2$. In the second case the holes are all collected, and contribute $Ne/2$, but the electron contribution remains reduced. The effect of the ultimate recombination of holes with the trapped electrons is not seen if the recombination time is also longer than the integration time τ, as assumed here. If the recombination occurred at a time intermediate between τ_c and τ then the situation would be represented by part (c) of the figure, showing a negative pulse due to recombination which may be interpreted as a reduction in the dark current in the counter. The total signal, subtracting this negative component, is now the same as in part (a) of the figure. This illustrates once again that it does not matter whether the recombination of the trapped charge is with a thermally generated carrier or one produced by the ionizing particle. It is the time needed for recombination which is important.

If the electrons suffered some trapping and some recombination their contribution to the signal would be broadened, with a rise time τ_c', as well as being reduced in magnitude.

Case IV: one carrier in category (i) the other in category (iv).

In each example so far the whole process of returning to a normal equilibrium situation in the counter has taken place in a time much shorter than the dielectric relaxation time τ_0. Consideration of the electrical neutrality has therefore been unnecessary. However, a carrier in category (iv) remains trapped without recombination for a time longer than the dielectric relaxation time, and by definition the counter will by this time have become electrically neutral everywhere. This happens by an interaction between the trapped charge and the carriers normally present in the counter, and it must therefore affect the signal.

To give a detailed description of what happens it is again easiest to take a specific example. Imagine that the counter is an n-type semiconductor, and that the carrier in category (iv) is the hole, *i.e.* the minority carrier. Initially the counter will be neutral, and it remains so after the absorption of the ionizing particle. But after the electrons produced by the particle have been collected, making their contribution to the signal, the counter has a net positive charge due to trapped holes. If these are distributed as shown in Fig. 3.9(a), surrounded by a uniform distribution of majority carriers (electrons), they will modify the field in the counter from the uniform one initially present (shown dotted) to one in which there are two distinct fields, one higher and one lower than the

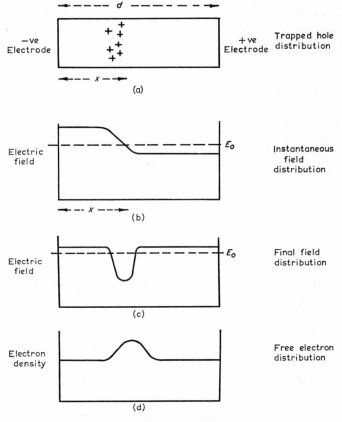

FIG. 3.9 Charge amplification

initial field. Instantaneously electrons at the left-hand end of the counter are in a higher field and will move faster than those on the right. This cannot, however, be a steady state, for current continuity must exist, and therefore a higher carrier velocity can only occur where there is a lower carrier density. The majority carriers in the counter will therefore rearrange

S.N.R.—4*

themselves to cause a further redistribution of field. It is not hard to see that the stable field distribution to which the system tends is that shown in Fig. 3.9(c). Near the trapped charge the field is somewhat lower than initially, and assuming that the voltage applied to the specimen is constant it will be correspondingly higher elsewhere. Electrical neutrality and current continuity can now be maintained by the majority carriers slowing down near the trapped holes, so that their time-averaged effect is to create a dipole. The total number of free electrons in the specimen has to be higher than initially by the amount of charge trapped. Now the effect of increasing the average density of free charge carriers and maintaining the same voltage on the counter must be to increase the current through it. The signal due to the ionizing particle will therefore consist of a fast pulse due to the electrons, decaying with the circuit time constant to a current higher than the initial one, and finally to the original current with a time constant τ_r the recombination time for the holes in the traps. Various waveforms are possible, of which the two most characteristic are shown in Fig. 3.10.

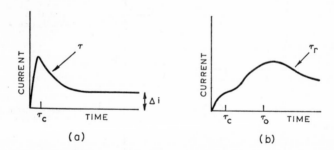

FIG. 3.10 Current pulses with charge amplification due to trapping (After NORTHROP and SIMPSON[4])

The total charge in the signal, represented by the areas under these curves may be much greater than the amount Ne generated by the ionizing particle. It is given in the situation of Fig. 3.10(a) by

$$Q = \int_0^{\tau_r} \Delta i \, \mathrm{d}t \qquad (3.12)$$

Q/Ne being the charge amplification of the counter. To get some idea of its possible magnitude take the case where a charge Ne is trapped, and subsequently compensated by an additional Ne majority carriers. These will cross the crystal every τ_c seconds, τ_c being as little as a microsecond in many practical counters. It will continue to recross the crystal for a time τ_r which may easily be a millisecond and could be seconds. So instead of an extra Ne holes crossing the crystal to give a pulse signal Ne, electrons cross the crystal τ_r/τ_c times. Their effect would be 10^3 to 10^6 times as great, *i.e.* the charge amplification would be in this range, but the signal due to a single particle would spread over the proportionately long time τ_r.

This mechanism is the basis of the highly sensitive cadmium sulphide gamma-ray flux detectors which will be described in more detail in a later chapter. The effect of irradiation over times longer than τ_r gives a large standing current which is a measure of the mean flux during the previous τ_r.

Carried to extremes the trapping of minority carriers for long periods in a counter may be turned to advantage in this way, but in general it is a troublesome thing, to be avoided at all costs. It causes successive events to produce overlapping signals, even at low repetition rates, and it causes signals not proportional to the energies of individual particles, so that the counter is not a useful particle spectrometer. The inverse process in which majority carriers are trapped is equally troublesome, and has no known uses. These will cause a net reduction in the number of free majority carriers, and hence a reduction in the steady state current.

These four cases are far from exhaustive, but they present enough of the basic ideas for any other situation to be worked out, at least qualitatively. Many indications have been given of how to deal with more complex situations. These often become very complicated algebraically, which is why they have been avoided here. For example, obliquely incident particles, or beta particles or gamma rays would give a distribution of values for x, the position of absorption relative to the electrodes; it is possible that both carriers might be liable to trapping or recombination, and so on. These situations do arise with depressing regularity in practice, but armed with the above concepts it should be possible to diagnose them, if not cure them.

REFERENCES

For this chapter

1. Tavendale, A. J., *Nuclear Instr. and Methods*, **25**, 188 (1963).
2. Shockley, W., *Czech. J. Phys.*, **B11**, 81 (1961).
3. Chynoweth, A. G., *Proceedings of Asheville Conference*, NAS-NRC Publications, **871**, 95 (1961).
4. Gibson, W. M. and Miller, G. L., *Brookhaven National Laboratory, report* No. BNL **5391**.
5. Lindhard, J. and Nielsen, V., *Physics Letters*, **2**, 209 (1962).
6. Baldinger, E., Czaja, W. and Gutman, J., *Proceedings of Symposium on Nucl. Instr.* (Harwell, Sept. 1961), edited J. B. Birks, Heywood & Co. (London, 1962).
7. Shirato, S., *Jap. J. Appl. Phys.*, **3**, 326 (1964).
8. Gunn, J. B., *Solid-State Electron*, **1**, 739 (1964).
9. Northrop, D. C. and Simpson, O., *Proc. Phys. Soc.*, **80**, 262 (1962).

For general reading

Shockley, W., *Electrons and Holes in Semiconductors*, Van Nostrand (Princeton, N.J., 1950).

Mott, N. F. and Gurney, R. W., *Electronic Processes in Ionic Crystals*, Oxford University Press (Oxford, 1940).

CHAPTER 4

NOISE LIMITATIONS AND THE
PERFORMANCE OF REAL COUNTERS

4.1 Statistical limitations

An important application of semiconductor counters is in particle spectrometry, where the amplitude of the signal is used as a measure of the energy of the incident particle. An ideal counter for this purpose would be one in which particles of equal energy always produce signals of the same amplitude, but in practice this never quite happens. There will always be a certain spread in the pulse amplitudes due to a set of mono-energetic particles which introduces an uncertainty into the measurement. This can conveniently be expressed as the standard deviation[1] in the set of measurements, σ; the smaller σ the better is the counter as a spectrometer. The standard deviation will be made up of a number of independent contributions, some fundamental, and others a function of the way in which the counter is constructed and used. In the discussion which follows it is assumed that the counter is large enough to absorb the incident particles completely, and that these are heavy charged particles. Other types of radiation, such as beta particles or gamma rays, are more complicated to deal with because the ways in which they are absorbed are more complex than those of heavy particles. These complications can be introduced as further contributions to the standard deviation after the general pattern has been established for the simpler case.

The most fundamental contribution to the standard deviation is that due to fluctuations in N, the number of ion pairs produced by a particle, and this is the standard against which other contributions can be judged. The signal in this discussion is $\bar{q}$, the charge collected at the electrodes of the specimen after the absorption of a single particle. When the charge collection is perfect the charge collected after any one event is

$$q = Ne \qquad (4.1)$$

If the ionization process described earlier, leading to the production of N ion pairs, terminates in N entirely independent events, then the standard deviation in N would be $\sqrt{N}$. If, however, there is some correlation between the N events the standard deviation of q becomes

$$\sigma = e\sqrt{(FN)} \qquad (4.2)$$

where F is the Fano factor, defined in Section 1.4 by the equation $F = \sigma_n^2/N$ where σ_n is the standard deviation in N.

It is convenient to define the energy resolution of the counter for this type of particle as $\sigma/\bar{q}$ so that due to this particular cause the resolution is

$$\sigma/\bar{q} = \sqrt{\frac{F}{N}}$$

or, expressing N in terms of the particle energy W and the mean energy per ion pair w

$$\sigma/\bar{q} = \left(\frac{Fw}{W}\right)^{\frac{1}{2}} \qquad (4.3)$$

It is obvious intuitively that the resolution will improve as the particle energy increases, and as the mean energy per ion pair decreases. Both changes increase the total number of ion pairs produced. In silicon $w = 3\cdot6$ eV, so that for 1 MeV particles this resolution is $0\cdot19$ per cent, when $F = 1$.

Two alternative methods of specifying the resolution of a counter are in common use, and need to be mentioned at this stage. First, an alternative to the above, which will be frequently used in this discussion, is the energy of a particle which would produce a signal equal to the standard deviation, i.e. $\dfrac{\sigma w}{e}$,

$$\frac{\sigma w}{e} = \sqrt{FwW} \qquad (4.4)$$

For 1 MeV particles in a silicon counter the resolution is
1·9 keV when $F = 1$. In either of these definitions the combined effect due to several contributions is obtained by adding
the squares of the resolutions and taking the square root of
the sum in the usual way. A more commonly used quantity
is that measured experimentally by plotting the pulse height
spectrum obtained from the counter under bombardment by
mono-energetic particles and measuring the full width of this
distribution at its half maximum valves (FWHM). This can
again be expressed either as an energy or as a ratio or percentage. These quantities are related to those previously
defined by the actual shape of the pulse height spectrum, and
where this is Gaussian the FWHM is 2·35 times the resolution
defined from the standard deviation.

For minimum ionizing particles, or especially thin counters,
there will be a worsening of the resolution due to the Landau
effect (see Section 1.4). This is applicable wherever the number of high-energy secondaries generated by the primary
particle is small, or in other words where the actual energy
deposited in the counter suffers statistical fluctuations. It can
be a noticeable effect in dE/dx counters.

4.2 Incomplete charge collection

Failure of all the charge to reach the electrodes can affect
the resolution of the counter in three quite different ways, and
it is important to distinguish clearly between them. In the
first place charge carriers may recombine in the particle
track after moving distances so small that their contribution
to the signal is negligible. For densely ionizing particles, and
particularly for fission fragments, this can be important ,and
has been discussed in Section 3.3, but in most cases the loss
of resolution due to direct recombination of this kind is smaller
than that due to statistical fluctuations in N.

The other two causes of line broadening operate when some
or all of the charge leaving the track of an ionizing particle
fails to reach the electrodes. In the first case it is assumed that
the electrode separation is very much larger than the mean
drift length of the carriers, so that the contribution of each
carrier is determined solely by its lifetime and the applied

field. The fraction of charge carriers remaining at time t after the ionization event is $\exp(-t/\tau_r)$, when the average carrier will have moved a distance $x = \mu E t$. Thus the probability of any carrier having a total path length between x and $x + dx$ is

$$P(x) = \frac{1}{\lambda} \exp\left(-\frac{x}{\lambda}\right) dx$$

where $\lambda = \mu E \tau_r$ and λ and τ_r are the values in the conditions under which the counter operates. Using a theorem of statistics the probability $P(y)$ that the sum of the path lengths of all N carriers is y must be

$$P(y) = y^{(N-1)} \exp(-y/\lambda) \left(\frac{1}{\lambda}\right)^N \Big/ \Gamma(N)$$

From this we obtain σ, the standard deviation in total path, by subtracting the square of the mean path length from the mean square value.

$$\sigma^2 = \frac{\left(\frac{1}{\lambda}\right)^N}{\Gamma(N)} \int_0^\infty y^{(N+1)} \exp(-y/\lambda)\, dy - N^2\lambda^2$$

$$\sigma^2 = \frac{\left(\frac{1}{\lambda}\right)^N}{\Gamma(N)} \cdot \frac{\Gamma(N+2)}{\left(\frac{1}{\lambda}\right)^{(N+2)}} - N^2\lambda^2$$

$$\sigma^2 = N(N+1)\lambda^2 - N^2\lambda^2 = N\lambda^2$$

so that the resolution is $\sigma/\bar{q} = \dfrac{1}{\sqrt{N}}$ (4.5)

The standard deviation in this case is identical to that due to variations in ionization when the Fano factor is unity, so it is a comparatively small effect. It only applies to devices large compared with λ, or those with contacts which allow re-injection of charge, so that the total path length is limited by recombination after an integral number of passages through the crystal. The final, and by far the most common, situation is that in which carriers may be divided into two classes:

(a) those whose path length is terminated by reaching an electrode

and (b) those which are trapped or recombine before reaching an electrode.

The fraction of carriers in each category will depend on the position of the ionizing event relative to the electrodes, and it turns out that the greatest standard deviation arises when events occur at randomly distributed positions. This case is calculated by considering the rectangular block of semiconductor shown in Fig. 4.1. The plane electrodes are separated

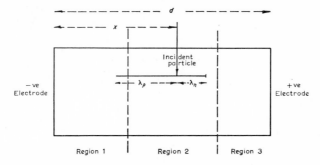

FIG. 4.1 Geometrical effects of incomplete charge collection

by a distance d with a uniform electric field E between them. Uniform production of carriers is assumed throughout the semiconductor, with a total of N_0 electron-hole pairs. This ionization pattern would be characteristic of gamma radiation, or of charged particles incident in a direction at right angles to the electric field, but not of charged particles incident through one electrode.

Consider a slice of the semiconductor of thickness dx, taken parallel to the electrodes.

Number of electrons in elementary slice $= \dfrac{N_0}{d}\, dx$

Probability of any one of these having a total path between

y and $y + dy = \dfrac{1}{\lambda_{\mathrm{n}}} \exp(-\, y/\lambda_{\mathrm{n}})\, dy$

Charge pulse due to these electrons $= \dfrac{N_0 e y}{d^2 \lambda_n} \exp(-y/\lambda_n)\, dx\, dy$

Probability of travelling at least the distance x to the electrode

$$= \exp(-x/\lambda_n)$$

The total pulse due to all the electrons produced in the slice is given by integrating the first of these expressions over values of y from zero to x, and adding the appropriate fixed amount of charge for the remaining electrons reaching the electrode, i.e. the total charge pulse due to electrons produced in thickness dx is

$$q_n = \frac{N_0 e\, dx}{d^2 \lambda_n} \int_0^x y \exp(-y/\lambda_n)\, dy + \frac{N_0 e}{d^2}\, x \exp(-x/\lambda_n)\, dx$$

$$q_n = \frac{N_0 e \lambda_n}{d^2} \left\{ 1 - \exp(-x/\lambda_n) \right\} dx \qquad (4.6)$$

By symmetry the total charge pulse due to electrons and holes generated in the slice is

$$q_n + q_p$$

$$= \frac{N_0 e}{d^2} \left\{ \lambda_n + \lambda_p - \lambda_n \exp(-x/\lambda_n) - \lambda_p \exp\left(-\frac{d-x}{\lambda_p}\right) \right\} dx$$

where λ_n and λ_p are the mean drift lengths for electrons and holes respectively in a uniform field E in an infinite slab of the semiconductor.

The total charge pulse for the whole crystal is obtained by integrating the separate electron and hole contributions above with respect to x over the range between zero and d.

Thus the mean value of the pulse due to electrons is

$$\bar{q}_n = \int_0^d \frac{N_0 e \lambda_n}{d^2} \left\{ 1 - \exp\left(-\frac{x}{\lambda_n}\right) \right\} dx$$

$$\bar{q}_n = \frac{N_0 e \lambda_n}{d^2} \{ d - \lambda_n + \lambda_n \exp(-d/\lambda_n) \}$$

and, by symmetry, the mean value of the total pulse is

$$\bar{q} = \frac{N_0 e}{d^2} \{(\lambda_n + \lambda_p)\, d - \lambda_n^2 - \lambda_p^2 + \lambda_n^2 \exp(-\,d/\lambda_n)$$
$$+ \lambda_p^2 \exp(-\,d/\lambda_p)\} \quad (4.7)$$

As would be expected intuitively this is zero when λ_n and λ_p are zero, and $N_0 e$ when λ_n and λ_p are large (it is necessary to expand the exponentials as power series in order to show this clearly).

The standard σ can be found from the usual relation

$$\sigma^2 = \bar{q^2} - (\bar{q})^2$$

where $\bar{q}$ is given by equation (4.7) and $\bar{q^2}$ is found by integration

$$\bar{q^2} = \frac{1}{d} \int_0^d (q_n + q_p)^2 \, dx$$

where q_n and q_p are given by equation (4.6).

The value of σ cannot be calculated simply, and the results have therefore been computed.* Some cases of particular interest are shown in Figs. 4.2 and 4.3. They present a rather complex picture the important features of which may not be immediately apparent. A simpler, but approximate, treatment has been given by Northrop and Simpson[2] which yields comparatively simple values for σ and $\bar{q}$ in analytical form, and which may therefore give a clearer physical picture of the situation. Unfortunately, it is inaccurate for values of λ_n and λ_p approaching d, which is the region of greatest interest for most applications.

It is clear from Fig. 4.2 that incomplete charge collection can lead to serious loss of energy resolution, and therefore it is advisable, whenever possible, to arrange for the charged particles to be incident through an electrode. In this way the ionization produced by each particle is always distributed in the same way with respect to the electrodes, fixing x in effect, and reducing the standard deviation due to incomplete charge collection to zero. Unfortunately, this is not always feasible, and the exceptions are important. The most obvious case is gamma rays, where absorption occurs at virtually any point in the volume of a counter, generating secondary electrons travelling at any angle to the gamma ray path. One condition which has to be fulfilled in a good gamma ray spectrometer is

* This is to be published by Day, R. B., Dearnaley, G. and Palms, J. M.

therefore long carrier drift lengths for both electrons and holes i.e. longer than the electrode separation. Another case in which the same requirement might arise is that of very high energy charged particles. These might easily have ranges longer than the largest attainable electrode separation, which is set by the need for the electric field strength to be below the breakdown stress of the material, but above that which makes the drift lengths satisfactorily large. In practice the

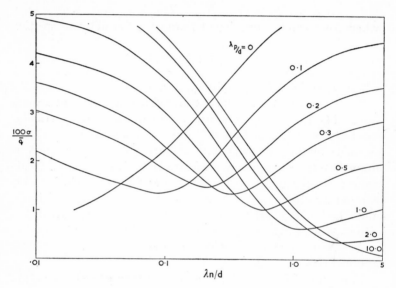

FIG. 4.2 Resolution $\sigma/\bar{q}$ as a function of the electron drift length parameter λ_n/d, for a range of values of the hole drift length parameter λ_p/d.

greatest useful electrode separation is likely to be between 1–2 cm. It is attractive for particles of greater range than this to have them incident at right angles to the field, since it then becomes much easier to enlarge the crystal in the appropriate dimension. However this is exactly the situation analysed above, and considerable caution is necessary in using it.

Anticipating what is to come in the sections dealing with junction counters, it should be noted that where the electric field is not uniform the standard deviation is rather larger than that calculated here.

Looking at the results in greater detail, Fig. 4.2 plots the resolution $\sigma/\bar{q}$ as a function of λ_n/d for a range of values of λ_p/d. It is seen that an increase in λ_n/d does not always lead to an improved energy resolution, and at first this may seem surprising. On consideration however it is clear from the symmetry of the problem that for a given value of $\lambda_n + \lambda_p$ the best resolution will occur at $\lambda_n = \lambda_p$. It is also clear that as λ_n and λ_p both become small the results will approximate to the case where no carriers reach the electrodes, and where the standard deviation is $1/\sqrt{N}$. This is not to say that short carrier drift lengths are good, for although the resolution due to this particular cause improves the signal, $\bar{q}$ becomes smaller, and other sources of noise relatively more important. It is invariably better to aim for a large signal, and hence for large values of λ_n and λ_p.

This feature is more clearly illustrated in Fig. 4.3 which is a section cut through the two surfaces $\sigma/\bar{q}$ and $\bar{q}/Ne$, plotted as

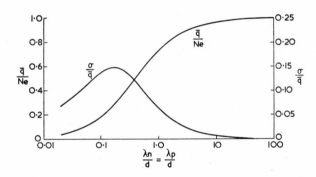

FIG. 4.3 Charge collection efficiency $\bar{q}/Ne$ and resolution $\sigma/\bar{q}$ as a function of the (equal) drift length parameters λ_n/d and λ_p/d.

functions of λ_n/d and λ_p/d. The section is defined by the plane $\lambda_n/d = \lambda_p/d$. Although the charge collection efficiency $\bar{q}/Ne$ increases monotonically to unity as λ_n and λ_p increase, the resolution $\sigma/\bar{q}$ rises to a maximum of 0·15 for $\lambda_n/d = \lambda_p/d = $ 0·19 and then improves again towards large values of λ_n and λ_p. To attain a resolution of 1 per cent (F.W.H.M. 2·35 per cent) it is necessary that $\lambda_n/d = \lambda_p/d = 7$ i.e. the carrier drift lengths must be seven times the electrode separation. In many nuclear physics experiments better resolution than this is required.

Finally it should be noted that it is important for both carriers to play their part in building up the charge pulse. Resolution is worst when one carrier has zero drift length. In this case (Fig. 4.2) the resolution deteriorates as the other drift length increases, reaching a value of almost 0·5 when the drift length of the useful carrier is equal to the electrode separation.

4.3 Thermal noise

Various kinds of electrical noise in the circuit can also super-impose fluctuations on the signals and thereby contribute to the resolution of the counter. All these kinds of noise arise fundamentally because the counter is not a perfect dielectric; it contains electrons and holes in thermal equilibrium with the lattice in addition to any carriers generated by incident radiation. In calculating the effect of noise on the resolution of a counter it is necessary to specify something of the circuit used for the measurement. For this purpose the circuit of Fig. 4·4 is assumed to limit the bandwidth of the measuring system, feeding into a circuit of greater bandwidth. This is not how the counter would be used in practice, for the signal : noise

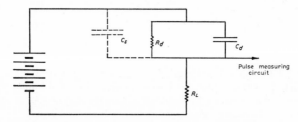

FIG. 4.4 The effective circuit of a counter

ratio can obviously be optimized by adjusting the band-width of the measuring system suitably. But the question of how to do this can only be answered with a complete know-ledge of the frequency distribution of the noise power and of the signal power in any individual case. Certain basic limitations on the bandwidth through which both signal and noise can be observed are set by the circuit which is used to apply the necessary field to the counter. The circuit shown is the barest minimum which can perform this function and allow measurement of what is happening in the counter. R_d and C_d are the resistance and capacitance of the counter, shown in parallel with the stray circuit capacitances C_s. R_L is the load resistor. It is convenient to define

$$C = C_d + C_s$$

and
$$R = \frac{R_L R_d}{R_L + R_d} \tag{4.8}$$

and the circuit time constant $\tau = CR$.

Normally τ will be made greater than the charge collection time τ_c for both carriers, or where there is trapping greater than τ_c'. The observed voltage across the load resistor R_L will then decay according to the equation

$$V = \frac{Ne}{C} \exp\left(-t/\tau\right) \tag{4.9}$$

where Ne is the total charge collected. (Because electrical noise is an independent source of line broadening, complete charge collection is assumed throughout this discussion.) As explained in Chapter 3, τ will be made much shorter than τ_0 the dielectric relaxation time. Since

$$\tau_0 = \frac{\rho\varkappa}{4\pi} = C_d R_d \tag{4.10}$$

this means that R_L must be less than R_d.

Noise is most conveniently expressed as the energy of an ionizing particle which would produce a signal equal to the r.m.s. noise. This definition is consistent with the earlier use of the standard deviation of pulse height, so that the overall resolution of any counter can still be found by adding the squares of all the various contributions and taking the square root of the sum.

Thermal noise, or Johnson noise, occurs in any conductor, whether a current is flowing or not. It arises because the velocity distribution of the carriers leads to a fluctuating and, in general, non-uniform distribution of these carriers in the conductor. This shows up as a fluctuating voltage between the ends of the conductor whose average value is zero, but whose r.m.s. value is given by the familiar expression

$$\overline{V^2}(f)df = 4kTRdf \tag{4.11}$$

where $\overline{V^2}(f)df$ is the r.m.s. noise voltage in a bandwidth df observed across a resistor R at absolute temperature T. k is Boltzmann's constant.

Thermal noise has a 'white' spectrum, $i.e.$ the power is uniformly distributed over an infinite frequency band. The mean square voltage observed across the load resistor R_L is limited to an upper frequency set by C and R, which may be regarded as a filter, or as forming a frequency dependent potentiometer. The integrated r.m.s. voltage seen by the measuring circuit is therefore

$$\overline{V^2} = \int_0^\infty \frac{\overline{V^2}(f)df}{1 + \omega^2 C^2 R^2}$$

$i.e.$
$$\overline{V^2} = \int_0^\infty \frac{4kTRdf}{1 + \omega^2 C^2 R^2} \tag{4.12}$$

giving
$$\overline{V^2} = \frac{kT}{C}$$

The number of ion pairs necessary to produce a signal $(\overline{V^2})^{\frac{1}{2}}$ is

$$\Delta N = \frac{C}{e} \left(\frac{kT}{C} \right)^{\frac{1}{2}}$$

and the energy of a particle necessary to give this number is $w\Delta N$ so that

$$\Delta W = \frac{w}{e} (kTC)^{\frac{1}{2}} \tag{4.13}$$

Somewhat surprisingly the magnitude of the thermal noise contribution to counter resolution depends on C and not on R, but this is due entirely to the bandwidth of the counter circuit.

A typical example is provided by taking the case of silicon, with $w = 3\cdot6$ eV, at room temperature, when

$$\Delta W = 1\cdot4 C^{\frac{1}{4}} \text{ keV} \qquad (4.14)$$

where C is in pF. A conduction counter of 1 cm cube would have a capacitance of about 1 pF so that C is determined by stray capacitance of perhaps 15-20 pF. For most purposes ΔW would then be negligible. At the other end of the scale, a large area p-n junction counter could have a capacitance up to 1000 pF, when ΔW would be nearly 45 keV, and might make a sizeable contribution to energy resolution.

4.4 Current noise

Additional noise arises when a field is applied to the counter. The resulting current is made up of discrete movements of electrons and holes which may be introduced and withdrawn at electrodes or trapped, recombined or generated thermally within the counter. Any process which interrupts the movement of carriers destroys the continuity of the current, and constitutes an additional source of noise in the counter. A complete treatment of current noise in a solid would be extremely involved, and none has yet been produced. The best that can be done is to deal with the main causes of noise as if they were independent.

(a) Shot noise

Shot noise occurs in a system most clearly exemplified by an electron beam where each carrier crosses continuously from one electrode to another and all electrons have the same transit time. The current is built up of a number of square pulses each of duration equal to the transit time. When there is no correlation between charge carriers, as in a low-density electron beam, the shot noise associated with a mean current I is

$$\overline{I^2(f)}df = 2Iedf \qquad (4.15)$$

When the current through a semiconductor counter takes this same form the mean square noise voltage seen in the measuring circuit will be

$$\overline{V^2} = \int_0^\infty 2Ie\,\frac{R^2}{(1 + \omega^2 C^2 R^2)}\,df$$

Putting N_c for the number of carriers in the counter, and $\tau = CR$ this can be reduced to

$$\overline{V^2} = \frac{N_c \tau}{2\tau_c} \cdot \frac{e^2}{C^2} \tag{4.16}$$

τ_c being the transit time in the absence of trapping. The number of ion pairs needed to generate a signal equal to the r.m.s. noise voltage is

$$\Delta N = \left(\frac{N_c}{2}\right)^{\frac{1}{2}} \left(\frac{\tau}{\tau_c}\right)^{\frac{1}{2}}$$

and the resolution due to this cause

$$\Delta W = w \left(\frac{N_c}{2}\right)^{\frac{1}{2}} \left(\frac{\tau}{\tau_c}\right)^{\frac{1}{2}} \tag{4.17}$$

in normal operation of the counter $\tau > \tau_c$ so that according to this formula ΔN will have a minimum value of about $N_c^{\frac{1}{2}}$.

This can be seen by a purely physical argument, as follows. If the applied field were suddenly switched on when a particle was in the counter, and turned off again after a time τ_c when all the ionization generated by the particle had reached the electrodes the total charge collected would be $N + N_c$. If the charge carriers are generated by independent thermal processes the standard deviation of N_c will be $N_c^{\frac{1}{2}}$. The situation becomes worse as the circuit integration time τ increases, the noise grows in proportion to the square root of the charge collected, *i.e.* $(\tau/\tau_c)^{\frac{1}{2}}$. This argument is equivalent to the one implicit in the somewhat more rigorous derivation of the shot noise expression given above, and may help to give a clearer picture of what is happening.

Equation (4.17) actually gives a pessimistic answer for shot noise in a counter, for it assumes no correlation whatever between the separate charge carriers. Just as space charge fields in an electron beam smooth out current fluctuations and reduce shot noise, so any process which tends to keep the semiconductor electrically neutral will thereby reduce shot noise also. Such processes are the trapping or untrapping of charge, or the generation or recombination of pairs of carriers, which are themselves sources of noise, so before a complete assessment of shot noise can be made these other noise sources must be assessed.

(b) Generation-recombination noise

One way in which a current in a semiconductor differs from that in an electron beam is the contribution made to current noise by the generation and recombination of pairs of carriers at points in the bulk of the material. Such carriers traverse only part of the distance between the electrodes, and so contribute current pulses which are shorter than those due to electrons and holes which traverse the specimen completely. Short pulses also come from single carriers which are trapped for varying times, and cross the crystal in two or more stages. Any effects of this kind which further disrupt the current are clearly additional sources of noise. They are generally grouped together, since they can be treated in the same way mathematically, and the resulting noise is called generation-recombination noise. Van der Ziel[3] has shown that it takes the form

$$\overline{I^2(f)}df = \frac{4\overline{\Delta N_c^2}e^2}{\tau_c^2}\frac{\tau_1^2}{(1 + \omega^2\tau_1^2)} \cdot df \qquad (4.18)$$

where N_c is the total number of carriers in the counter, and τ_1 is the mean free time of the carriers. The equation is only valid under the restriction $\tau_1 < \tau_c$, i.e. when the mean free time is less than the transit time across the counter in the absence of trapping. This is not a serious limitation since generation-recombination noise becomes really important only when τ_1 is short enough for most carriers to cross the counter in several steps.

$\overline{\Delta N_c^2}$, the variance in N_c, depends on the kinetics of carrier generation, and has to be worked out for each case on its merits. Sautter[4] has done this for a number of cases, of which two are specially noteworthy. In an impurity semiconductor with fully ionized donors or acceptors $\overline{\Delta N_c^2}$ is zero because all the carriers are free all the time. There is no generation recombination noise in this case. On the other hand, when only a small percentage of the impurities is ionized $\overline{\Delta N_c^2} = N_c/2$. Using equation (4.18) this gives for the mean square noise voltage in the measuring circuit

$$\overline{V^2} = \int_0^\infty \frac{2N_c e^2}{\tau_c^2} \cdot \frac{\tau_1^2}{(1 + \omega^2\tau_1^2)}\frac{R^2}{(1 + \omega^2 C^2 R^2)}\,df \qquad (4.19)$$

For normal counter operation $\tau > \tau_c$, so that, with the added restriction $\tau_1 < \tau_c$ (for the validity of equation (4.18)) $\tau \gg \tau_1$. Integrating equation (4.19) and applying this last inequality gives

$$\overline{V^2} = \frac{N_c e^2 \tau_1 R}{2\tau_c^2 C}$$

The number of ion pairs necessary to produce a signal equal to the r.m.s. voltage is

$$\Delta N = \frac{C}{e}\left(\frac{N_c e^2 \tau_1 R}{2\tau_c^2 C}\right)^{\frac{1}{2}} = \left(\frac{N_c}{2}\right)^{\frac{1}{2}}\left(\frac{\tau \tau_1}{\tau_c^2}\right)^{\frac{1}{2}} \qquad (4.20)$$

and the energy resolution is

$$\Delta W = w\left(\frac{N_c}{2}\right)^{\frac{1}{2}}\left(\frac{\tau \tau_1}{\tau_c^2}\right)^{\frac{1}{2}} \qquad (4.21)$$

It is easy to confuse shot noise and recombination noise because of the similarity between the formulae of equations (4.21) and (4.17); they are identical if $\tau_1 = \tau_c$. This is not really so surprising, for the calculations are based on very similar models, and when $\tau_1 = \tau_c$ the carriers all get right across the counter so that only shot noise occurs. The physical processes leading to the two kinds of noise are quite distinct. Shot noise is due to the lack of correlation between electrons, which all pursue the same path across the counter. Generation-recombination noise is due to a breaking up of individual electron trajectories into separate parts. The usual treatment of generation-recombination noise simplifies the problem by giving all carriers the same mean free time, so making it appear even more like shot noise.

A further complication exists in that, for purely physical reasons, shot noise and generation-recombination noise are often mutually exclusive. The shot noise formula gives a maximum value for the case where there is no correlation between carriers, and where mechanisms exist to introduce correlations shot noise will be reduced. Similarly the magnitude of generation-recombination noise depends on $\overline{\Delta N_c^2}$. In the two cases worked out for generation-recombination noise it is of interest to see what reduction of shot noise is expected. In the first case of a fully ionized impurity semiconductor generation-recombination noise is zero, but as there is no mechanism for charge correlation the full shot noise will occur. Where the percentage of impurities ionized is small charge carrier correlations can occur, so that shot noise is reduced but generation recombination noise takes a much higher value. These sources of noise are to some extent mutually exclusive each giving a maximum value of ΔN around $N_c{}^{\frac{1}{2}}$. For a silicon counter containing a total of 10^6 charge carriers either could give an energy resolution

$$\Delta W = 3 \cdot 6 \text{ keV}$$

Both these kinds of current noise could be important in large volume counters or with counter materials of insufficiently low charge carrier density.

(c) Excess noise

As its name implies excess noise is that part of the current noise not attributable to shot noise or generation-recombination noise. Often, in semiconductor devices, it makes the largest contribution of the three, so it is unfortunate that comparatively little in the way of detailed explanation of its physical causes can be given. Almost invariably excess noise is a predominantly low-frequency effect, having a power spectrum proportional to $1/f$ or to some power of it. In this it resembles flicker noise in vacuum tubes.

Excess noise is often associated in a rather unpredictable way with the nature of the electrodes used, or with the surface treatment which the semiconductor has undergone. This generally means that there is some scope for altering the processing of any device in the hope of reducing excess noise to unimportant proportions. A further possibility is to deal with it by reducing the low-frequency response of the amplifier or detecting circuit. In the case of a counter where the signals are fast, it is possible to eliminate a lot of low-frequency noise without greatly reducing the signal.

In his book on noise van der Ziel[3] deals at some length with excess noise in semiconductors, and in vacuum tubes and metallic films, in all of which the same $1/f$ spectrum, or something like it, is observed. He concludes that there is a slow diffusion mechanism involved, which may in a semiconductor be the migration of ions on the surface, and that this modulates the generation of electrons and holes in a way which will give predominantly low-frequency noise. He also concludes that excess noise is by no means a necessary property of semiconductors because resistors made from nickel and lithium oxides show very little of it.

This whole topic is a very involved one, in which conjecture plays a greater part than is desirable, and therefore it is unnecessary to say much more about excess noise here. This is not to minimize the practical importance of such noise, for it is the predominant kind in many counting devices, but unfortunately the theory, as it exists at the moment, is not very helpful in diagnosing the causes of excess noise, or in dealing with them, and it is therefore not helpful to deal with it at length.

4.5 Hot electrons and high field effects

Throughout this discussion it has been assumed that the charge carriers remain in thermal equilibrium with the lattice as far as their velocity distribution is concerned. This is not always the case when high electric fields are applied to the counter, as has been found experimentally. Conduction electrons absorb energy from the applied field which appears as extra kinetic energy. The scattering processes which limit the drift velocity of carriers normally remove this energy gained from the field and convert it into thermal energy of the crystal lattice so that the mean drift velocity remains small compared with the thermal velocity of the carriers. There is a limit to the rate at which the scattering processes can transfer kinetic energy from the electrons to the lattice, and when the rate at which energy is gained from the applied field exceeds this then the electrons gain in total energy and are no longer in thermal equilibrium with the lattice.

Shockley[5] first described this phenomenon, and found that the new velocity distribution function was approximately a Boltzmann distribution with an effective temperature T_e greater than the lattice temperature. Shockley called such carriers 'hot'.

Thermal noise derives from the velocity distribution of the

charge carriers, and therefore the effective temperature T_e should be used in place of the lattice temperature in equations (4.11) to (4.13). Shockley's calculated value of T_e reduces to

$$\frac{T_e}{T} = \left(\frac{3\pi}{32}\right)^{\frac{1}{2}} \frac{\mu E}{v_s}$$

(4.22)

when $\mu E \gg v_s$, v_s being the velocity of sound in the semiconductor. Shockley's theory has been improved upon in detail, but the ideas are basically right for a semiconductor whose carrier mobilities are limited by scattering by the acoustic modes of the lattice. Again, taking silicon as an example, v_s is about 7×10^5 cm/sec at room temperature, so that for electrons with a mobility of 1200 cm^2 volt^{-1} sec^{-1} the field which makes μE comparable with v_s is less than 600 volts cm^{-1}. When the applied field approaches this value thermal noise will begin to increase.

As the field is increased the mobility decreases at the same time as the electrons become hot. Shockley derives the equation

$$\mu = \frac{\sqrt{2}\,\mu_0}{\left[1 + \left\{1 + \frac{3\pi}{8}\left(\frac{\mu E}{v_s}\right)^2\right\}^{\frac{1}{2}}\right]^{\frac{1}{2}}}$$

(4.23)

Again the derivation is not completely accurate, and in practice the mobility becomes different from the low field value μ_0 at lower fields than the equation predicts. This has been explained by taking into account the shape of the energy bands of the semiconductor. The details of this are largely irrelevant here; it is necessary to note, however, that carrier mobility decreases at high electric fields.

Ultimately another scattering process, due to interaction with the optical modes of the lattice, takes over and provides a very efficient means of dissipating excess kinetic energy. It is so effective that the drift velocity tends towards a maximum value

$$v_{\max} = \frac{h\nu_0}{m^*}$$

(4.24)

where $h\nu_0$ is the energy of an optical phonon, and m^* is the effective mass of the carriers.

Prior[6] has measured the current density as a function of electric field in both n-type and p-type germanium and silicon. Only in n-type germanium is there really clear evidence of saturation, but in all cases there is a marked reduction of mobility for field strengths in excess of 1000 volts cm^{-1}, resulting in corresponding departures from Ohm's Law. Prior's results for n-type germanium and n-type silicon are reproduced in Fig. 4.5.

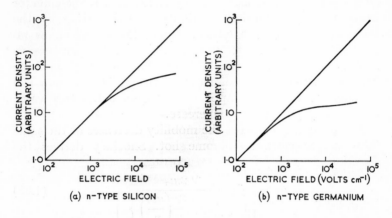

FIG. 4.5 Variation of the electron mobility with electric field in silicon and germanium (after PRIOR)

These effects of high applied fields in first increasing thermal noise and then in reducing carrier mobilities have to be weighed carefully when considering what field to apply to a counter. It is often attractive to increase the field to obtain faster pulses and higher charge collection efficiencies but obviously a point is reached when the noise is increasing rapidly with applied field and the collection of charge is hardly improving at all. Exactly similar limitations apply to ideas of increasing the signal size by avalanche ionization in a high electric field, in a way analogous to Geiger counter operation, and in this case there is the additional hazard of noise due to impact ionization by thermally generated carriers. This is not to say that either of these ideas is completely unprofitable: it is a question of knowing where to stop.

4.6 Materials for semiconductor counters

So far the properties of semiconductor counters have been discussed by assuming them to be rectangular solids of homogeneous material with a uniform electric field applied between two parallel faces. This is a satisfactory way of presenting a physical picture of their important features with the minimum mathematical complexity. As is well known many of the devices in current use are not of this simple form, but consist of rectifying junctions in which the electric field is non-uniform, and where the thickness of the sensitive volume is a function of the applied voltage. Before describing junction counters in greater detail it is worth examining the implications of the theory, to see what properties would be required of a material in order to make good homogeneous counters. Comparison of the properties of real materials with the theory then provides experimental confirmation of the major conclusions reached, and at the same time shows the junction counter to be a logical way of overcoming practical difficulties at the cost of greater complexity. There is no doubt that a homogeneous counter has great advantages of simplicity and flexibility of design over a junction, so it is of interest to summarize the properties necessary in a good counter. They are:

(*i*) Low carrier density to minimise current noise: since this depends on the total number of carriers in the volume of the counter the minimum acceptable energy gap is a function of counter volume. For 1 c.c. it is about 1·4 eV, at room temperature.

(*ii*) Freedom from traps to minimise loss of signal and various slow effects.

(*iii*) High carrier mobilities for short pulse rise times.

(*iv*) A low value for the mean energy per ion pair, w, to give a low ultimate limit to the energy resolution.

(*v*) High atomic number for good stopping power, particularly for photoelectric absorption of gamma rays.

(*vi*) Long carrier lifetimes to allow efficient charge collection.

It is immediately clear that some of these requirements conflict with one another. For example (*iv*) requires a small energy gap, since w is directly related to E_g, and this is in direct conflict with (i), the condition for low carrier density. In any particular application a suitable compromise must be made, and where feasible the counter should be cooled, to bring about a reduction in the free carrier density without a corresponding increase in w. A more immediate practical difficulty also presents itself. Long carrier lifetimes and freedom from traps imply a material developed to a stage where lattice defects and impurity concentrations have been reduced to a very low level. Silicon and germanium are the only materials falling in this category which are suitable in other respects for use as counters, and even these fall short of the requirements of low carrier density and high atomic number.

Table 4.1 lists a number of materials which have been seriously considered for counting applications. The list is by no means exhaustive, but it includes a selection of materials which are near optimum as regards each of the separate requirements. The contents of the table are largely self explanatory, but nevertheless it is worth drawing some general conclusions from it. Silicon and germanium are immediately attractive because they are readily available in a state of high purity and crystalline perfection (less than 10^{12} impurities per c.c.) and moreover they are well understood materials whose technology is highly developed. They have long minority carrier lifetimes and large mobilities. However their energy gaps are too low for operation as homogeneous counters at room temperature and their atomic numbers are lower than ideal for gamma ray work. It is the clearest possible comment on the present shortcomings of other materials that ways have been found of overcoming these difficulties.

Of the materials with energy gaps higher than the somewhat arbitrary 1·4 eV level gallium arsenide and cadmium telluride are the most interesting, the former having the higher mobilities and the latter the greater atomic number. However in their present state of development they are not yet ready for this application. Their purity is not much better than 10^{17} atoms per c.c., which is much worse than silicon and germanium, and therefore high resistivity material is always compensated, i.e. the concentration of ionized donors N_D, is nearly equal to the concentrations of ionized acceptors N_A, so that

TABLE 4.1

Semiconductor	Energy Gap (eV) at 300°K	Electron Mobility (cm² volt⁻¹ sec⁻¹) at 300°K	Hole Mobility (cm² volt⁻¹ sec⁻¹) at 300°K	Electron lifetime in p-type (sec)	Hole lifetime in n-type (sec)	Atomic Number
Silicon	1·08	1500	500	3×10^{-3}	3×10^{-3}	14
Germanium	0·67	3800	1800	10^{-3}	10^{-3}	32
Diamond	~6 eV.	1800	1200			6
Gallium Arsenide	1·43	8500	420	10^{-7}	10^{-7}	31,33
Gallium Phosphide	2·25	140	150	10^{-8}	10^{-8}	31,15
Cadmium Sulphide	2·4	300	10	$\sim 10^{-3}$ limited by traps	$< 10^{-8}$	48,16
Cadmium Telluride	1·5	~100	~100	4×10^{-5}	$> 10^{-5}$	48,34
Indium Antimonide	0·17	78000	750	$\sim 10^{-7}$	$\sim 10^{-7}$	49,51
Gallium Antimonide	0·67	4000	1400	$\sim 10^{-8}$	$\sim 10^{-8}$	31,51

the number of conduction electrons $n = N_D - N_A$ is small. Where the acceptors would not by themselves be ionized thermally (deep acceptors of ionization energy $E_A >> kT$) the compensation may be very accurate, as is illustrated in Fig. 4.6 for the case of an n-type semiconductor. Here the total number of deep acceptors can exceed the number of donors, and the acceptors are ionized by accepting electrons from the shallow donors, all of which are assumed to be

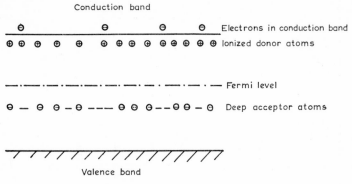

FIG. 4.6 Compensation of n-type silicon

ionized. It is possible in this way to achieve an electron concentration far lower than the initial donor concentration – in gallium arsenide electron concentrations at room temperature of 10^7 cm^{-3} have been reported for specimens whose total impurity concentration is greater than 10^{16} cm^{-3}. Such materials are non-homogeneous, are not easily reproduced, and have not proved useful as nuclear counters. A study of gallium arsenide by Northrop, Thornton and Trezise[7] reveals many of the difficulties likely to be encountered in any compensated high energy gap material. Gallium arsenide has been the subject of more work than any other compound listed in Table 4.1, so that there must be a general lack of confidence that the others will be better. This is not, of course, an argument for ignoring them, merely a warning against over-optimism. Indium antimonide deserves a mention because of its very high electron mobility and very low energy gap, which promise a fast response and small mean ionization energy. In fact, its energy gap is much too low from the point of view of free carrier concentration, and even cooling to very low temperatures does not bring the noise to acceptable limits. This is because a mechanism of conduction due to interactions between impurities (called impurity band conduction) becomes important, making the concentration of carriers independent of temperature.

Gallium antimonide is a substance similar in many ways to germanium, but with a higher atomic number. It has been studied very little, and could repay more work, especially in the field of gamma ray spectrometry. Gallium phosphide has comparatively little to recommend it except its high energy gap.

The two remaining materials in the table, diamond and cadmium sulphide, occupy rather special positions in the history of semiconductor counters. Diamond was the first material to be fully investigated as a homogeneous conduction counter, though its energy gap and the price of large single crystals both appear prohibitively high to allow its widespread use. However, much of the early work was of high quality.[8] It deserves attention for two reasons; firstly, because it prepared the way for the rapid development of semiconductors which has taken place in recent years, and secondly, because of the methods it explored for making use of diamond in practical circuits. For example, the judicious use of background illumination on the specimen can often improve its performance by changing the electron population in traps, either by immediate re-excitation of carriers from the traps into the bands, so that they continue to contribute to the signal, or alternately by keeping the deep traps filled in order to minimise the trapping of carriers produced by ionizing particles. By the standards now set for counters it seems likely that any device needing such measures would be automatically sub-standard as regards energy resolution. Nevertheless it is possible that it might find application outside nuclear physics, e.g. in radiation monitoring. But perhaps the greatest importance of this early work is to those developing new counter materials for they form a basis for diagnosing many of the difficulties likely to be met in the early stages of such work.

Cadmium sulphide was probably the first semiconductor to be widely used for detection of nuclear radiation. It differs from the other compounds discussed in that it sublimes at a temperature below its melting point, and has to be crystallized from the vapour phase. It is therefore much harder to produce stoichiometric crystals without large concentrations of lattice defects, and purification techniques such as vacuum melting and zone refining are not available. Even the best cadmium sulphide is therefore full of traps and recombination centres, resulting in its mode of operation being that described as Case IV in Section 3.4. Its normal use is therefore as an integrating flux counter, the potential and uses of which are discussed in Chapter 9. It can in principle be used as a pulse counter in this mode, and if the carriers make an integral number of circuits before recombining then the system can retain its linearity and energy resolution, sacrificing only time constant in order to obtain amplification. Very large pulses have been reported due to alpha particles in cadmium sulphide,[9] but there are no quantitative data available.

A final and very important feature of the table is the very long minority carrier lifetimes exhibited by germanium and silicon. The low lifetimes in other materials are due in part to high impurity concentrations, but they are also due in part to their energy band structures. In germanium and silicon the energy-momentum curves (see Section 3.2(a)) do not have both their extrema at $k = 0$ so that direct radiative transitions between the bottom of the conduction band and the top of the valence band are improbable, owing to the large change in momentum vector which would be involved. Recombination therefore occurs non-radiatively which in practice means via recombination centres that have energy levels near the centre of the forbidden gap. Carrier lifetimes are therefore strongly dependent on the density of such levels and can be long when the density is low. On the other hand, gallium arsenide, cadmium sulphide, cadmium telluride, indium antimonide and gallium antimonide all have energy bands where the extrema are at $k = 0$ so that the direct radiative process is allowed and sets an upper limit to carrier lifetimes, which is thought to be a few microseconds, even in completely pure crystals. Gallium phosphide is an 'indirect gap' material like silicon and germanium, which is an additional reason for including it in the table. Of course, the figures given should only be taken as a rough guide, because they depend critically on the constitution of the material, and are hard to measure with any accuracy.

4.7 Electrodes

Little mention of electrodes has so far been made, but it has been implied that ohmic contacts could be made to the counter which would enable a field to be applied without modifying the charge carrier concentration anywhere in the counter. At the same time they must be capable of introducing and withdrawing charge so that a continuous current can flow. This in itself raises some difficulty, because in operating the counter the field must be sufficiently high that

$$d/\mu E = \tau_0 < \tau_r \qquad (4.25)$$

That is, the collection time τ_0 for carriers of either sign must be shorter than the recombination time τ_r in which the semiconductor reverts to its thermal equilibrium number of free charge carriers. If carriers produced by an ionizing particle traverse the counter without coming into thermal equilibrium with the lattice then so must those introduced by the electrodes, if the counter is completely homogeneous. This situation leads to space charge limited currents, analogous to the space charge current in a vacuum diode, in which the semiconductor is neither electrically neutral, nor does it have its thermal equilibrium carrier population. Such currents have been observed in cadmium sulphide by Ruppel and Smith[10] and have been treated theoretically by Rose and Lampert,[11] and Lampert.[12] These higher currents are associated with a non-uniform field distribution and therefore cause both extra noise and less efficient charge collection than in a homogeneous counter, and are to be avoided.

An ohmic contact necessarily involves a transition region between the metal electrodes and the high resistivity semiconductor whose function is to regulate the rate of movement of charge to what is required for the maintenance of thermal equilibrium in the bulk of the semiconductor. The density of charge carriers must increase very substantially in passing from the semiconductor into the metal, and this normally means that both the field and the carrier mobility must decrease to give current continuity, since in equilibrium the current density is

$$J = E \, e(n\mu_n + p\mu_p) = \text{Constant} \qquad (4.26)$$

It also follows from equation (4.25) that the carrier lifetime τ_r has to be lower near the electrodes than it is in the bulk of the semiconductor.

In many high-resistivity materials and insulators the field distribution is automatically adjusted near the electrodes by the trapping of charges. This gives a space charge reduction of the applied field which preserves current continuity at a level determined by the situation in the bulk material. Figure 4.7 shows diagrammatically what happens in an n-type

FIG. 4.7 Trapped electrons from the negative electrode in an n-type semiconductor

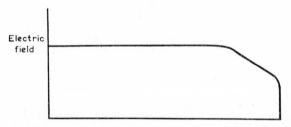

FIG. 4.8 The field distribution in the specimen (the trapped electrons near the negative electrode lower the field and impede the entry of more electrons)

semiconductor which contains electron traps which are not normally occupied at room temperature. Electrons entering the material from the negative electrode are trapped for periods depending on the depth of the traps, giving that end of the crystal a net negative charge. The field distribution which results is shown in Fig. 4.8 which can be simply deduced from the lines of force drawn in Fig. 4.7. There are obvious dangers in trying to use this method of making ohmic contact to conduction counters, since it results in two conflicting conditions which have to be applied to the trap density in the material. A lower limit is set by the electrode considerations outlined above, but an upper limit has already been imposed by the requirement of efficient and prompt charge collection. There is no guarantee that a working margin exists between these two limits, and in most cases it does not. What appears to be needed is a graduated trap density, presumably produced after the counter has been cut to size, so that the lower limit of trap density near the electrodes and the upper limit in the bulk of the material can be satisfied separately. This is essentially the aim of the two kinds of technique which give the best results.

In the first method an impurity is diffused into the semiconductor, a donor impurity if it is an n-type semiconductor, or an acceptor if it is p-type, the diffusion being through the electrode faces. Near the electrodes this produces a material with shorter lifetime and much higher carrier density than in the bulk. The extra free carriers reduce the field in the same way as the trapped charge in Figs. 4.7 and 4.8. Moving away from the electrode region the resistivity and lifetime gradually change to those of the bulk semiconductor. This is often referred to as an n, $n +$ contact; it is exactly analogous to the p, $p+$ contacts made to p-type semiconductors by diffusing in suitable acceptors. A safe working rule for this kind of contact is that the Fermi level should change relative to the conduction band by less than kT per carrier diffusion length, so that carriers are held in thermal equilibrium with the lattice over distances small compared with the impurity diffusion depth. Diffusion processes are capable of sufficient control to achieve this aim fairly easily.

The second method is to alloy the impurity, recrystallizing from the alloy to get a graduated impurity concentration. This is a much less controlled method than diffusion, but it can be made to give perfectly satisfactory results in most cases. It has the very important advantage of being a much lower temperature process than diffusion so that it can be carried out with far less chance of damage to the semiconductor.

A third method which can work equally effectively is to rely on surface states, i.e. energy levels associated with adsorbed or chemically combined layers on the surface of the material, or with variations of lattice periodicity at the surface. These can act as traps, allowing evaporated or electroplated metals to replace alloyed or diffused contacts. Surface states play an important part in the formation of surface barriers, and will be discussed in detail in Chapter 5. They have the disadvantage of being much harder to control than diffusion or alloying processes.

Two other conditions apply to the electrodes. In the first place they should contribute no electrical noise; they must be sound mechanically and have the correct kind of structure as outlined above. Secondly, they must be accurately defined spatially, so that the electrode separation, d, has a definite value, and each ionization event generates the same signal in an external circuit. There may be problems in achieving this when relying on varying trap distributions near the electrodes to produce the other properties outlined above.

4.8 Performance of homogeneous counters

Amongst the best results obtained with homogeneous counters are those of Gibbons and Northrop[13] who worked with compensated silicon cooled at 90° K. They made a number of counters of different sizes and shapes, chosen, to suit particular applications, of which two examples are chosen.

For energy spectrum measurements on 30 MeV protons 6 mm cubes were used, with alloyed aluminium electrodes on opposite faces. They were used with protons incident through one electrode, to minimize the loss of resolution due to incomplete charge collection. It was found that the energy resolution depended somewhat on the direction of the electric field, as would be expected when the carrier drift lengths are unequal and comparable with the electrode separation. Fig. 4.9 shows the results obtained for the best field direction where the energy resolution is about 1.5 per cent F.W.H.M. The small group of high energy protons is well resolved, and generally the performance compares well with scintillation counters in this energy range.

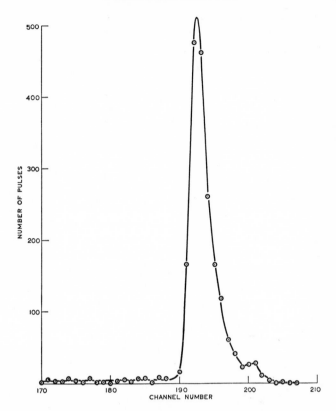

Fig. 4.9 Pulse height spectrum due to 30 MeV protons
(After Gibbons and Northrop[13])

A second set of results concerns a group of counters of
different values of λ_n/d and λ_p/d, the drift lengths λ_n and λ_p
having been measured experimentally by determining the
pulse heights due to α-particles incident through an electrode.
Fig. 4.10 shows the pulse height spectra for four of these
irradiated with gamma rays from ^{137}Cs. Their resolutions
follow the general pattern predicted in Section 4.2, even
though extra contributions due to inhomogeneity and current
noise make the actual resolution worse than that predicted for
incomplete charge collection alone. It is particularly noticeable that the resolution is better for $\lambda_n/d = \lambda_p/d = 0.5$, than
for $\lambda_p/d = 0.9$, $\lambda_n/d = 0.5$ even though the latter gives the

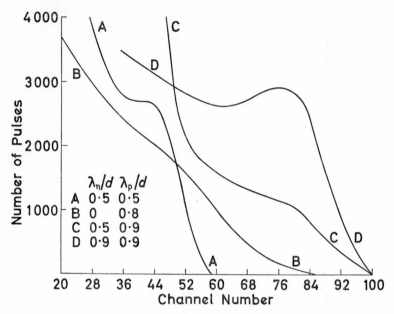

FIG. 4.10 Pulse height spectra due to ^{137}Cs gamma rays
(After GIBBONS and NORTHROP[13])

larger signals. It is also obvious that, for silicon, only the
Compton spectrum is observed, the photoelectric absorption
being quite insignificant at this energy.

4.9 The design and operation of counters

The theoretical treatment of semiconductor counters in
this and the preceding chapter has been kept deliberately
general. It therefore says very little about how to design and
operate a counter for a specific application, although it
should contain the material necessary to make such decisions.
In later chapters various kinds of counter will be described
in terms of this theory and their uses and limitations discussed.
The type of amplifier used and its bandwidth are other variables which may be used to optimize performance, and these
will also be discussed. All this illustrates the use of the theory,
and gives an overall picture of what existing materials and
techniques can achieve; it answers the question 'what existing
device serves my purpose best?' In addition it is worthwhile,

particularly for the solid state physicist, to take a rather more farsighted view by asking what materials and techniques would broaden the scope or improve the performance of the existing devices. Again a lot of the information necessary to begin answering this question has been given, and it will be clear, for example, that high resistivity materials with long carrier drift lengths would make possible important advances in the directions of accurate gamma-ray spectrometry, and high-energy charged particle spectrometry. Along these lines it is a valuable exercise to use the theory to choose the material, the geometry and the operating conditions of a counter to give optimum performance for spectrometry of say 30 MeV protons or 500 keV gamma rays.

Equally important advances may come from improvements in device technology, such as methods of presenting counters in a form where they can be stacked or built into an array, so as to give better performance than a single counter. The relative simplicity of the two approaches has then to be carefully assessed. It is intended to discuss future developments of this kind in the chapters relating to existing devices.

Finally, in any practical system, a pulse amplifier is an integral part of the set up, and therefore the performance of the combination of counter and amplifier is the important thing. The type of amplifier, its noise and its bandwidth, are further variables which may be used to improve performance, and their importance is discussed in a separate chapter.

REFERENCES

For this chapter

1. Brownlee, K. A., *Industrial Experimentation*, H.M.S.O. (London, 1949).
2. Northrop, D. C. and Simpson, O., *Proc. Phys. Soc.*, **80**, 262 (1962).
3. van der Ziel, A., *Noise*, Prentice Hall (New York, 1954).
4. Sautter, D., *Progress in Semiconductors*, 4, 127 (1960).
5. Shockley, W., *B.S.T.J.*, **30**, 990 (1951).
6. Prior, A. C., *J. Phys. Chem. Solids*, **12**, 175 (1959).
7. Northrop, D. C., Thornton, P. R., and Trezise, K. E., *Solid-State Electron*, **7**, 17, (1964).
8. Champion, F. C., *Phil. Mag. (Suppl.)*, **5**, 383 (1956).

9. Private Communication, P. Fochs *et al.*, A.E.I. Research Laboratory, Rugby.
10. Ruppel, W. and Smith, R. W., *R.C.A. Review*, **20**, 702 (1959).
11. Lampert, M. A. and Rose, A., *Phys. Rev.*, **121**, 26 (1961).
12. Lampert, M. A., *Phys. Rev.*, **125**, 126 (1962).
13. Gibbons, P. E. and Northrop, D. C., *Proc. Phys. Soc.*, **80**, 276 (1962).

For general reading

van der Ziel, A., *Noise*, Prentice Hall (New York, 1954).
Sautter, D., *Progress in Semiconductors*, **4**, 127 (1960).
Shockley, W., *Electrons and Holes in Semiconductors*, Van Nostrand (Princeton, N.J., 1950).

CHAPTER 5

RECTIFYING JUNCTION COUNTERS

5.1 Semiconductor rectifiers

Semiconductor junction counters are the type most widely used at the present time, and their properties and the forms they take will be discussed at length. Before coming to this it will be helpful to consider in general terms some of the properties of semiconductor rectifiers as they affect the counting properties, and for this purpose it is simplest to consider the junction between an n-type region and a p-type region in a semiconductor crystal. In the n-type region the charge carriers are virtually all electrons, and in the other holes, so that at the junction each set of carriers will tend to diffuse over into the other region. Each of these diffusion processes constitutes an electric current flowing from the p-type material into the n-type, so clearly they cannot continue without the supply of power. The current is in fact inhibited by a built-in voltage at the junction due to the ionized impurities in each region. Excess positively charged donors in the n-type region and negatively charged acceptors in the p-type region form a charged double layer which repels the free charges and prevents their crossing the boundary. Figure 5.1 shows the distribution of electrons and holes, of charged donors and acceptors, and, finally, the total charge for such a system in equilibrium. An entirely equivalent picture is presented in the energy band diagram for a p-n junction in Fig. 5.2. The Fermi level, which is the electrochemical potential of electrons, must be constant throughout the crystal, so that at the junction the bands follow the shape given. A potential difference across the junction acts as a barrier to both electrons and holes, such that at the interface the electron currents in each

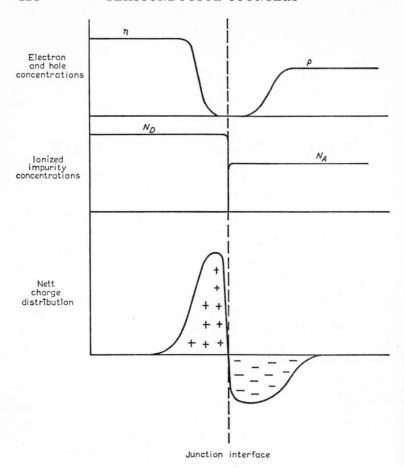

FIG. 5.1 The charge distribution in a p-n junction

direction and the hole currents in each direction balance. It is clear from the energy band diagram that the built-in voltage will normally be rather less than the energy gap of the material.

The forward direction for the rectifier is that where the applied field opposes the built-in field, *i.e.* with the n-type material biased negative. Electrons are then driven into the p-type material and holes into the n-type, and clearly once the built-in voltage is exceeded there is no region which has less than its thermal equilibrium complement of carriers.

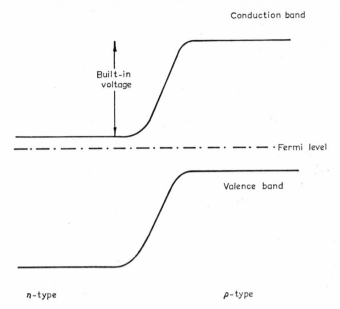

FIG. 5.2 Energy band diagram for a *p-n* junction

When a junction is to be used as a counter the forward direction is not of very great interest; it is in the reverse biased condition that it acquires the necessary properties. With the *n*-type region biased positive it is clear by an extension of the above arguments that the applied voltage assists the built-in voltage in removing free charges from the junction interface and the regions on either side of it. It is here, in the so-called charge depletion layer, that the conditions for counter operation can exist, for the application of a reverse bias is seen to reduce the free carrier populations below their thermal equilibrium numbers, thereby reducing the current noise generated in the depletion layer. Moreover, the field in the crystal distributes itself in the steady state according to the current continuity equation

$$J = E\, e(n\mu_\mathrm{n} + p\mu_\mathrm{p}) \qquad (5.1)$$

where E is the electric field, J is the (constant) current density and p and n are the local concentrations of holes and electrons. Most of the applied voltage, therefore, appears across the

126   SEMICONDUCTOR COUNTERS

depletion layer, suiting the purpose of using this region as a counter remarkably well.

The hope is then that a material which would have too high a carrier density to be used as a bulk counter, but which has the necessary carrier lifetimes and is available in uniform single crystals, might still be used in the form of a reverse biased rectifier. The price to be paid is the limited volume of such a counter, for there will obviously be limits to the extent to which the carrier concentrations can be reduced by the applied field. To assess the properties of junction detectors it is therefore necessary to calculate the width of the depletion layer, which will determine not only its thickness as a counter, but also its capacity and the thermal noise it generates. The reverse current must also be calculated to find its contribution to the noise.

5.2 The depletion layer thickness

The distance to which the depletion layer penetrates into each region of the crystal will be determined by a solution of the current continuity equation (6.1) together with Poisson's equation. For the p-type region this is:

$$\frac{\partial^2 V}{\partial x^2} = \frac{4\pi e}{\varkappa} (N_A + n - p) \tag{5.2}$$

where N_A is the acceptor impurity concentration, n and p are again the local electron and hole densities and $\varkappa$ is the dielectric constant of the crystal.

An exact solution of these equations is rather formidable,[1] but fortunately it is possible to learn a great deal about the junction using a rather drastic approximation, namely that throughout the depletion layer n and p are small compared with N_A. Poisson's equation then reduces to

$$\frac{\partial^2 V}{\partial x^2} = \frac{4\pi e}{\varkappa} N_A \tag{5.3}$$

and successive integrations give

$$\frac{\partial V}{\partial x} = \frac{4\pi e N_A}{\varkappa} (x - x_p)$$

and
$$V = \frac{4\pi e N_A}{\varkappa} (x^2 - 2xx_p) + V_0$$

x_p being the end of the depletion layer where $N_A + n - p = 0$ (on this model the depletion layer ends abruptly) and V_0 is the potential at the junction interface, $x = 0$.

When $x = x_p$, $V - V_0 = V_p$, the potential difference across the p-type region,

$$\therefore \quad x_p{}^2 = \frac{V_p \varkappa}{2\pi N_A e} \tag{5.4}$$

Similarly the extension into the n-type region is

$$x_n{}^2 = \frac{V_n \varkappa}{2\pi N_D e} \tag{5.5}$$

On our model the excess charge in the n-type region is equal and opposite to that in the p-type region, for the field is confined to the depletion layer in this approximation.

Thus

$$x_p N_A = x_n N_D \tag{5.6}$$

The depletion layer penetrates the two regions in the inverse ratio of their ionized impurity concentrations, or alternatively in the direct ratio of their resistivities measured away from the influence of the junction. Normally it will happen, because of the way the junction is made, that the ionized impurity concentration is very different on the two sides of the junction. Then the depletion layer exists almost entirely in the high-resistivity material. If this is the p-type material the depletion layer width is approximately

$$x^2 = \frac{\varkappa}{2\pi e} \frac{V}{N_A}$$

and if all the acceptors are ionized, the resistivity of the material is

$$\rho = \frac{1}{N_A e \mu_p}$$

so that

$$x = \left(\frac{\varkappa \mu_p}{2\pi} \rho V \right)^{\frac{1}{2}}$$

Similarly, for n-type material

$$x = \left(\frac{\varkappa \mu_n}{2\pi} \rho V \right)^{\frac{1}{2}} \tag{5.7}$$

In p-type silicon this gives approximately

$$x = 3 \cdot 2 \times 10^{-5} (\rho V)^{\frac{1}{2}} \text{cm}$$

and for n-type $\quad x = 5 \cdot 3 \times 10^{-5} (\rho V)^{\frac{1}{2}} \text{cm}$

where ρ is expressed in Ω cm and V in volts. These depletion layer thicknesses are in the ratio of the square roots of the majority carrier mobilities. The capacity of the reverse biased junction will, to the same order of approximation, be that of a parallel plate condenser of thickness x with a silicon dielectric.

i.e. $$C = \frac{\varkappa A}{4\pi x}$$

substituting for x from equation (6.7) gives

$$C = A \left(\frac{\varkappa}{8\pi\mu_{\text{p}}\rho V} \right)^{\frac{1}{2}} \tag{5.8}$$

for p-type material.

To give a general idea of the numerical values likely to be met in practice in the case of p-type silicon provides as good an example as any. It is reasonable to consider 10^4 Ω cm material, and to bias a rectifier made with it to 100 volts in the reverse direction. This would give $x = 333$ μ and $C = 30$ pF cm^{-2}. ORTEC[2] have prepared a nomograph based on equations (5.7) and (5.8) which is reproduced as Fig. 5.3. It gives the depletion layer thickness and capacity as a function of resistivity and bias for both n-type and p-type material.

In spite of the approximations made, equation (5.8) gives an accurate value for the incremental capacitance dQ/dV, because the profile of the charge distribution advances with little change of shape when the voltage is increased, and the incremental charge is deposited at the face of the profile, giving a good approximation to the situation in a parallel plate condenser. Equation (5.8) is not a good value for the total capacitance Q/V because it ignores the fact that the change is distributed throughout the depletion layer. Noting that $Q = Nex$ per unit area the total capacitance can be derived from equation (5.5) as

$$C = A\left(\frac{\varkappa}{2\pi\,\mu_\text{p}Pv}\right)^{\frac{1}{2}}$$ (5.9)

i.e. twice the parallel plate value.*

Usually the incremental capacitance will be the important one, because either the a.c. measuring voltage will be much smaller than the d.c. bias voltage, or alternatively the additional charge produced by a signal will be small compared with the total charge already present in the depletion layer. When this condition is not satisfied, for example if the ionization density due to incident radiation is large then the capacitance and field distribution of the depletion layer will change.

5.3 Noise and energy resolution in junction counters

Thermal noise will again depend on the capacity of the detector, as derived for the general case in Chapter 4. Into an open bandwidth this gives for the r.m.s. thermal noise

$$\overline{V^2} = \frac{kT}{C},$$

and for the energy resolution

$$\varDelta W = \frac{w}{e}(kTC)^{\frac{1}{2}}.$$ (5.10)

For silicon at room temperature this reduces to

$$\varDelta W = 1{\cdot}4\,C^{\frac{1}{2}}\,\text{keV}$$

where C is in pF. For a large area counter, of a few square centimetres C could be as high as 500 pF, particularly if the resistivity and bias were low. The resolution due to thermal noise alone would then be 31 keV (FWHM 73 keV), which might well be unacceptable for many applications. Where energy resolution is important it is therefore worthwhile to use high resistivity material and high bias voltages, as far as these are consistent with low current noise, and to use the smallest area counter possible.

An explanation of the current which flows in a rectifier under reverse bias must begin with a detailed study of the

* This was pointed out by A. Moat of A.W.R.E., Aldermaston.

RESISTIVITY VS BIAS VOLTAGE VS SILICON DEPLETION DEPTH

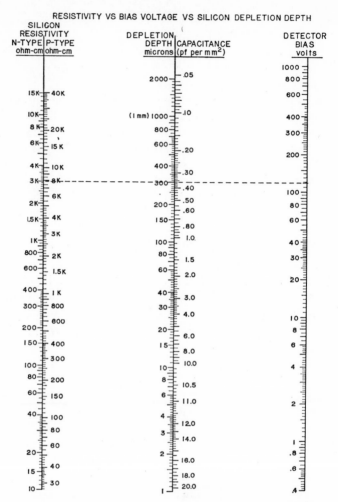

FIG. 5.3 Nomogram to determine depletion layer thickness
(*By courtesy of Oak Ridge Technical Enterprises Corporation,
Oak Ridge, Tennessee, U.S.A.*)

properties of recombination centres.[3, 4] Figure 5.4 shows a
recombination centre in the forbidden energy gap and the
four possible electron transitions to and from the centre
which control the free carrier populations. Electrons may be
captured from the conduction band or may be released into

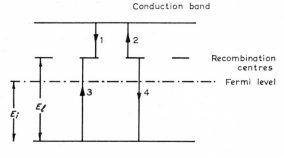

<figcaption>FIG. 5.4 Transitions of electrons to and from recombination centres</figcaption>

the conduction band (processes 1 and 2) similarly electrons may be captured from or generated into the valence band (processes 3 and 4); these latter two are usually called hole generation and hole trapping respectively. For any one centre not all of these processes are possible at any one time; an electron has to be captured before it can be released, so that a centre has either a probability of electron capture or of hole capture, but not both simultaneously. One of the functions of such centres is the restoration of equilibrium after excess carriers have been generated by light or by nuclear radiation. A centre can capture first an electron and then a hole, which amounts to restoring the electron to the valence band in two stages. The characteristic time for this process is the recombination time τ_r, which has been shown by Shockley and Read[3] to be

$$\tau_r = \frac{(n + n_1)}{(n + p)}\tau_p + \frac{(p + p_1)}{(n + p)}\tau_n \qquad (5.11)$$

τ_p is the lifetime for hole capture by a centre which is in a state where it can capture holes and τ_n is the lifetime for electron capture by a centre which is in a state to capture electrons. These quantities are multiplied by the number of centres in these two states, n and p are the electron and hole concentrations and n_1 measures the location of the state in the band gap, being defined as $n_1 = n_i \exp \dfrac{(E_i - E_1)}{kT}$ where E_i is the centre of the band gap, E_1 is the energy of the recombination centre, and n_i is the intrinsic electron concentration. n_1 and p_1 are related by $n_1 p_1 = n_i^2$. These recombination centres are responsible for two kinds of current in reverse biased junctions which will now be considered in turn.

The diffusion current is that normally encountered in conventional semiconductor rectifiers, and it arises in the following way. In the p-type material of the junction shown in Fig. 5.2 there will be a low concentration of electrons, n_p, given by the relation $n_p p_p = n_i^2$. Those generated from recombination centres in the field-free region within a diffusion length of the depletion layer can diffuse into it and will then be swept away by the field. The generation rate G, for electrons is given by the equilibrium equation

$$G\tau_r = n_p \tag{5.12}$$

τ_r being the same for electrons and holes since they have to recombine in pairs. The carrier diffusion length is simply $L = (D_n \tau_r)^{\frac{1}{2}}$ where D_n the diffusivity is $\dfrac{kT}{e}\mu$. The diffusion current density is simply the product of the generation rate and the diffusion length, $i.e.$

$$J_D = \frac{e n_p D_n^{\frac{1}{2}}}{\tau_r^{\frac{1}{2}}} \tag{5.13}$$

There will be a similar contribution from holes on the n-type side of the junction, but this can be ignored in comparison with the above current because the material will be heavily doped, causing the minority carrier concentration to be very small. τ_r will also be smaller, but the total current density will be dominated by the carrier density. As an example, 1000 Ω cm p-type silicon, having a hole concentration of about 10^{13} cm^{-3}, will have an electron concentration of about 10^7 cm^{-3} (from $np = n_i^2 \simeq 10^{20}$). If τ_r is 1 μsec $J_D \simeq 5 \times 10^{-9}$ amp cm^{-2}. This current is independent of applied voltage above some small threshold value. As the resistivity of the material rises, so does the minority carrier concentration and the diffusion current. A long lifetime reduces the current, but only as the inverse square root.

There is a second contribution to the junction current due to those recombination centres within the depletion layer, which is usually called the space charge generated current and will be denoted here by the current density J_s. The applied field in the depletion layer will have removed almost all the free electrons and holes, so that the recombination centres can no longer capture free carriers. They are left with only two possible functions, namely, generation of holes and electrons, alternately, first an electron, then a hole, then another electron. These two generation rates, which must be equal, contribute a current in the circuit of one electron per ion pair generated, and hence the current density J_s is proportional to the depletion layer thickness, x, and to the generation rate. Sah, Noyce and Shockley[5] have shown this to be

$$g = n_i^2/(\tau_p n_1 + \tau_n p_1) \qquad (5.14)$$

The two terms in the denominator contain the probabilities of thermal excitation of holes and electrons through the exponential character of n_1 and p_1. The current density is thus

$$J_s = exg \qquad (5.15)$$

The generation rate g can be rewritten in terms of the actual lifetime which the carriers would experience if the depletion layer field were removed,

$$g = \frac{n_i^2 \left[\dfrac{(n + n_1)}{(n + p)}\tau_p + \dfrac{(p + p_1)}{(n + p)}\tau_n \right]}{\tau_r \qquad (n_1\tau_p + p_1\tau_n)} \qquad (5.16)$$

Calculation of the current thus involves a knowledge of the capture probabilities of the centres for electrons and holes, and the location of the energy level in the forbidden gap. These parameters are usually unknown, but it is nevertheless possible to reduce the equation to simpler terms by making reasonable assumptions. If the material is p-type with $p \gg n$ and if the electron and hole lifetimes τ_n and τ_p are equal.

$$g = \frac{n_i^2}{\tau_r} \frac{(p + n_1 + p_1)}{p\,(n_1 + p_1)} \qquad (5.17)$$

When $n_1 + p_1$ is small compared with p this becomes

$$g = n_i^2/\tau_r(n_1 + p_1) \qquad (5.18)$$

which has a maximum value

$$g_{max} = \frac{n_i}{2\tau_r} \qquad (5.19)$$

when $n_1 = p_1 = 2n_i$, *i.e.* when the recombination centre is at the centre of the forbidden gap.

Alternatively, when $n_1 + p_1$ is large compared with p the generation rate is

$$g = \frac{n_i^2}{p\tau_r} \qquad (5.20)$$

This would be the case when the carriers generated from the recombination centres dominated the conductivity of the material from which the junction was made.

Taking the least favourable case of the maximum generation rate the current density is

$$J_s = \frac{en_i}{2\tau_r} x \qquad (5.21)$$

where x is the depletion layer thickness. This current is therefore proportional to $(\rho V)^{\frac{1}{2}}$, because of the variation of x, and τ_r^{-1}. For a counter biased to give a depletion layer thickness of 10^{-2} cm, and with a carrier lifetime of 100 μsec the maximum current density is 10^{-7} amp cm^{-2}.

In the vast majority of cases greater currents are observed than can be accounted for by either the diffusion current or the space charge generated current and they are assumed to be surface currents. They may, however, have the same voltage dependence as the space charge generated current if the contamination of the surface gives rise to energy levels in the surface layers of the crystal which act as efficient recombination centres, so providing a conducting path in parallel with the volume of the main space charge region. It is therefore an oversimplification to think of surface currents as being due to conduction in a surface film of contaminating material. This warning should serve to emphasize the importance of the surface of a junction counter, which should if possible be 'passivated' by a covering of material which does not cause surface recombination centres.[6] Unfortunately this is not very easy, and in spite of a great deal of experimentation[7] surface currents remain the principal source of current noise in semi-conductor junction counters.

The noise due to reverse currents can be stated in terms of the total number of charge carriers in the depletion layer. This will be the total generation rate gx per unit area, multiplied by the carrier transit time across the depletion layer, $\tau_c = x/\mu E$. The total number of electrons in the depletion layer is therefore

$$N_{cn} = \frac{n_i A x^3}{2\tau_r \mu_n V} \tag{5.22}$$

where x is the depletion layer thickness, A the area of the junction, V the applied voltage and μ_n the electron mobility. The hole content is

$$N_{cp} = \frac{n_i A x^3}{2\tau_r \mu_p V} \tag{5.23}$$

making the total

$$N_c = \frac{n_i A x^3}{2\tau_r V}\left(\frac{1}{\mu_n} + \frac{1}{\mu_p}\right) \tag{5.24}$$

The space charge generated current will be subject to full shot noise, because the generation events are all independent of one another, but there will be hardly any generation recombination noise, since the carriers are not subject to retrapping whilst crossing the depletion layer. This quantity may be used in equation (4.17) to give for the resolution due to space charge generated current noise

$$\Delta W = w\left\{\frac{n_i A x^3}{4\tau_r V}\left(\frac{1}{\mu_n} + \frac{1}{\mu_p}\right)\right\}^{\frac{1}{2}}\left(\frac{\tau}{\tau_c}\right)^{\frac{1}{2}} \tag{5.25}$$

As before $(\tau/\tau_c)^{\frac{1}{2}}$ may be taken as unity to calculate an order of magnitude for ΔW. As a numerical example consider again a counter made with 1000 Ω cm p-type silicon biased at 100 volts, with an area of 1 cm². The depletion layer thickness is then 10^{-2} cm, and the carrier lifetime is assumed to be 100 μsec, giving for the total number of carriers

$$N_c \simeq 1\cdot 5 \times 10^3$$

and for the energy resolution

$$\Delta W = 0.095 \text{ keV}$$

Similarly the noise due to the diffusion current may be calculated, giving an effective number of electrons in the depletion layer

$$N_c = \frac{n_p D_n^{\frac{1}{2}} x^2}{\tau_r^{\frac{1}{2}} \mu_n V} \tag{5.26}$$

The current will again be subject to full shot noise giving a resolution

$$\Delta W = w \left(\frac{n_p D_n^{\frac{1}{2}} x^2}{2\tau_r^{\frac{1}{2}} \mu_n V}\right)^{\frac{1}{2}} \left(\frac{\tau}{\tau_c}\right)^{\frac{1}{2}} \tag{5.27}$$

Using as an example the same junction as above gives

$$N_c = 4.5$$
and $$\Delta W = 8\text{eV}$$

The diffusion current in this example contributes a quite negligible amount of noise, and this is true of almost all other cases.

Two final conclusions to be drawn from this analysis are, firstly, that a long carrier lifetime is important in minimizing both diffusion and space charge generated currents, and, secondly, that quite large space charge generated currents can be permitted provided that they generate no more than normal shot noise. For example 10 μA flowing in the above example would give less than 1 keV resolution into a wide band amplifier, which is by no means excessive. It must therefore be concluded that in many cases excess noise is the limitation.

This treatment is somewhat rough and ready, ignoring completely the fact that the field is not constant in the depletion layer. In practice, however, the fact that it tails off at increasing distances from the junction interface as the free carrier density increases has very little effect on the results derived above. The junction capacity will have about the value given and will vary as $V^{-\frac{1}{2}}$, and the reverse current will vary as $V^{-\frac{1}{2}}/\tau_r$, provided that the crystal contains only fully ionized donors or acceptors. Where the occupancy of localized energy levels changes with applied field then both these laws may become inaccurate. This is best illustrated by taking a number of special cases. If the p-type material contains acceptors which are not completely ionized in thermal equilibrium then they will become more highly ionized in a high electric field, according to the mechanism described by Larrabee.[8] Their thermal ionization rate remains constant, but because the field reduces the free carrier concentration, recombination slows down. On balance, the higher the field the greater is the fraction of acceptors ionized. Allowing for the variation of field across the depletion layer this will lead to N_A becoming a function of x in equation (5.3). The situation is not unlike that in a narrow junction in low resistivity material where the variation in impurity concentration at the interface causes the capacity to vary as approximately $V^{-\frac{1}{3}}$. In the wide depletion layer with variable acceptor ionization C might vary in any way between $V^{-\frac{1}{2}}$ and $V^{-\frac{1}{3}}$. In an extreme case the depletion layer might be much narrower than expected, for N_A might be much larger than the thermal equilibrium hole concentration, and if the field fully ionized the acceptors the depletion layer would be narrower than the value given by equation (5.7) by the factor $(N_A/p)^{\frac{1}{2}}$. Pronounced effects of this kind can also occur in compensated crystals where one of the impurity levels has a large activation energy.

One final thing not brought out by the simplified model of the charge depletion layer is the importance of the carrier lifetime τ_r in determining the charge collection efficiency, or alternatively the effective thickness of the counter. The capacity calculated above refers explicitly to the charge and field distributions in the depletion layer, and not to the distance over which charges can be collected without appreciable recombination losses. Clearly, for a given field distribution the longer the recombination time τ_r the greater the effective thickness of the counter, so that, once again, it pays to have a large value of τ_r as well as a high resistivity.

5.4 Pulse rise time in junction counters

The pulse produced in a junction counter is governed by the same considerations as that in a homogeneous counter, but it differs considerably in detail because of the non-uniform field in a junction counter. Several authors have dealt with this problem, notably Tove and Falk[9,10] and Hansen.[11] They use essentially the same methods and make the same assumptions.

The calculation is based on the argument given in Section 3.3 that in a parallel electrode system the charge flowing through the external circuit when charges in the counter move is

$$\Delta q = \frac{e}{d} \, dx \qquad (5.28)$$

for each electron moving a distance dx in a direction perpendicular to the electrodes, d being the electrode separation. The pulse shape can be derived using this expression for the pulse induced in an external circuit for a given charge movement, and by considering the positions of the charges as a function of time as they move in the junction field. Consider a junction made with n-type material, so that the junction field at a distance x from the p-type layer (assumed very thin) is that derived in Section (5.2) by the integration of Poisson's equation,

$$E = -\frac{dV}{dx} = -\frac{4\pi e N}{\varkappa}(x - d) \qquad (5.29)$$

Consequently the equation of motion of an electron is

$$\frac{dx}{dt} = \mu_n E$$

or

$$\frac{dx}{(d - x)} = \frac{4\pi e N_0 \mu_n}{\varkappa} \, dt$$

$$\frac{dx}{(d - x)} = \frac{dt}{\tau_0} \qquad (5.30)$$

where $\tau_0 = \varkappa p/4\pi$, the dielectric relaxation time of the material from which the junction was made. (The assumption is made that the only charge carriers in the initial material arise from the donors, so that $\sigma = 1/p = N_0 e \mu_n$).

An electron produced at x_1 at time $t = 0$ drifts away from the p-type surface into the low field region, and its position at any time t is found by integrating equation (5.30)

$$x(t) = d - (d - x_1) \exp(- t/\tau_0) \qquad (5.31)$$

x approaches d only as t approaches ∞, so that strictly speaking there is no finite charge collection time for electrons; it is only possible to talk of the time necessary for a given percentage of the charge to be collected.

The corresponding equation of motion for holes is

$$\frac{dx}{(d - x)} = - \frac{dt}{\beta\tau_0} \qquad (5.32)$$

where $\beta = \mu_n/\mu_p$ the ratio of the carrier mobilities. And the position of a hole starting from $x = x_1$ at $t = 0$ is

$$x(t) = d - (d - x_1) \exp(t/\tau_0) \qquad (5.33)$$

Holes move into a region of increasing field and so have a finite collection time τ_p found by putting $x = 0$ into equation (5.33)

$$\tau_p = \beta\tau_0 \ln \frac{d}{(d - x_1)} \qquad (5.34)$$

To calculate the form of the charge pulse in the external circuit one further assumption is made, namely that the specific ionization of the particle is constant and equal to W/x_0, where W is the total energy of the incident particle, and x_0 is its range. The pulse due to electrons produced over the incremental length dx at $x = x_1$ is then

$$q(t) = - \frac{e}{w} \frac{dW}{dx}\left(1 - \frac{x_1}{d}\right)(1 - \exp - t/\tau_0)dx \qquad (5.35)$$

and integrating over all values of x from 0 to x_0 the pulse due to all electrons is

$$Q_n(t) = - \tfrac{1}{2}Ne(2 - b_0)(1 - \exp - t/\tau_0) \qquad (5.36)$$

where Ne is the total electronic charge and b_0 is the reduced range x_0/d.

The pulse due to holes is found similarly, though the algebra is a little more involved because the holes move towards a high field region, causing holes starting at different points to have different collection times (equation (5.34)) whereas electrons all have the same collection time (equation (5.31)). The final result is

$$Q_p(t) = -\frac{1}{2}\frac{Ne}{b_0}\left[1 - \exp(-t/\tau_0) - (1 - b_0)\left(\exp\frac{t}{\beta\tau_0} - 1\right)\right]$$

(5.37)

At $t = \infty$ the total contributions to the signal from electrons and holes are found to be

$$Q_n(\infty) = -Ne\left(1 - \frac{b_0}{2}\right)$$

(5.38)

$$Q_p(\infty) = -\frac{Neb_0}{2}$$

(5.39)

They add to give $|Ne|$ as expected, and their proportions depend upon the reduced range b_0.

Thus it is possible to define a charge collection time for the electrons equal to the dielectric relaxation time of the initial material.

$$\tau_n = \tau_0 = \frac{\varkappa\varrho}{4\pi} = \varrho - 10^{-12} \text{ seconds for silicon}$$

(5.40)

and as already explained collection goes to completion exponentially. But for holes collection is complete at time τ_p, obtained by putting $x_1 = x_0$ in equation (5.34) which yields

$$\tau_p = \beta\tau_0 \ln \frac{1}{(1 - b_0)}$$

(5.41)

which is a function of b_0 for a given detector.

Taking $\beta = 3$ for silicon

$$\tau_p = 3\varrho \ln \frac{1}{(1 - b_0)} \times 10^{-12} \text{ seconds}$$

When the junction is made with p-type silicon the roles of electrons and holes are reversed and the electron and hole pulses are

$$Q_p(t) = \tfrac{1}{2}Ne(2 - b_0)(1 - \exp - t/\tau_0)$$

(5.42)

$$Q_n(t) = \tfrac{1}{2}\frac{Ne}{b_0}\left[1 - \exp\left(-\frac{\beta t}{\tau_0}\right) - (1 - b_0)\left(\exp\frac{\beta t}{\tau_0} - 1\right)\right]$$

$$(5.43)$$

Tove and Falk[10] have compiled a nomogram for both n- and p-type junctions which gives the 10–90 per cent pulse rise times as a function of resistivity and reduced range. It is reproduced in Fig. 5.5. The method of using it is to put a straight edge between the reduced range and the resistivity appropriate to the counter and to read the rise time as the intersection on the time scale. It is noticeable that for junctions made with p-type silicon of a given resistivity the pulse rise time decreases monotonically as b_0 increases. This is because a greater proportion of the signal is due to the more mobile electrons. Using n-type material the situation is a little more complicated. As b_0 increases from zero the rise time initially falls because the average distance travelled by carriers decreases, but the trend is reversed as the less mobile holes become responsible for a higher percentage of the signal.

Although it admittedly contains a number of assumptions the nomogram is found to give a good indication of the pulse rise times to be expected in practice.

5.5 Surface barrier rectifiers

The first four sections of this chapter deal with the properties of the charge depletion layer in a reverse biased rectifier, without being specific about the exact form the rectifier takes. Diodes can be made in a number of ways, resulting in devices whose properties differ because the method of preparation changes the physical properties of the initial material, and also because different methods of fabrication lead to different device geometries.

The most straightforward device to understand is the conventional p-n junction made by diffusion of an impurity into a semiconductor crystal. It behaves in exactly the way described in the earlier sections of this chapter, and is made by processes that are understood and readily controlled. Its advantages lie in its robustness, for it is mechanically indistinguishable from a uniform single crystal, and in the inherently

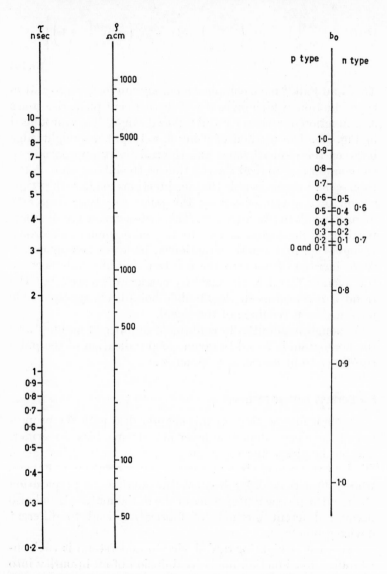

FIG. 5.5 Nomogram giving pulse rise time for junction counters as a function of the resistivity of the counter material and the reduced range of the incident particles (after TOVE and FALK[10])

high yield of the diffusion process. Important disadvantages are that the high temperatures used (800–1000° C for silicon) inevitably lead to a reduction of minority carrier lifetime and consequently an increase in current noise in the junction, and that the 'window thickness' of the diffused layer cannot be made less than a few tenths of a micron. Surface barrier junctions are made by processes carried out at or near room temperatures and therefore they hold out the possibility of better energy resolution than diffused junctions. They do so at the cost of greater fragility, and probably a much lower success rate in fabrication, though this latter point would be hard to substantiate because different workers have different standards of success. But because most users of junction counters require the best possible energy resolution surface barrier counters outnumber other types. It is therefore important to summarize what is known of their nature.

It has long been recognised that a potential barrier should exist[12,13] when a metal and a semiconductor come into intimate contact. When the two materials are separate they are internally in equilibrium, and the Fermi energy of each will have a particular value relative to that of an electron in the vacuum outside the crystal. In general the Fermi energies will be different. When the two materials come into contact a new equilibrium is established which includes the electrons in the metal and the semiconductor. It is characterized by the Fermi energy becoming the same throughout both solids. This is only possible if an electrostatic potential difference (the barrier height) is established between the two solids such that an electron taken round a complete cycle from metal to semiconductor and back through the vacuum does no nett work. This potential will indeed be established by the diffusion of charge carriers across the junction, exactly as in a p-n junction. Fig. 5.6 shows the energy levels of the metal and semiconductor (a) when they are well separated and (b) when they are in contact. It is clear that when they are in contact the potential barrier, as defined above is simply equal to the difference in Fermi energy of the separate materials. i.e.

$$eV_0 = \zeta_1 - \zeta_2 \qquad (5.44)$$

where V_0 is the barrier height.

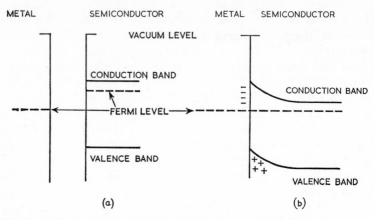

FIG. 5.6 The energy levels of a metal and a semiconductor (*a*) when
they are well separated, (*b*) when they are in contact. Electrons accumulate at the metal surface, and holes near the semiconductor surface
establishing a dipole layer resulting in the Fermi level and the vacuum
level being continuous.

It will be clear that in this Shottky barrier the magnitude and direction of the barrier height will depend on choice
of metal, and on the position of the Fermi energy relative to
the band edges in the semiconductor. Commonly it is found
that the measured barrier does not depend markedly on the
metal chosen, and this has led to a search for other phenomena which might affect the barrier height. Bardeen[14] was the
first to suggest that 'surface states' existed at the surface of a
semiconductor differing in energy from those in the bulk of
the crystal, and that the filling or emptying of such electron
levels could modify the barrier height by screening the
crystal, wholly or partially from external electric fields. This
is saying, in effect, that there may be other electrostatic
potentials not drawn in Fig. 5.6 due to charge double layers
at the surface of the semiconductor from causes other than the
exchange of conduction electrons.

There are four distinct ways in which a charged double
layer can arise at the surface of a semiconductor.[15]

(*i*) The kinetic energy of thermal motion of the electrons
in the crystal, although insufficient to carry them out
of the influence of the lattice can nevertheless take

them outside the outermost positive ion cores, before they turn back. This creates a charged double layer at the surface with the negative charge outermost.

(*ii*) At the semiconductor surface the periodic lattice ends, more or less abruptly. It is unlikely, therefore, that the energy levels of the bulk crystal which depend so strongly on the lattice periodicity will extend to the extreme surface layers. This problem was first tackled by Tamm[16] who considered a finite linear lattice in which the atomic fields were represented by square potential wells. He found an energy level in the forbidden gap due to the finite nature of the lattice. Shockley[17] considered a three-dimensional crystal and predicted a two-dimensional surface band half filled with electrons and with a surface density of states of about 10^{15} cm^{-2}, i.e. one per surface atom. This high density of surface charge can constitute a polarization of the electrons with respect to the ion cores and hence a charge double layer at the surface.

(*iii*) A further contribution to the double layer could be due to deformation of the ion cores near the surface, because of the asymmetric forces acting on them.

(*iv*) Finally, adsorbed monolayers of gas on the surface of the crystal may themselves be polarized, for they are held by a directional bond of some kind. In this case the degree of polarization would depend on the nature of the adsorbed layer.

It is not possible at this stage to say dogmatically what is the nature of the surface barrier effective in the silicon and germanium junctions used as nuclear particle counters, for the evidence does not fit clearly any of the four cases defined above. From the method of preparation and the kinds of deterioration associated with surface barrier counters it is clear that adsorbed layers are very important, for oxygen and water vapour both need to be present in the atmosphere in order to make a really good junction.

However, many workers find that the Bardeen model does not adequately describe their experimental results, and report junctions whose properties depend on the evaporated metal

very markedly. Indeed the use of gold as a rectifying contact
and aluminium as an ohmic one in the standard surface
barrier procedure illustrates a very marked difference of this
kind.

The most hopeful attempt to resolve this difficulty has been
made by Siffert, Laustriat and Coche[18,19], who have studied
the long term stability of surface barriers made with various
evaporated metals. It has long been known that surface
barriers undergo an ageing process after the gold evaporation,
and it has recently become apparent that evaporated aluminium contacts also change, although much more slowly, and
that they eventually become rectifying, with characteristics
very like those of the gold-silicon interface. Changes in the
back contact result in a shelf life of only a few months for
devices required to operate into high speed circuits or with
high fields at the back contact. Siffert and Coche have found
that all surface barriers on silicon become rectifying and
eventually acquire very similar electrical properties if they are
allowed to age for a long enough period. In some cases this
may be a year or more. They suggest that the adsorption of
oxygen and its diffusion into the oxide layer on the surface of
the silicon are the important steps in establishing the equilibrium surface states on the silicon, and further they contend
that this takes place only after the deposition of the metal.
The evidence for this is that the metals which yield rectifying contacts comparatively easily are those with work functions higher than that of silicon so that the resulting electric
field favours the migration of oxygen anions through the
oxide layer. Such metals include gold, antimony, tin, chrom-
ium platinum, aluminium, lead, silver, bismuth and zinc. On
the other hand, manganese, magnesium and the rare earth
elements which have work functions lower than that of silicon
give very good ohmic contacts initially, and revert only slowly
to rectifying barriers. The inference is that Bardeen's theory
is substantially correct for the silicon-silicon oxide system, but
that equilibrium is established at a rate determined by the
electric field which either assists or hinders the migration of
oxygen through the oxide layer. Where no external field is
applied the rate depends on the work function of the metal.

There are naturally many features of this theory which

require close examination, and experimental confirmation could be sought for the effect of electric fields on the formation of barriers, for example. Equally it is necessary to allow for the chemical affinity of the various metals for oxygen, their permeability to it, and any ageing effects in the metal itself. The best judgement that can be made at the moment is that much circumstantial information supports the theory; it agrees with most people's findings that the electrical properties of surface barriers show a much larger variation immediately after fabrication than they do after a period of ageing, and it is in line with recent findings on metal-oxide-silicon transistors.[20, 21]

A second puzzling feature of the process is that oxygen and water vapour have been observed to have opposite effects on silicon (and on germanium). Oxygen on n-type crystals adheres as an anionic impurity by accepting an electron from the conduction band. The bands therefore bend upwards at the surface corresponding to a depletion of electrons in the surface layers of the crystal. Water vapour on the other hand has been found to adsorb as a cationic impurity on p-type material by donating an electron to the valence band. Unfortunately there is no clear evidence of the roles of oxygen and water vapour adsorbed together on n-type silicon or germanium. Such evidence as there is will form part of Chapter 6 dealing with the fabrication and testing of junction counters.

5.6 Ion implantation doping

Another method of making junctions without heating has been attempted with considerable initial success by Martin, King and Harrison.[22] Its intention is to make a single crystal structure broadly similar to a diffused junction, but using a doping process consisting of accelerating ions in a Van de Graaff accelerator and embedding them in the surface of a silicon crystal. The method has one important disadvantage compared with diffusion, and one extra degree of freedom, which may prove to be a great advantage, in addition to the more obvious advantage that there is no need of heating which might reduce the minority carrier lifetime.

The disadvantage is the damage to the crystal lattice, in

the form of atoms knocked into interstitial positions leaving behind vacant lattice sites. Radiation damage of this kind is discussed more fully in Chapter 10, and here it is sufficient to say that it can have serious effects in reducing minority carrier lifetime and mobility and in changing the charge carrier populations. These changes only occur in that part of the crystal penetrated by the radiation and not throughout its volume, as happens during heat treatment.

The extra degree of freedom is that of controlling the impurity profile, which can be achieved by varying either the ion bombardment energy or the angle of incidence during the implantation experiment. Thus it is possible to have the maximum concentration of impurity at the surface, or at maximum depth, or to have a linear variation, or any other by arranging the experiment suitably. Whether any variation of concentration with depth would give better junctions than that achieved by diffusion is uncertain.

Martin, King and Harrison[22] used boron ions accelerated to either 100 keV or 500 keV scanned across the surface of an n-type crystal, and they varied the impurity profile by changing the angle of incidence during the irradiation. They were able to limit the window thickness to 0·5 microns, but found it necessary to implant at least 5×10^{11} atoms per cm^2 of surface in order to obtain a junction. They attribute this threshold to the need to overcome the n-type surface states. To minimise the effect of radiation damage they found it necessary to carry out the irradiation at liquid nitrogen temperatures and then to anneal at 300° C for 4 hours. It is suggested that the annealing consists of the 'recombination' of interstitial atoms with vacant lattice sites, and that the low temperature of irradiation prevents the diffusion of one type of defect to the surface, which would make the subsequent removal of the second one much more difficult.

The counters were completed by evaporating aluminium on the p-type surface and depositing nickel on the n-type surface using the method of Sullivan and Eigler.[23] The best results with comparatively large counters (120 mm^2) made on 10,000 ohm cm silicon gave resolutions as good as 50 keV at 40 volts reverse bias, comparing well with diffused junctions made by conventional techniques. It would be interesting to extend the method to other impurities and to compare manufacturing costs with those of other methods.

5.7 Lithium ion-drift in *p-n* junctions

The thickness of the depletion layer in a *p-n* junction given by equation (5.7) is limited by the resistivity and the break-down voltage of the junction. Using the best commercially available silicon and conventional fabrication techniques the upper limit of thickness is about 1 mm. Many applications call for greater thicknesses than this, and therefore attempts have been made both to increase the breakdown voltage of junctions and the resistivity of the starting material. The first of these two possibilities is discussed in the next chapter, since it is largely a question of methods of fabrication. We now deal with two techniques for increasing the resistivity of silicon and germanium.

The most difficult impurity to remove from silicon is boron, so that the purest available crystals are *p*-type containing boron as the most important source of charge carriers. The

Conduction band

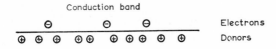

Electrons

Donors

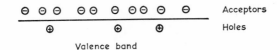

Acceptors

Holes

Valence band

FIG. 5.7 Compensated semiconductor with fully ionized impurities

boron is fully ionized at room temperature. Fig. 5.7 shows the energy level situation of a closely compensated semiconductor in which the concentration of ionized donors is almost equal to the ionized acceptor concentration, so that the concentration of extrinsic carriers is equal to the difference between the two impurity concentrations and is much smaller than either. Clearly if the two impurity concentrations were equal there would be the intrinsic concentration of holes and electrons and the only difference between this and truly intrinsic silicon would be lower carrier mobilities and lifetimes due to processes at the charged impurity centres.

The best available method of producing accurately compensated silicon and germanium is the lithium ion drift process due to Pell.[24] Lithium is a fast interstitial diffusant in silicon and germanium, diffusing in an ionized state. It therefore follows from the Einstein relation $D = (kT/e).\mu$ that its mobility in an electric field will be high, and that it will move in response to an applied field at temperatures where purely thermal diffusion is negligible.

The principle of the process is illustrated in Fig. 5.8. Starting with a p-type crystal with ionized acceptor concentration N_A, a p-n junction is made near the surface by diffusing lithium, to obtain a donor concentration gradient

$$N_D = N_0 \text{ erfc}\left[\frac{x}{2(Dt)^{\frac{1}{2}}}\right] \qquad (5.45)$$

where N_0 is the surface concentration and N_D the donor concentration at depth x, D is the diffusion constant of lithium at the appropriate temperature and t the diffusion time. The junction interface is at $x = c$, where $N_D = N_A$.

The junction is then biased in the reverse direction whilst held at a temperature at which the ion drift in the depletion region is appreciable, and is much larger than the temperature-controlled diffusion.
i.e.

$$E\mu N_D >> D\nabla.N_D \qquad (5.46)$$

Under these conditions lithium ions drift from the donor rich region $x < c$ to the region $x > c$, but N_D cannot become less than N_A for $x < c$, since if it did this would simply increase the field bringing in more ions from the left hand side. Similarly N_D cannot exceed N_A in the region $x > c$ because this would introduce field changes tending to reduce N_D where it exceeds N_A. Thus an accurately compensated (intrinsic) region is built up on both sides of $x = c$ by the transfer of

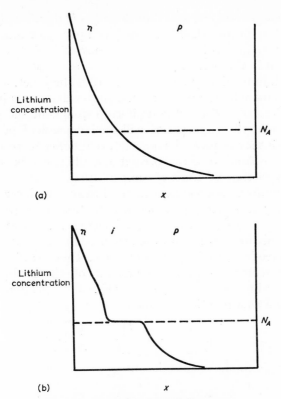

FIG. 5.8 The lithium ion-drift process
(a) After diffusion   (b) After drifting

lithium ions from the donor rich to the acceptor rich sides of
the junction. The maximum width of the intrinsic region is
reached when at its edges

$$E\mu N_{\mathrm{D}} = D\nabla.N_{\mathrm{D}} \tag{5.47}$$

i.e. the drift is exactly equal to the back diffusion. Pell[24] has
calculated this width to be

$$\frac{w^2}{8L} = \int E\mu\mathrm{d}t \tag{5.48}$$

where $L = 2Dt/c$ and $W << L.$

At room temperature lithium ion diffusion is still appreciable over long periods of time, and tends to reduce the width

of the compensated region, but there is a stabilizing effect due to the formation of lithium-boron complexes of much lower mobility than free lithium ions. The use of this effect will be described in Chapter 6.

It will immediately be recognized that the junction so produced is more like a homogeneous counter than a p-n junction, for the electric field will be uniform throughout the intrinsic region, and the capacitance will be independent of applied voltage if the compensation is exact. In practice there are small departures from these two predictions, which can be used as a measure of the exactness of compensation.

The uniform electric field in the intrinsic region results in different pulse shapes and charge collection times from those found in p-n junctions. If a charged particle is incident through the p-type surface the holes are produced in a column touching the electrode to which they will move. They do so with constant velocity, so that the amount of charge in motion decreases linearly with time and the hole collection may be expressed as a function of time by

$$Q_{\mathrm{p}}(t) = Ne\beta \, \frac{t}{\tau_{\mathrm{p}}}\left[1 - \frac{t}{2\tau_{\mathrm{p}}}\right] \qquad (5.49)$$

where τ_{p} is the hole collection time

$$\tau_{\mathrm{p}} = \beta \frac{d^2}{\mu_{\mathrm{p}} V} \qquad (5.50)$$

d being the total thickness of the device, V the applied voltage and β the reduced range of the particle. It is commonly arranged that the compensated region fills the whole thickness of the device, in which case d would be equal to W, the width of the intrinsic material.

Electron collection passes through a number of stages for which different charge collection rates apply. Under the simplifying assumption that the compensated region fills the whole of the device, there are two clearly defined regions. First the electrons are moving uniformly towards the positive electrode without any appreciable reduction in their number giving a linear charge collection

$$Q_{\mathrm{n}}(t) = - Ne(1 - \beta)\frac{t}{\tau_1} \qquad (5.51)$$

in the interval $0 \leqslant t \leqslant \tau_1$

where
$$\tau_1 = \frac{d^2}{\mu_n V}(1 - \beta) \qquad (5.52)$$

the time when the first electron reaches the electrode. From $t = \tau_1$ to $t = \tau_2$, where

$$\tau_2 = \frac{d^2}{\mu_n V} \qquad (5.53)$$

the time taken for the last electron to reach the electrode, the charge collection is like that for holes, and

$$Q_n(t) = - Ne\frac{(1 - \beta)}{\beta}\frac{(t - \tau_1)}{\tau_1}\left[1 - \frac{(1 - \beta)}{2}\frac{(t - \tau_1)}{\tau_1}\right] \qquad (5.54)$$

Typical values of charge collection time in a silicon detector with a compensated region a few millimetres thick lie in the range $10^{-7} - 10^{-6}$ secs, the electron collection time depending only on the thickness of the compensated region and the applied voltage and the hole collection time depending on these factors and the reduced range of the incident particles. Clearly for particles incident on the n-type surface of the device the roles of holes and electrons are reversed, but the general pattern of events is otherwise unaltered.

5.8 Transmutation doping

A second way of increasing the resistivity of silicon by compensation uses the nuclear reaction

$$\mathrm{Si}^{30} + n \; \rightarrow \; \mathrm{Si}^{31} \xrightarrow[2.6 \text{ hrs}]{} \mathrm{P}^{31} + \beta$$

Starting with p-type silicon it should be possible to create as many phosphorus atoms (donors) as there were acceptors initially, and so achieve perfect compensation. The isotopic abundance of Si^{30} is 3·09 per cent and its transmutation cross-section is 110 mb, so that exact compensation of 1000 Ω p-type silicon could be achieved in about 24 hours in a flux of 10^{12} neutrons cm^{-2} sec^{-1}. It is fortunate that the resulting Si^{31} atoms decay with such a short half life to the stable P^{31}, and that the more abundant Si^{28} and Si^{29} isotopes merely absorb neutrons in transmuting to other stable isotopes. The only real problem therefore is the same as that in ion implantation doping, namely that of minimizing and annealing out radiation damage caused by elastic collisions between nuclei and neutrons, and also that due to atoms recoiling after nuclear reactions. Since neutrons of more than 200 eV kinetic energy can cause lattice damage in this way the irradiation flux should as far as possible exclude neutrons having more than this energy. Since neutrons are required in quantities only readily available in the core of a reactor this is not an easy condition to satisfy, but nevertheless it is possible to do something to improve on the natural flux, by using absorbers and scatterers, and it is important to take this as far as possible.

The best results obtained by this method are those of Messier, Le Coroller and Merlo Flores[25]. They irradiated silicon of good uniformity with thermal neutron fluxes greater than 10^{16} neutrons cm^{-2}, and followed this by annealing the crystals at 500° C for up to 40 hours, after which no further change in conductance was observed. The phosphorus concentrations, deduced from measurements of Hall coefficient before and after irradiation agreed within 10 per cent with those calculated from the neutron flux and the number and cross section of the Si^{30} nuclei.

Diffused junctions made with the annealed material have depletion layer thicknesses of several millimetres at 200 volts bias. The best resistivity indicated in this way is 200,000 ohm cm, and lifetime measurements on finished devices have shown values of 3–10 microseconds.

The method has obvious interest and promise, and should not prove expensive if silicon can be irradiated in comparatively large quantities. It is therefore important to compare it with the lithium drift technique of achieving the same end product. Two important advantages of the lithium drift process are

(i) It compensates the acceptor concentration accurately whether it is uniform or not, whereas the irradiation technique produces a uniform phosphorus concentration, so magnifying the percentage inhomogeneity of the starting material.

(ii) Devices can be made at low temperatures, and without

irradiation, so that there is every prospect of the lithium drifted counters having the greater minority carrier lifetime.

Two advantages of the irradiation method are

(*iii*) The positional stability of the compensating centres is not in doubt.

(*iv*) The diffused structure which results is quite straightforward to make, and can have a combination of thin window ($\sim$ 0·5 micron) and physical robustness not yet attained with lithium drifted devices (see Chapter 6).

The first of these points is the vital one, for silicon of sufficient uniformity for the nuclear transmutation process is not readily available, and has usually to be selected, but in spite of this there are probably some requirements better met by the nuclear transmutation method.

It should be noted that pulse rise times will be the same in irradiation compensated junctions as in lithium drifted devices since the potential distribution is the same for both.

5.9 Junction counters with amplification

The voltage signals from junction counters are rather small, and it would be extremely attractive to amplify them in some way in the counter, assuming that this could be done without loss of performance in other respects. So far comparatively little has been done to this end. Bearing in mind the basic similarity between solid state counters and gas ionization chambers, the idea which comes first to mind is to obtain amplification by impact ionization, looking for something analogous to the proportional counter.

Controlled amplification by impact ionization in *p-n* junctions was first reported by McKay and McAfee[26] over ten years ago, but it is only recently that Huth, Trice and McKinney[27] have obtained useful gain in a semiconductor counter by this mechanism. These conditions have to be satisfied before useful amplification is attained:

(*i*) The junction must be capable of biasing to the point where internal amplification in the bulk occurs before surface breakdown.

(*ii*) The internal field must produce impact ionization by charges of one sign but not the other, for if both exceed their respective ionization thresholds complete electrical breakdown occurs.

(*iii*) The reverse current must be low, since this too will be amplified, adding to the noise generated in the junction.

Huth, Trice and McKinney satisfied these conditions in *p-n* junctions made on 50 ohm cm silicon by a rather deep (75 micron) gallium diffusion. The length of the surface conduction path is increased by lapping the edges of the slice at an angle of 6–10° to the normal to the junction interface. This proved sufficient to suppress surface breakdown, so that the junctions showed bulk breakdown at 1850 volts or more, as expected for this resistivity, with appreciable amplification above 1300 volts. Above this bias the window thickness is less than 10 microns and the depletion layer thickness of 200 microns is sufficient for complete absorption of 200 keV electrons. Amplification factors as high as 15 at 1840 volts bias were found for 1 MeV electrons, but for less uniform specific ionizations the amplification depends on particle range, because the junction field is not uniform, and therefore amplification does not occur uniformly throughout the volume of the depletion layer.

This technique shows great promise, for the characteristics of the devices were particularly stable in a variety of ambient atmospheres including vacuum, and the amplification was obtained without appreciable deterioration of noise or speed of response. Where only one type of charge carrier exceeds its threshold energy for impact ionization the amplification proceeds as a cascade through the depletion layer, moving with the drift velocity of the carriers taking part. No increase in pulse rise time is therefore expected, and none was found. The noise line width remains remarkably constant at just over 10 keV over the whole range of bias voltages, although the reverse current doubles from approximately $5 - 10 \times 10^{-8}$ amp, indicating that the main sources of noise are elsewhere than the reverse current.

A transistor form of counter is possible, made by analogy with the photo transistor with the geometry shown in Fig.

5.9(*a*). A high resistivity silicon slice, assumed to be *p*-type in this case, has diffused *n*-type contacts made on both faces to act as collector and emitter. It is shown with a positive bias applied to the collector, with the emitter earthed, and the base not connected, as is usual with photo-transistors.

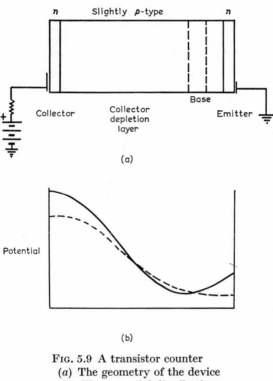

(a)

(b)

FIG. 5.9 A transistor counter
(*a*) The geometry of the device
(*b*) The potential distribution
—— quiescent   – – – after irradiation

The collector junction is reverse biased and therefore has a wide depletion layer, exactly like that of the normal junction counter. The emitter junction is forward biased and therefore has a very shallow space charge region and a very low field since its current is entirely controlled by the collector junction. The mode of operation is to arrange the thickness of the slice, its resistivity and the applied voltage so that the collector depletion layer is thick enough to absorb incident radiation completely, and extends to within 10 microns or less of the emitter junction. This is then the thickness of the transistor base.

When a charged particle is absorbed in the collector depletion layer the ion pairs are separated in the usual way, the electrons moving towards the collector and the holes towards the emitter, where they eventually enter the very low field of the base region. These excess holes is the base region disturb the potential distribution there, and are neutralized by excess electrons from the n-type emitter layer in a time equal to the dielectric relaxation time, (10^{-8} sec in 10^4 Ω cm p-type silicon.) A part of this injected electron current diffuses into the collector space charge region and gives an additional current. The magnitude of the current gain depends quite critically on the potential distribution in the base region and on its thickness. If the dark current through the structure is low the potential distribution is initially that shown by the full line in Fig. 5.9(b), with a minimum in the region of the base. This happens because there is a built-in field in the emitter junction opposing the flow of current in the absence of an applied field (as explained in Section 5.1). The applied field necessary to pass the collector junction current will not reverse this potential difference, so that the emitter junction also has a depletion layer rather like that of a reverse biased one. With this field distribution the holes can remain in the potential minimum for up to the carrier lifetime in the base. Meanwhile, if the base region is narrower than the electron diffusion length, many of the injected electrons will pass straight through the base region into the collector depletion layer. This current gain mechanism is analogous to that in cadmium sulphide with hole traps and has a maximum gain equal to the hole storage time in the base divided by the electron transit time across the base. Because the gain depends on the thickness of the base region it is liable to vary across the base, because of fabrication difficulties, so that transistor counters are never likely to be as good for particle spectrometry as are straightforward junctions. The rise time and pulse duration will also be longer.

In germanium a current gain of about 60 has been reported

for a structure such as that described above, but silicon transistors cannot yet be made with current gain at low values of emitter current. Williams and Webb,[28] in their silicon transistor counter, made a contact on to the base region in the way shown in Fig. 5.10. By passing a standing current between base and

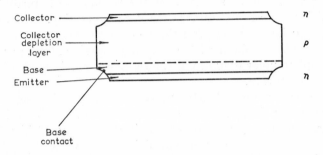

Collector — n

Collector depletion layer — p

Base — n
Emitter —

Base contact

FIG. 5.10 A transistor counter with base contact

emitter they have obtained current gain in the emitter-collector circuit of 200–300 under pulse conditions, or 600 with constant illumination with light, using the device as a phototransistor.

It is possible that the thermal noise in this device might be lower than that in a simple junction counter if the capacity of the emitter junction could be made lower than that of the reverse biased junction. This might be done by making it much smaller in area. Current noise would be much higher, however, for the current in the emitter junction now contributes its noise, and unfortunately this would probably be quite a large current in a high gain device. On the whole, therefore, the energy resolution of the transistor counter is unlikely to be as good as that of the simple junction, so that where resolution is important the counter is best made separately from the amplifier. Each can then be optimized rather more easily than when they have to be made in the same piece of silicon. However, when an array of counters is required, it might be advantageous to have larger signals so that long leads could be used to carry them to an amplifier. Then the transistor configuration might come into its own.

5.10 Position sensitive detectors

Growing interest is being shown in counters, or arrays of counters, which give signals indicative of the positions at which particles are absorbed. Detectors with this property could replace the photographic plate in a magnetic spectrometer with the advantage that the results are immediately available in a form suitable for data processing, instead of requiring development after the completion of the experiment. They might also be used in scattering experiments to acquire a complete polar diagram of the scattered particles at a high information rate.

The first successful attempt to make a position sensitive counter was that of Parkinson and Bilaniuk[29] who used the instrumental approach of combining an array of identical counters into a lumped constant delay line. Pulses of particles arriving over a time interval short compared with the electrical transit time along the delay line give signals which enter the amplifier at times after the event being observed which are proportional to length of delay line between the amplifier and the relevant detectors. The application of this system is limited to measurement of discrete pulses of particles, and relies on having a number of identical detectors if the transmission line is to have good electrical characteristics.

These limitations can be removed if detectors are made which are themselves position sensitive. The simplest counter of this kind is a rectangular one in which the back contact is an evaporated resistive film carrying a contact at the end of the long dimension of the rectangle (Fig. 5.11). Particles incident at the contact end of the device give rise to the largest voltage pulses because that part of the counter has the smallest resistance in series with the input impedance of the amplifier. For points of incidence further from the contact a greater series resistance is introduced consisting partly of the resistance of the evaporated film and partly of the undepleted silicon. A correlation is therefore established between voltage pulse height and position, although the conditions for a linear relation are not clearly defined. Positional accuracy about 0·3 mm, adequate for most magnetic analysers, can be obtained, and connection to a charge sensitive amplifier allows energy analysis to be performed using the same counter, although long time constants must be used in order to accommodate the spread in pulse shapes. Counters of this kind can accept a continuous flux of particles.

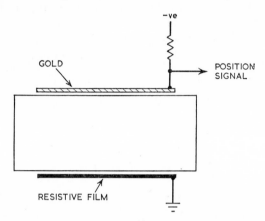

FIG. 5.11 Position Sensitive Detector using resistive film

Better linearity might be achieved by having the resistive film on the front of the counter, so that the resistance of the undepleted silicon is irrelevant to counter performance. The use of other metals than gold, or ion implantation doping are techniques which might give the required sheet resistivity.

The position sensitive detector with the best combination of properties has been developed by Ludwig, Gibson and Hood[30] using 'web' silicon. This is the name given to thin sheets of single crystal silicon grown between parallel pairs of dendritic crystals[31,32] with remarkable uniformity of thickness and resistivity. It may be made n- or p-type in the resistivity range 0·1 to 200 ohm cm or more, with lifetime around 10 microseconds. The thickness of the sheet is 50 to 250 microns and the width 5 to 10 mm. The length can be many metres. Crystallographically the material is quite good with less than 1,000 dislocations per cm^2, but there are usually several twin planes running parallel to the surface within the web, and these can affect the charge collection efficiency.

Using conventional surface barrier techniques counters were made with the geometry shown in Fig. 5.12. An evaporated gold electrode on one face forms the rectifying junction, and acts as the thin window of the counter. Two aluminium dots act as the ohmic contact. For each incident particle two signals are taken from the device. The signal derived at the gold electrode is proportional to the total energy deposited, and is independent of position, with charge collection efficiency greater than 98 per cent everywhere. Electrons moving to the back contact will divide between the two aluminium dots in

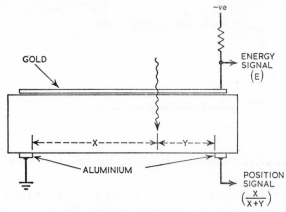

FIG. 5.12 Position Sensitive Detector using 'Web' silicon
(After LUDWIG, GIBSON and HOOD[30])

the inverse ratio of the resistances of the two paths. Thus the signal to one is proportional to $X/(X + Y)$, where X and Y are the distances from the incident particles to the two dots. Experiments show that this law is obeyed accurately and that a positional accuracy of 0·01 in. is attainable. Web silicon is also well suited to making position sensitive dE/dx counters, because it does not rely on any particular value of undepleted resistance. Additionally it has the advantage of greater strength than conventional dE/dx counters because of the dendritic crystals supporting it.

REFERENCES

For this chapter

1. Dabbs, J. W. T., Walter, F. J., Roberts, L. D. and Wright, H. W., *Oak Ridge National Laboratory*, Report No. **CF58-11-99** (1959).

2. ORTEC (*Oak Ridge Technical Enterprises Corporation*), Oak Ridge, Tennessee, U.S.A.
3. Shockley, W. and Read, W. T., *Phys. Rev.*, **87**, 387 (1952).
4. Brown, W. L., *Proceedings of Asheville Conference*, NAS-NRC Publication No. **871**, 19 (1961).
5. Sah, C-T., Noyce, R. N. and Shockley, W., *Proc. I.R.E.*, **45**, 1228 (1957).
6. Statz, H., *Proceedings of Asheville Conference*, NAS-NRC Publication No. **871**, 99 (1961).
7. Buck, T. M., *Proceedings of Asheville Conference*, NAS-NRC Publication No. **871**, 111 (1961).
8. Larrabee, R. D., *Phys. Rev.*, **116**, 300 (1959).
9. Tove, P. A. and Falk, K., *Nuclear Instr. and Methods*, **12**, 278 (1961).
10. Tove, P. A. and Falk, K., *Nuclear Instr. and Methods*, **29**, 66 (1964).
11. Hansen, N. J., *Progress in Nuclear Energy*, Vol. 4, Part 1, Pergamon Press (Oxford, 1964).
12. Mott, N. F., *Proc. Roy. Soc.*, **A171**, 27 (1939).
13. Schottky, W., *Z. Phys.*, **113**, 367 (1939).
14. Bardeen, J., *Phys. Rev.*, **71**, 717 (1947).
15. Spenke, E., *Electronic Semiconductors*, p. 345, McGraw Hill (New York, 1958).
16. Tamm, I., *Physik Z. Sowjetunion*, **1**, 733 (1932).
17. Shockley, W., *Phys. Rev.*, **56**, 317 (1939).
18. Siffert, P., Laustriat, G., and Coche, A., *I.E.E.E. Trans. Nucl. Sci.*, **NS 11**, No. 3, 244 (1964).
19. Siffert, P. and Coche, A., *I.E.E.E. Trans. Nucl. Sci.*, **NS12**, No. 1, 284 (1965).
20. Deal, B. E., Grove, A. S., Snow, E. H. and Sah, C-T., *Trans. Met. Soc.*, AIME, **233**, 524 (1965).
21. Snow, E. H., Grove, A. S., Deal, B. E. and Sah, C-T., *J. Appl. Phys.*, **35**, 2455 (1964).
22. Martin, F. W., King, W. J. and Harrison, S., *Proc. 9th Scintillation and Semiconductor Counter Symposium*, Washington (1964).
23. Sullivan, M. V. and Eigler, J. H., *J. Electrochem. Soc.*, **104**, 226 (1957).
24. Pell, E. M., *J. Appl. Phys.*, **31**, 291 (1960).
25. Messier, J., Le Coroller, Y. and Merlo Flores, J., *Proc. 9th Scintillation and Semiconductor Counter Symposium*, Washington (1964).
26. McKay, K. G. and McAfee, K. B., *Phys. Rev.*, **91**, 1034 (1953).
27. Huth, G. C., Trice, J. B. and McKinney, R. A., *Rev. Sci. Instrum.*, **35**, 1220 (1964).

28. Williams, R. L. and Webb, P. P., *Proceedings of Asheville Conference*, NAS-NRC Publication No. **871**, 182 (1961).
29. Parkinson, W. C. and Blanuik, O. M., *Rev. Sci. Inst.*, **32**, 1136 (1961).
30. Ludwig, E. J., Gibson, W. M., and Hood, J. S., *I.E.E.E. Trans. Nucl. Sci.*, **NS-12**, No. 1 (1965).
31. Dermatis, S. N. and Faust, J. W. Jr, *I.E.E.E. Trans. Commun. Elect.*, **65**, 194 (1963).
32. O'Hara, S. and Bennett, A. I., *J. Appl. Phys.*, **35**, 686 (1964).

For general reading

Shockley, W., *Electrons and Holes in Semiconductors*, Van Nostrand (Princeton, N.J., 1950).

CHAPTER 6

PREPARATION AND PROPERTIES OF SEMICONDUCTOR JUNCTION COUNTERS

6.1 Diffused junctions

Many techniques and precautions are common to the methods of making all kinds of semiconductor junction. They will be described in detail in this first section and taken for granted in subsequent descriptions of other methods. It should also be borne in mind that many variations of technique are possible, so that there are many satisfactory ways of making junction counters – probably as many as there are people making them. All that can be attempted here is a description of one self-consistent method with indications of how it may be varied to suit individual needs and facilities.

Silicon and germanium crystals suitable for all kinds of junction counters are now available commercially, normally in the form of floating zone refined crystals of very uniform cross-section. Resistivity and carrier lifetime measurements have usually been made by the manufacturer at regular intervals along the crystal, so that it is possible to pick the material for making a counter with a considerable degree of confidence as to the outcome. The problems are concerned with maintaining the resistivity and lifetime of the material whilst making a junction of the desired size and shape, and of controlling surface contamination.

The first step is to cut the crystal into slices, mounting it with strong wax or a potting plastic on a firm base, and cutting with a precision diamond loaded annular saw. This is a technique which has found wide application in semiconductor technology because it can cut any desired thickness of slice down to about 0·005 in. accurately and with no more than 0·005 in. of waste per cut. It also has the great advantage that it minimizes the damage to the cut surface, because the tension applied to the outer diameter of the annular saw can be adjusted to allow very little whip or vibration of the inner cutting edge. Mechanical damage to the crystal caused by cutting or abrading creates recombination centres which greatly reduce the carrier lifetimes, and it is therefore necessary to remove all damaged material before making a junction. This can be done straightforwardly by lapping (by hand or by machine) with successively finer grades of polishing powder, finishing with about 8 or 10 micron aluminium oxide and removing in all about 0·003 in. of crystal. Boiling toluene in an ultrasonic bath is a good way of removing each successive grade of lapping powder, followed after the last polish by washing first in chromic acid and then in deionized water to remove all traces of grease, prior to etching. After this, slices should never be handled or come into contact with metals. Plastic tweezers and beakers should be used exclusively to avoid metal contamination or grease marks from fingers. These latter are extremely difficult to remove, and either kind of contamination can have a serious effect on the properties of the finished device. The final stage of slice preparation is to etch* in CP4A† at 45° C for about $1\frac{1}{2}$ min using 50 cc of fresh etch for each slice. This removes a further 0·001 in. of silicon, including all the residual damage due to the final stage of polishing and leaves the surface flat. It is usually true that damage in lapping or polishing extends below the polished face to a depth of about two diameters of the polishing powder, though with diamond it may be rather deeper. Other etches and temperatures have been proposed to achieve

* It is convenient to hold the slice in the jaws formed by splitting a polythene or P.T.F.E. rod into three segments down its length. This ensures even etching on both faces and reduces the danger of splashing acid as compared with the all too common method of swilling the slice around in the bottom of a beaker.

† CP4A etch consists of: conc. hydrofluoric acid (48 per cent) – 3 parts by volume; conc. nitric acid (71 per cent) – 5 parts by volume; glacial acetic acid (100 per cent) – 3 parts by volume. Mix carefully and store in polythene container.

this end, and, indeed, etching may be used to the exclusion of mechanical polishing to remove all the damage due to the saw cut. Generally speaking, however, the longer the etching time and the greater the amount of material to be removed the harder it is to achieve a flat polished finish to the slice, and the above procedure is felt to be somewhere near optimum. This etch, and all subsequent ones, should be 'quenched', that is, they should be diluted with deionized water, partially decanted, and then diluted again, preventing air reaching the crystal until the acid is extremely weak. This is necessary to avoid surface oxidation. The slices may then be rinsed in ethyl alcohol, dried under an infra-red lamp and should be stored in a vacuum desiccator until the next stage of the process is to be performed. The slices are then clean and damage-free, and ready for diffusion, they should be stored and handled separately as quite slight contact between them can cause further damage in the form of chips and scratches, so ruining the whole of the preparation. For very thin counters the procedure is basically the same, but with careful polishing with $\frac{1}{4}$ micron alumina to the desired thickness and correspondingly less etching.

Silicon is preferred in most cases for junction counters because they work at room temperature whereas germanium counters must be cooled to reduce leakage currents. The techniques will therefore be described for silicon. Most diffused junction counters are made from p-type silicon for the somewhat slender reasons that it is slightly easier to obtain high resistance, long lifetime material of this type, and because it is a little easier to diffuse phosphorus than boron or gallium. The process will be described for p-type material and can easily be modified for application to n-type material.

Phosphorus is the most convenient donor for diffusion into silicon, and can be applied in the form of a paint[1] to the face of the silicon slice. This has the advantage over the more normal gaseous diffusion that a second impurity can be diffused simultaneously from the other face of the slice to make an ohmic contact to the back of the junction. No masking is needed to keep the two diffusants separate, and only a single heating cycle is necessary to make the whole counter structure. The process, which has been described by Moncaster,

Raines and Northrop,[2] consists of evaporating a film of aluminium about 0·5 μ thick on one face of the slice, using a mask to keep the edges of the slice clean.

It would be hard to over-emphasize the importance of scrupulous care and cleanliness at every stage in the preparation of all kinds of semiconductor counter. Most manufacturers find it necessary to carry out all operations in clean rooms or glove boxes under controlled conditions of humidity and temperature, and to use special overalls including overshoes and headgear if they are to achieve a good yield of high quality devices. Equal care must be taken in selecting the chemicals and apparatus to be used and in protecting this from contamination. This generally means that equipment used for counter production cannot be used for other purposes. Departures from these standards lead to poor and non-reproducible results.

Phosphorus is then painted on the other face in the form of a solution of phosphorus pentoxide in ethylene glycol, approximately 2 cc of P_2O_5 to 10 cc of ethylene glycol. (This should be mixed cautiously in a fume cupboard and allowed to stand two days with occasional stirring before use.) It is best painted with a camel-hair brush in a plastic holder, without metal parts, painting successive coats and drying them under an infra-red lamp until a uniform coat is produced. The diffusion is carried out in a furnace in a flow of dry argon, taking the temperature up to 800° C in an hour, maintaining it there for a further hour, cooling to 500° C in the next hour, and then switching the furnace off to cool to room temperature. The phosphorus diffuses into the silicon, probably to a depth of about one micron. The ethylene glycol residues char and leave the silicon covered with a black deposit. Aluminium alloys with silicon at 577° C and then aluminium diffuses from the alloy to give a heavily doped p-type layer below the metal film.

When cold the slice is soaked in concentrated hydrofluoric acid to remove charred material and the phosphorus glass. It is then washed in deionized water, rinsed in ethyl alcohol and dried under an infra-red lamp. The basic structure shown in Fig. 6.1 is now complete with a thin rectifying contact and a rather thicker ohmic contact made to high resistivity p-type silicon. It may be mounted whole, or cut up to give a number of smaller counters, as desired. Pressure contacts to the two

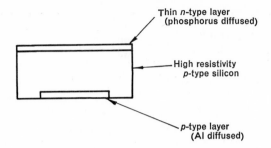

Thin *n*-type layer
(phosphorus diffused)

High resistivity
p-type silicon

p-type layer
(Al diffused)

Fig. 6.1 Diffused *n-p-p+* diode

faces are perfectly adequate, and small counters may be mounted on standard transistor headers under a spring clip as illustrated in Fig. 6.2. Alternatively, wires may be fixed to the faces using a conducting cement such as Johnson Matthey's F.S.P.49. Other methods of preparing and mounting diffused

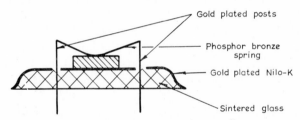

Gold plated posts

Phosphor bronze spring

Gold plated Nilo–K

Sintered glass

Fig. 6.2 Small area counter mounted on transistor header

junction counters are outlined in Section 6.4 under the heading of encapsulation and surface treatment.

6.2 Surface barriers

Surface barrier rectifiers are made on *n*-type crystals of silicon or germanium where spontaneous oxidation gives an inversion layer on the surface having properties very like a diffused *p*-type layer. Because the oxidation occurs at room temperature this offers a method of making a rectifier without heating and therefore without deterioration in the carrier lifetime. The cutting and preparation of the crystal slice are exactly the same as for diffused junctions, though once again different workers recommend recipes widely different in detail. For example, Dearnaley and Whitehead recommend cooling the CP4A etch in iced water to prevent over-rapid reaction rates, and they allow the etch to continue for twice the time taken to produce a mirror finish on the slice, discarding any slice which does not give a mirror finish as unsuitable. It is hard to say what property of the crystal makes it both unsuitable for surface barrier counters and impossible to etch smoothly, but no doubt it is an empirical rule to be respected by those who follow the Dearnaley and Whitehead[3] method.

Given a smooth and damage-free slice it is usually sufficient to leave it in clean, dust-free, air for 12–36 hours before evaporating a gold film over it to form a rectifying contact. Typically, slices might be left overnight in a sealed plastic container. Precisely what happens during this time is not clear, and indeed there are conflicting accounts of what is actually observed. Archer,[4] and Andreyeva and Shishakov[5] have measured the rate at which oxygen is taken up on an etched semiconductor surface, and the latter's results, reproduced in Fig. 6.3 show the formation of a stable oxide layer and a volatile component, probably oxygen. The thickness of the oxide increases with time to about 70 Å. Undoubtedly oxygen plays an important part in surface barrier formation, but oxidation alone is not enough. Water vapour too has a role, and it has been found by many workers that good surface barriers do not form in completely dry air. In fact, Klema[6] has obtained good results by holding his silicon slice in the surface of boiling water for 30 minutes before gold evaporation. Siffert, Laustriat and Coche[7] have shown that rectification occurs only after a period in oxygen or air after the gold deposition, and most other workers would agree that the traditional ageing of surface barrier devices goes on for a considerable time after completion.

No coherent explanation of all the experimental observations reported in the literature has been given, but there is little doubt that surface treatment before gold evaporation is important, and that wet air gives lower leakage currents, higher breakdown voltages and better stability in vacuum than other ambients.[8] Whether the ageing after evaporation is

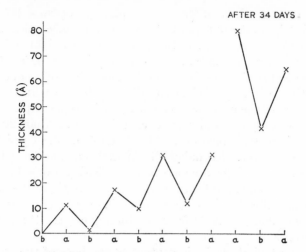

Fig. 6.3 The reversible take-up of oxygen on semi-conductors. The thickness of an adsorbed film on germanium is measured during a repeated cyclic process of (a) Exposure to the atmosphere for 20–30 mins. (b) pumping for 6 hours. (after ANDREYEVA and SHISHAKOV[5]).

a continuation of this process or an ionic rearrangement in the oxide layer is not known.

At this stage it may be advantageous to apply an edge protection around the area which will form the rectifying contact. This is not essential in junctions for use at moderate voltages or those made with material of resistivities greater than about 300 ohm cm, for in these cases the surface field is not high enough to cause troublesome surface breakdown. In the case of shallow depletion layer devices of low resistivity material, junctions to be biased to very high voltages, and those likely to be exposed to humid or corrosive atmospheres an edge protection such as that used by Fox and Borkowski[9] described in section 6.4 should be used.

Next a gold film is evaporated over the front surface of the crystal to form a thin rectifying contact. Gold is chosen because it evaporates easily to form a film which is continuous and a good conductor at the required thickness, and which does not tarnish. It has also been found to give a better rectifying contact than other metals, perhaps because its work function is most appropriate to do so on oxidized silicon. The thickness of gold is not critical, and surface weights of 20-50 μgm cm^{-2} are adequate. Some compromise can be made between good surface conductance, and low absorption of energy from the incident particle, depending on the range and specific ionization of the particles to be measured. For example, fission fragments might require an even thinner film than 20 μgm cm^{-2}, whereas for protons a thick film of low sheet resistance would be better. Dearnaley and Whitehead take the precaution of evaporating a second much heavier layer of gold on the small area to be used for connecting a lead to the surface. This minimizes the risk of damage by spring contacts, or of penetration of contaminants from conducting cement through the gold film.

The best kind of ohmic contact to the base of the rectifier is that described by Andrews,[10] who uses a thick layer of evaporated aluminium. It has a low carrier injection rate and so is particularly useful for counters in which the depletion layer extends right through the slice. This evaporation and that of the gold are perfectly straightforward, requiring only normal vacuum techniques, but it is a sensible precaution to evaporate through masks of freshly cleaved mica or other suitable material to ensure that no metal or other contamination reaches the sides of the slice. The counter is now ready for mounting, which can be done using conducting pastes or cements exactly as for diffused junctions, though germanium junctions, which have to be cooled to 90° K, are better with indium soldered contacts, or indium pressure pads. Once again, consideration of encapsulation and edge protection is reserved to a later section.

6.3 Lithium ion-drift junctions

(a) *Silicon*

The technique first described by Mayer[11] for making lithium ion-drift junction detectors in silicon follows that originally used by Pell[12] in studying the mechanism of the ion-drift process. A silicon crystal slice is prepared for diffusion by cutting, lapping and etching as described above, the only differences from the method used for making a conventional diffused junction are that the slice would be thicker – between 1 and 10 mm – and that it would be p-type in the resistivity range 1000 to 2000 ohm cm. Mayer used a lithium in oil suspension (obtained from the Lithium Corporation of America), painting it on one face of the crystal and drying in an inert atmosphere at 200° C. There is some difficulty in obtaining uniform coverage of the surface, which is lessened if the surface is lightly lapped. Recently, however, many workers[13,14,15,16,17] have favoured evaporation of lithium in vacuum as a way of overcoming the difficulty.

The lithium is then diffused into the silicon at a temperature between 300 and 500° C for a time between 1 and 10 minutes. Typically a 5 minute diffusion at 400° C is used for crystals of resistivity greater than 100 ohm cm, with higher temperatures for lower resistivities to keep the surface concentration of lithium about 103 times that of the acceptors in the crystal. The diffusion may be carried out in an oven in an inert atmosphere, or in the vacuum chamber used for the lithium evaporation. Dearnaley and Lewis, and Goulding and Hansen both used the latter method, though Goulding and Hansen preheat the silicon to 400° C before the evaporation and cool rapidly with water passing through a cooling coil after a one minute diffusion. Dearnaley and Lewis evaporated on a cold substrate, and carry out the diffusion as a separate operation.

Resistivity measurements and chemical staining techniques show diffusion depths of about 200 microns. After washing the slice in an alcohol-water mixture to remove excess lithium a check of the thickness and uniformity of the diffusion may be made by a four point probe measurement of sheet resistivity for comparison against the data published by Backenstoss.[18]

Before the drift process can begin contacts have to be made to both the n- and p-type surfaces of the slice. Aluminium or gold containing 1 per cent boron may be alloyed to the p-type surface to give a good p^+ contact, and pure gold or gold containing 1 per cent antimony to the n-type surface. Alternatively both faces may be nickel plated by the so-called electroless method described by Sullivan and Eigler,[19] or gold plated using one of the commercially available gold potassium cyanide solutions (e.g. from Engelhard Industries, or Sigmund

Cohn Inc.). Alloyed contacts are relatively simple to make on silicon which forms eutectic alloys with gold just below 400° C and with aluminium just below 600° C. All that is necessary is to heat the silicon to the eutectic temperature for about one minute in contact with the alloying substance in the form of a pellet or an evaporated film. On cooling a layer of heavily doped material silicon crystallizes first, followed by the eutectic alloy, giving a good thermal contact.

Because of the difference in thermal expansion coefficient between silicon and the alloy, large area contacts of this kind may be brittle. This should not be a serious obstacle with low resistivity silicon which does not require large area contacts (say greater than 1 mm diameter). Nevertheless some workers prefer to use plated contacts, sometimes 'firing-in' the nickel at about 600° C and still others prefer to diffuse phosphorus into one face and aluminium or boron into the other. This has to be done before the lithium diffusion because the high temperatures involved would distribute large quantities of lithium throughout the slice.

The structure is now a p-n junction and is ready for the lithium drift process described in Section 6.5. Temperatures of 100–200° C are commonly used for this, and there are two basic methods of attaining them, with many minor modifications.

The first method was evolved by Mayer[11] who used a stirred silicone oil bath, limiting its temperature and the drifting voltage so that the electrical power dissipation in the junction was less than 2 watts. This maintained the specimen temperature uniform, but led to very long drift times for deep compensated regions. Miller, Pate and Wagner[20] showed that the width of the compensated region is proportional to the cube root of the electrical energy dissipated in the junction during drift at constant temperature. Rapid drift rates therefore require high power dissipation and efficient removal of heat from all points in the device, the limit being set by the phenomenon of 'thermal runaway'. If a part of the junction heats up carrier generation increases and so therefore does the power consumption, leading to a further temperature rise. Drastic local overheating can cause complete electrical breakdown of the diode.

Miller, Pate and Wagner proposed a refinement of the constant temperature drift process employing a fluorocarbon (Minnesota Mining and Manufacturing Co. F.C.43) as a vapour phase coolant in the region of nucleate boiling. The improved cooling efficiency allowed a large and constant mean power to be fed to the diode by discharging a condenser through it

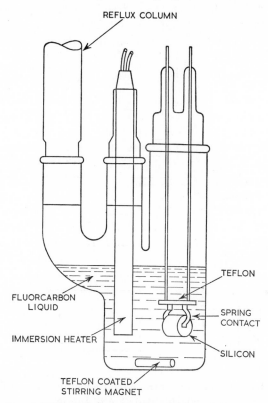

FIG. 6.4 Vapour phase cooling lithium drift apparatus. (after MILLER, PATE and WAGNER[20]).

at a preset frequency. Fig. 6.4 shows a diagram of their apparatus. They obtained drift rates of 4 mm in 28 hours at 15 watts, and 11 mm in 240 hours at 45 watts.

Dearnaley and Lewis[14] pointed out that dissipation of the excess heat in a fluid that surrounds the diode on all sides must lead inevitably to radial temperature gradients and

differences in drift rate across the junction area. They consider
it preferable to use a pair of plane metal cooling plates in
contact with the end faces of the device and to carry out the
drifting in air. Theirs is thus not a constant temperature
method, but one which seeks to achieve zero temperature
gradient at right angles to the drift field. Again a constant
power is fed to the diode, this time by a d.c. supply, but the
diode current is regulated by controlling the temperature of
the metal end plates. This is done by balancing a cooling air
blast against heat supplied to the end plates through a silicon
controlled rectifier. This gives rapid control of temperature

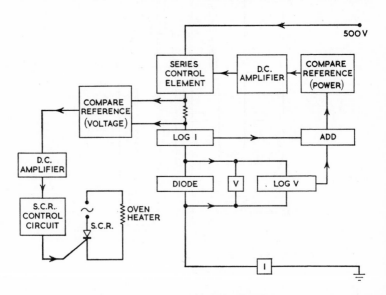

FIG. 6.5 Block diagram of control circuit for lithium ion-drift in silicon
(after DEARNALEY AND LEWIS[14])

either upwards or downwards. A block diagram of their control circuit is shown in Fig. 6.5. Drift rates are 4 mm in 20
hours or 7 mm in 65 hours for a power input of 15 watts.

This kind of servo mechanism was first proposed by Blankenship and Borkowski,[21] and something very similar has also
been described by Goulding and Hansen[15] who heat the silicon
by incorporating it in the heat sink of a 30 watt power tran-

sistor and use a water cooling arrangement for rapid temperature control.

Several methods are available for determining the width of the compensated zone after a period of drifting. One is by room temperature capacitance measurements, another is by chemical staining either with a staining etch (HF with about 0.25 per cent HNO_3) or by copper plating. This last method consists of reverse biasing the diode immersed in a bath of copper sulphate solution. Copper deposits only on the uncompensated lower resistivity part of the crystal. These are all methods which involve the interruption of the lithium drift process, and none of them offers any direct control over the drifting. But when a lithium drifted junction is used as a charged particle detector it is necessary to ensure a thin entry window, to minimise the energy loss before the particles reach the sensitive volume. The initial lithium diffusion produces a window 100 to 200 microns thick, which would be most undesirable, and this has led to attempts by Miller, Pate and Wagner,[20] and Dearnaley and Lewis[14] to continue the drift process to the back face of the slice, and to form a thin window surface barrier junction there. Miller *et al.* actually stopped the drifting short of the back face and ground off the uncompensated material, but Dearnaley and Lewis arranged their control apparatus so that when lithium reached the back face of the slice, causing an *n-i-n* structure to be formed passing a heavy current the drifting apparatus switched itself off. They then etched the slice before making a surface barrier on the exposed intrinsic material. Goulding and Hansen[15] have also described an automatic apparatus in which two electrodes are placed on the back face, and the change of impedance between them when lithium drifting is complete again switches off the apparatus. The electrode structure is then etched away.

The contact to the *n*-type lithium diffused face can be made in a variety of ways. Dearnaley and Lewis used a layer of evaporated aluminium, and connected a lead to this with conducting silver paste. They also showed that it is possible to etch away the lithium diffused layer and make a thin *n*-type contact to the compensated silicon by means of evaporated aluminium. Then the entire volume of silicon is sensitive to radiation.

There have been varying reports of the stability of lithium drifted silicon detectors during storage over periods of months. Without encapsulation there does appear to be a deterioration in the current-voltage and capacitance-voltage characteristics, which can be reduced by storage under a reverse bias of about 100 volts. On the other hand some fully encapsulated commercial detectors suffer no appreciable change over six months or more without storage bias. This evidence suggests strongly that the changes take place at the surface and are in some way catalysed by contact with the atmosphere. Recent work by Norgate and McIntyre[22] has shown that the original impurity also affects stability, presumably because lithium forms stable lithium-acceptor complexes of varying mobility and stability. After studying boron, indium, gallium and aluminium doped silicon they conclude that gallium gives the greatest stability and boron the least – a fact which may prove of considerable value where stable lithium configurations are required over long periods of time.

Gibbons[23] has proposed an interesting method for making stable lithium drifted counters with thin windows. He points out that the lithium in the compensated region is positionally stable because of the lithium-boron pairs formed, and suggests a procedure which stabilizes all the lithium in this way. A slice of high resistivity p-type silicon is prepared by diffusing n-type and p-type contacts into opposite faces. This could be done by simultaneous diffusion of phosphorus and aluminium, as described earlier, or by separate diffusion of any suitable impurities. Lithium may now be diffused into the silicon at 700° C, holding the lithium source at a much lower temperature, to give a uniform lithium concentration somewhat in excess of the acceptor concentration in the original material. Lowering the lithium source temperature reduces the lithium concentration attained in the silicon. There results a rectifying contact between the p-type diffused contact and the lithium doped bulk of the material, and a reverse bias at 200–300° C causes excess lithium to drift into the p-type contact where it becomes stabilized in the form of lithium-acceptor pairs. By doping down to 100 ohm cm before the out-drifting of lithium, compensated regions about 2 mm thick have been obtained.

The attraction of lithium ion-drifted junctions with two

thin windows, as described by Gibbons and by Dearnaley and Lewis is that they can be stacked one above another to give total absorption of very energetic particles, but with individual time constants much shorter than that of a single counter of the same total thickness.

(b) Germanium

Recently much attention has been focussed on the lithium ion drift process in germanium, mainly because germanium has a sufficiently high atomic number to give appreciable cross sections for photoelectric absorption of gamma rays.

The classic work on lithium in germanium was by Reiss, Fuller and Morin[24], who studied solubility and ion pairing. Because of the low solubility of lithium in germanium diffusions must be used which yield lithium concentrations exceeding the solubility at the drifting temperature. The excess lithium is then liable to precipitate in an electrically inactive form at lattice defects, and it has been shown that oxygen in the crystal accelerates the precipitation. Germanium crystals for lithium drifting should therefore contain very low oxygen concentrations if accurate compensation is to take place.

Surface states also have a stronger effect on the characteristics of germanium diodes than on silicon, and this necessitates drifting in a dry atmosphere. Finally it appears more difficult to make non-injecting contacts on compensated germanium than on compensated silicon and encapsulation is made more difficult because of the requirement to operate germanium detectors at liquid nitrogen temperatures.

The first germanium lithium drifted counters were prepared in Britain by Freck and Wakefield[25] in 1962. Starting with 5 ohm cm material they carried out a lithium diffusion exactly as for silicon, and then performed the drifting in an oil bath at a regulated temperature. Compensation was achieved to a depth of 4 mm. The resulting detectors gave an energy resolution as good as 6 keV for gamma rays at $90° K$, but this important work escaped attention. During 1963 other groups began similar work and by 1964 the great potentialities of the new detector were widely appreciated.

The best germanium for lithium drifted detectors is produced by zone levelling in a reducing atmosphere. It has a low oxygen content and is very uniform in composition. Hansen and Jarrett[26] drew attention to the work of Carter and Swalin[27] who had shown that the precipitation of lithium at defect sites in the lattice, which is catalysed by oxygen, can be inhibited by copper diffused to fill these sites before lithium diffusion. Hansen and Jarrett achieve this by copper plating the germanium at 425° C for a few minutes, and then removing excess copper from the surface by soaking in nitric acid.

Lithium is generally applied by evaporation in vacuum and the diffusion can be carried out either in an inert atmosphere or in the vacuum system, although recently electrolytic deposition from a eutectic of KCl and LiCl at 400° C has been used successfully. Palms[28] finds that preheating the crystal to 425° C before evaporating the lithium gives the best results, but Hansen and Jarrett recommend heating on a hot plate for 5 minutes at 425° C in a nitrogen atmosphere. They place a $\frac{1}{4}$ inch graphite plate between hot plate and germanium to minimise the thermal shock, and cool the crystal quickly in order to freeze the lithium ions in the lattice and minimise precipitation. Cooling may be achieved via an air cooled or water cooled copper block by turning on the flow of coolant at the end of the diffusion. It is then best to cut away the edges of the crystal and etch with 3:1 nitric acid-hydrofluoric acid mixture. The lithium diffusion then covers one face of the crystal which is ready for contacts to be applied prior to drifting. Tavendale[29] uses the electroless nickel plating method which is often employed on silicon, and has made extremely good detectors in this way, but Hansen and Jarrett describe a much more convenient method in which liquid metal contacts of gallium-indium eutectic (3 parts gallium : 1 part indium, melting point 15° C) are painted on. Such contacts give good thermal contact during the drifting.

Techniques for drifting the diodes are very similar to those described for silicon except that the temperatures are lower. Tavendale drifted diodes in air at temperatures up to 60° C and bias voltages up to 100 volts. Hansen and Jarrett maintained rather lower temperatures, and also used up to 100 volts bias. Both stress the importance of remaining below the temperature at which the germanium in the uncompensated device becomes intrinsic. Clearly, above this temperature electrons and holes generated thermally by excitation across the energy gap are more numerous than the holes due to ionization of acceptors and the ionized acceptor concentration. Under these conditions the electric field becomes uniform, and the ionized acceptors are electrically screened resulting in precipitation of lithium at lattice defects.

Constant power, constant current methods of drifting have been favoured for germanium. Hansen and Jarrett use a modification of the technique described by Goulding and Hansen for silicon. They use a power transistor as the source of heat, but to carry away excess heat at the lower temperature (15° to 40° C in their case) they use a refrigerated heat sink at − 40° C connected to the heated plate by a brass tube. A simpler method used by Palms and Greenwood,[30] employs a thermoelectric element alternately as a heating and cooling device in order to maintain temperatures between 0° C and 60° C. A diagram of their control circuit is shown in Fig. 6.6. The apparatus takes the form of two thermoelectric elements between which the germanium slice is sandwiched. Cold water flows through coils attached to the outer face of each element to carry away excess heat. It is found necessary for germanium

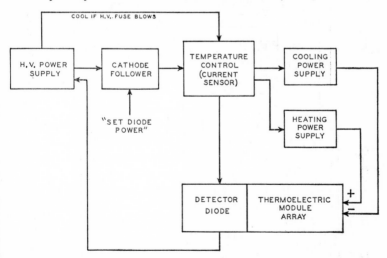

FIG. 6.6 (a) Block Diagram, and (b) Circuit Diagram for lithium in germanium drift experiment. (after PALMS and GREENWOOD[30])

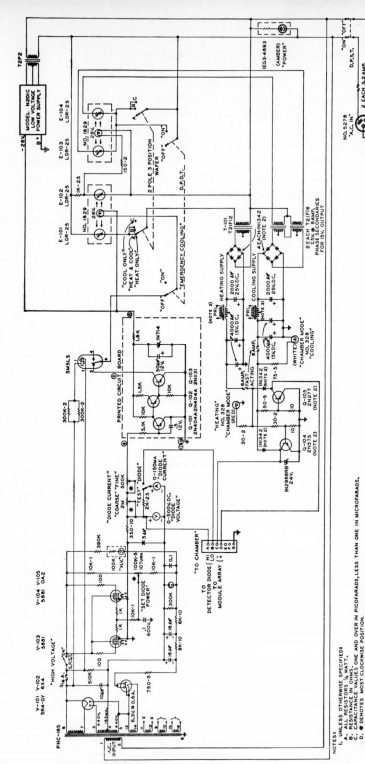

FIG. 6.6 (b)

182

to keep the crystal dry during, drifting, as otherwise a large increase in leakage currents results. Dry nitrogen is therefore passed through a plastic box enclosing the equipment.

These methods have produced compensated regions in germanium up to 12 mm thick, measured by the copper plating technique described for silicon. It is found however that above 8 mm thickness the charge collection efficiency is reduced, resulting in a degradation of energy resolution. Drift rates of 3 mm in 30 hours, 6 mm in 150 hours and 10 mm in 400 hours are typical, slower rates may mean that the crystal contains too much oxygen and should be discarded.

In contrast Tavendale[29] has developed a constant temperature process in which boiling chloroform (boiling point 61·3° C) was used to stabilise the temperature of the junction, probably 10–20° C above the boiling point. Diodes were drifted at 50–100 watts (30–50 volts drift bias), immersed in the chloroform bath. Drifting times up to 700 hours were used giving depletion depths of up to 11 mm. These diodes are amongst the very best made by any method; they have operated at 1200 volts bias with leakage currents of 15[9] amps and have yielded gamma ray spectra with a resolution of 3·5 keV at 122 keV. Unfortunately other workers have found the method difficult to control. Tavendale also describes a coaxial structure in which lithium is drifted from the curved surface of a cylindrical crystal until only a narrow core of p-type material remains. This is a way of making very large volumes without excessive drift times or excessive operating voltages. It is likely to be very important for high energy gamma ray spectroscopy.

After drifting it is usually necessary to clean the surface of the crystal before applying the final contacts. The Ga-In alloy can be wiped off with tissue soaked in trichlorethylene. Then all the crystal surfaces should be re-etched in a 3:1 mixture of nitric and hydrofluoric acids followed by soaking in hydrogen peroxide. The simplest contact method is again the gallium indium alloy using a very thinly wiped layer over the whole of the p-type surface and a small area at some point on the lithium diffused face. If the leakage current at 90° K exceeds 10^{-9} amps cm^{-2} at 300 volts bias the current noise will be the main factor determining energy resolution, and the device should be cleaned and re-etched to reduce leakage current. Sometimes, especially after long periods of drifting, the lithium concentration at the n-type surface is too low for any feasible contact to give good diode characteristics. Such diodes can often be reclaimed by carrying out a second lithium diffusion followed by a further short period of drifting to restore the compensation in the bulk of the crystal.

No entirely satisfactory method has been found for making a thin contact to the compensated germanium. Surface barriers made by gold evaporation exhibit large injection currents. Probably the best technique is that of Tavendale who formed an alloyed aluminium contact to the back face of the germanium before lithium diffusion, so that lithium drifted right through the crystal and into the alloyed region. The window thickness of these diodes is estimated to be only 6 microns. Other workers have experienced difficulty with this method, but until the problem is solved it will not be possible to build up stacks of detectors having good energy resolution and fast pulse rise time for high energy gamma ray studies. The importance of this field should provoke considerable attention to the problems of making thin window germanium detectors.

After completion the detector must be stored at a temperature of $-50°$ C or lower. Warming above this temperature for even a few hours can lead to a marked change in the lithium distribution and a deterioration in diode characteristics. However detectors held at temperatures below $100°$ K have remained stable for over six months.

6.4 Encapsulation and surface treatment

(a) Encapsulation

Above are outlined the bare essentials of methods by which various kinds of junction counter can be made. With proper care and control they will each give a high success rate. But is not enough to make the naked device; it must not merely work properly when newly made but must remain usable for as long as possible, and this means that the surfaces of the device must be prepared to have minimum surface leakage current and that they must then be kept that way. The solution of these problems is doubly important, for not only will it enable people to get the best out of their devices, but it is an essential preliminary to any manufacturer being able to make and market counters at sensible prices. To ensure this it is necessary to go beyond the stage of feeling fairly happy about one's own devices stored in one's own laboratory. They have to be capable of handling, transportation and long periods of storage at uncontrolled temperatures and humidities, just as valves and transistors are.

Clearly there are two kinds of function to be performed; one is to minimize surface leakage, and other leakage currents by providing the right kind of ambient atmosphere and in some cases the best electrode geometry. The second function is to provide some suitable physical barriers to prevent unwanted ambients replacing the selected one. In some methods of encapsulation such as straightforward canning, the two functions are performed separately, whereas, in others, such as potting in epoxy resin, they have to be considered together.

Purely geometrical considerations can be very important; for example, Fox and Borkowski[9] show that breakdown in surface barrier junctions occurs first at the edge of the gold electrode owing to the space charge layer in the silicon surface. They eliminate this by changing the sign of the surface charge at the edge of the electrode with a ring of amine-free epoxy resin doped with iodine and applied before evaporating the gold. Junctions made in this way will withstand 4000 volts without damage or breakdown though they become noisy above 1000 volts due to the charge inversion layer. They have succeeded in isolating this noise from the remainder of the structure with a guard ring electrode, giving a device similar to that depicted in Fig. 6.7. The method is to cement the prepared and oxidized slice into the ceramic ring with amine-free epoxy resin, to apply the ring of iodine doped epoxy, and finally to evaporate the electrodes. Where a guard ring is used a separate flying lead must be attached to the central gold area.

Clearly the surface barrier junctions, with their evaporated metal electrodes, are much more amenable to this kind of treatment than diffused junctions, and they have indeed been subject to many variations of the above theme. The general

criticisms to be made concern first the flimsiness of the
evaporated gold and aluminium films, at least one of which
must remain exposed as a window for the radiation. Secondly,
there is a general doubt about the reliability of epoxy resin
encapsulations: they are known to change composition with

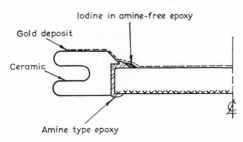

FIG. 6.7 Resin encapsulation of a surface
barrier detector (After Fox and
BORKOWSKI[9])

age, they may suffer tracking and surface breakdown in some
ambients, and they may not give a really durable bond to
silicon. These are all doubts rather than positive faults, but the
history of other semiconductor devices potted in this way is
very discouraging.

Diffused junctions offer the possibility of encapsulation in a
metal can mechanically fixed to the diffused layer, on the
lines described by Williams[31] and Moncaster, Northrop and
Raines.[2] Figure 6.8 shows schematically how this can be
accomplished. The main difficulty is to fix the top part of the
can around the edge of the diffused layer leaving most of it
exposed and giving a joint which is mechanically strong,
electrically sound, and makes a hermetic seal. Williams uses a
comparatively thick diffusion of 2-3 microns and has devised
a soldered joint between this and the can, by some means
unspecified. Moncaster, Northrop and Raines use a silver
cement to make the joint and cover it with insulating varnish
to get a better hermetic seal, and use a nominal 1 micron
diffusion. The lower half of the can may be sealed to the upper
by projection welding or cold pressure welding. The method
of making the back contact is basically the same in the two
cases; with a spring sealed through an insulated bead in the

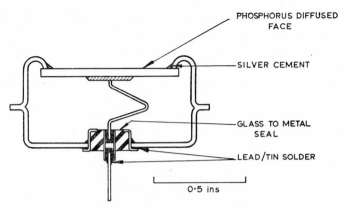

FIG. 6.8 Encapsulated diffused junction (After MONCASTER, NORTHROP and RAINES[2])

base of the can and making a pressure contact on the previously prepared back of the silicon counter.

A variation of this technique, applicable to those cases where energy resolution is not a prime consideration, was used on counters used for the exploration of radiation belts above the earth's atmosphere.[32] In these the active device was totally enclosed in a metal can with a thin window on one face. This was strong enough to withstand pressure differences of an atmosphere in either direction, but allowed protons and electrons to be counted and their energy distribution determined. This encapsulation is complete, and avoids the difficult vacuum seal between metal can and semiconductor slice. It would be a sensible way of making counters for many applications not requiring outstanding energy resolution.

If the counter behaves well before encapsulation it is best left alone, and this is easily achieved by encapsulation in a can, either evacuated or filled with a dry inert gas. Failing this it is a good idea to make the surface layer of different conductivity type from the bulk,[33] as with the iodine in epoxy resin of Fox and Borkowski's[9] method. This creates a rectifying barrier which isolates the surface film from the bulk of the crystal. In a similar way it is found that exposure to iodine vapour often improves the breakdown voltage of surface barrier detectors, presumably because the high surface density of negative charge reduces the field at the junction edge.

Epoxy resins suitable for both n-type and p-type crystals are being developed at present and should prove very useful for this kind of application. Also, it is worth mentioning that oxygen creates a p-type surface layer on germanium and silicon, which undoubtedly explains why surface barrier detectors made with n-type crystals last better in air than diffused junctions made with p-type crystals. On the other hand, adsorbed hydrofluoric acid creates an n-type surface, which is why soaking in HF improves the leakage current of diffused junction counters made with p-type crystals.

An important set of experiments has been reported by Buck, Wheatley and Rodgers,[32] who studied the effect of various surface treatments on the surface conductance and the surface Fermi level of silicon and the resulting leakage and stability of diffused junctions. They made p-n junctions by diffusing phosphorus into 10,000–20,000 ohm cm p-type silicon for 3 hours at 1050° C (diffusion depth 3 microns) and finally etched a mesa or flat topped island on the diffused face. Subsequent soaking in hydrofluoric acid produced a strong n-type inversion layer on the surface, resulting in a high leakage current, typically 50 μA at 100 volts with a noise linewidth of 85 keV. Boiling in deionized water gave a strongly p-type accumulation layer on the surface, and resulted in a low breakdown voltage.

A process was devised consisting of an HF soak followed by a series of dips in boiling deionized water of 5 seconds each to bring the leakage current down to 1 μA at 100 volts. Surface conductivity measurements can be fitted to a theoretical curve of surface conductance versus surface Fermi level and show that the best reverse characteristics occur with the surface slightly n-type.

Lithium drifted devices are much more sensitive to ambient atmospheres than are diffused junctions or surface barriers, and unfortunately there is not as yet either a complete understanding of the process nor a really satisfactory way of dealing with it. The most thorough investigation is that made by Llacer.[34] By probing the surface with a platinum point and measuring the potential with an electrometer he concludes that when exposed to normal ambient atmospheres the lithium compensated surface acquires an n-type skin. Moreover if the p-type material from which the counter is made is

300 ohm cm or less the surface of the p-type layer is inverted to n-type, giving a complete n-type surface path in parallel with the counter. Treatment with hydrofluoric acid or water gave a stronger n-type surface and potassium dichromate solution gave a strongly p-type surface with equally high conduction. Llacer suggests that most of the surface current originates with carrier generation near the i-p interface, where he finds very high electric fields. For this reason leakage currents should not depend markedly on the width of the compensated region. The conductance of the surface layer on the intrinsic region does not depend markedly on bias or position on the surface, but the number of surface states occupied increases with bias and with proximity to the high field region, its value in low fields being about 2×10^{10} cm^{-2}, or 10^{-4} times the number of surface atoms.

(b) Oxide protection and guard rings

An entirely different approach to the problem of stabilization of the junction surface has been proposed and realized by Hansen, Goulding and Lothrop,[35] and Hansen and Goulding.[36] They draw attention to the oxide masking technique used in making planar transistors in which silicon is first oxidised, and junctions are then made by diffusion through apertures in the oxide made by etching through a mask of photosensitive resin.* The diffusant 'undercuts' the oxide so that the junction interface is protected from atmospheric contamination by the oxide mask. In the conventional oxide masking technique surface conductivity is high, by the standards of the best particle detectors, although it is acceptable for transistors made with much lower resistivity material. Goulding and Hansen[37] have shown this surface conductivity to be associated with a surface concentration of about 5×10^{12} cm^{-2} donor states at the Si-SiO$_2$ interface. They show a correlation between the density of surface states and the oxygen content of the SiO$_2$ layer. By careful control of oxygen at all stages of their process they obtain reproducible interfaces and are able to compensate the donor states accurately by a diffusion of gallium (about 1 hour at 900° C). Before this a p^+ back contact is made by diffusing boron from boron tri-iodide at

* e.g. Kodak K.P.R. Photoresist.

1000° C for 3 hours, lapping or etching away this diffusion from all but the back surface. Then after the gallium diffusion an oxide mask is made and etched away before a phosphorus diffusion at 900° C for one hour to make the rectifying contact. A section of the structure is shown in Fig. 6.9. Hansen and

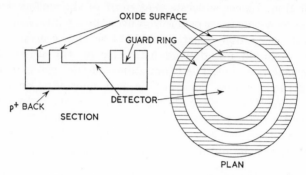

FIG. 6.9 Plan and Section of Oxide-Masked, Guard-Ring Structure (after HANSEN and GOULDING[35])

Goulding also use a guard ring electrode, as described by them in an earlier paper,[36] which prevents most of the noise associated with residual surface currents from appearing at the input of the amplifier circuit. The product of this technique is a high yield of uniform devices showing energy resolution typically 17 keV for 5 MeV α-particles over an active area of 1 cm diameter.

(c) Very thin detectors

Detectors of about 0·001 inch thickness, sensitive throughout, are of value in particle identification systems which measure the specific ionization $\mathrm{d}E/\mathrm{d}x$ and the total energy E. The very thin counter measures $\mathrm{d}E/\mathrm{d}x$. They present great difficulties at all stages of preparation because of the need to control thickness very precisely, and because of the need for edge protection which will preserve thin window geometry for the charged particle entering and leaving the device. (Fragility is not such a great problem as might be imagined.)

The most complete description of a fabrication process is that given by Madden and Gibson,[38] using about 400 ohm cm p-type silicon. They prepared their silicon by first lapping it on a bisurface planetary lapping machine using $303\frac{1}{2}$ grade alumina, which achieves a thickness variation less than 0·0001 in. Then 0·003 in. of silicon was etched from each face after a very careful cleaning, permitting a slow etch rate with minimum agitation to be used without bubbles forming at dust particles. The etch is a 20:1 HNO_3, HF mixture used at room temperature to give an etch rate of 0·001 in. in 20 minutes, and a method of rotating the beaker of etch and the slice was used which gives the same average rate of movement through the etch to each point on the surface of the slice. After etching the first side of the sample was oxidised at 650° C for 3 hours in 120 atmospheres of steam, and then phosphorus diffused from a phosphorus tribromide source through a 'frying pan' shaped hole in the oxide mask. The circular part of the frying pan is the useful area of the final device and the 'handle' provides a contacting area, as shown in Fig. 6.10. Finally the back contact is made by removing the oxide layer

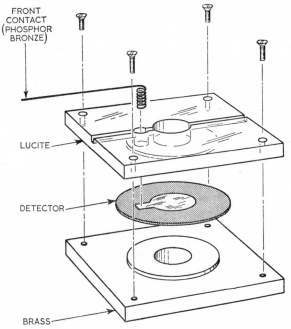

FIG. 6.10 Expanded view of thin dE/dx counter assembly (After MADDEN and GIBSON[37])

from the second face of the slice and etching as above to the desired thickness before evaporating a thin film of gold as the blocking back contact and allowing it to age.

The oxide film adds strength to the device, and by masking the interface between the n-type diffusion and the base material provides a measure of protection from contamination by the atmosphere. Leakage currents are relatively less important in dE/dx detectors, because the energy resolution is limited by the small amount of energy absorbed. It is therefore satisfactory to mount the detectors as shown in Fig. 6.10. It is important that particles should be incident in non-channelling directions of the crystal.

6.5 Electrical testing

(a) Rectification

A straightforward measurement of the current-voltage characteristic of the counter can give a lot of useful information very quickly. It can be made either by plotting point by point with a variable voltage source and an ammeter, or less tediously by applying an alternating voltage of controllable amplitude and displaying voltage and current as the x and y deflections on an oscilloscope. Figure 6.11 gives some idea of what one may see.

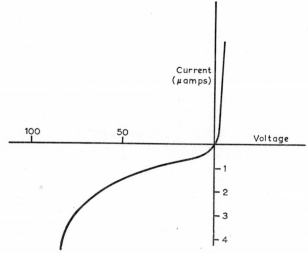

FIG. 6.11 Typical rectification curve

With experience it will be immediately obvious how low the reverse current is, though a display of this kind is not too good for making an accurate measurement of the current or the shape of the characteristic. A high value of the voltage at which breakdown occurs is also a hopeful sign, indicating not only that the depletion layer is likely to be wide but also that the surface of the device is clean. To be sure of these two facts it is necessary to check that the forward current rises sharply for small values of forward bias. If it does not there is a series resistance, either in one of the contacts, or, possibly, in the bulk of the crystal, or in the diffused or evaporated film at the junction, which could make the reverse characteristic look better than it really is. Such a resistance would almost certainly be very noisy. These electrical measurements, and all the others described below, should be carried out in darkness, as the junctions are very photosensitive, but as a final feature of the rectification test it is interesting to shine light on the counter to measure its photocurrent. Tens of μA at 2 or 3 volts in ordinary room lighting might be expected, and less than this could mean that the insensitive dead layer or window is too thick. Obviously this method would have to be carefully calibrated to give an accurate answer, and this will be dealt with in the section on window thickness measurements; it is suggested here as a quick and useful check.

(b) Reverse current

More accurate measurements of reverse current are easily made with a suitable current meter in series with the junction and a variable voltage supply. In most cases currents up to a few μA and voltages up to 100 or 200 volts would suffice, though occasionally voltages up to 4000 or 5000 volts are necessary to measure reverse breakdown. The things which can be learnt from these current measurements are, firstly, the predominant source of leakage current, and, secondly, the upper limit of voltage which the counter can stand. The first question is answered by finding the shape of the current voltage curve and the magnitude of the current. At low voltages the voltage independent diffusion current proportional to $\tau_r^{-\frac{1}{2}}$ will dominate, but at a few volts will be exceeded by the space charge generation current proportional to $\tau_r^{-1}(\rho V)^{\frac{1}{2}}$.

In each case the current is high for low carrier lifetimes τ_{r}. Surface leakage is a rather variable quantity, and can easily exceed either of these currents with a voltage dependence between V and $V^{\frac{1}{2}}$. A current which varies as $V^{\frac{1}{2}}$ can therefore indicate either a surface current or a space charge generation current, and to decide which it is requires a knowledge of the carrier lifetime. This can be determined by measuring the photoconductive decay time with a small applied voltage, or no bias at all, and using a pulsed light source of infra-red radiation. This gives absorption principally beyond the depletion layer, so that the current is due to diffusion of carriers into the depletion layer from a field free region and decays with a time constant equal to the carrier lifetime. Assuming that the level from which space charge generation occurs is in the centre of the energy gap the maximum value of space charge generated current density is, as deduced in Section 5.3,

$$ J_{\mathrm{s}} = \frac{e n_{\mathrm{i}}}{2 \tau_{\mathrm{r}}} x \qquad (6.1) $$

where n_{i} is the intrinsic carrier density ($1 \cdot 5 \times 10^{10}$ cm^{-3} in silicon at room temperature), τ_{r} is the carrier lifetime and x is the depletion layer thickness. If the current is greater than this it must be a surface current. Surface treatments with etches or gaseous atmospheres are likely to affect the magnitude of surface currents, and a study of this effect may be helpful in deciding how to reduce surface currents.

As the voltage is increased the current will eventually become very noisy, and, ultimately, breakdown will occur due to impact ionization either on the surface or in the volume of the counter. The exact mechanism can be determined from the shape of the current voltage curve near breakdown, and by direct observation of the light emission at points of localized breakdown (microplasmas). It was from such a study that Fox and Borkowski[9] were able to design their high-voltage counter and that Goulding[39] designed his guard ring structure to isolate the noise due to surface currents from the signal.

In the case of lithium ion drifted germanium detectors it is necessary to test the reverse current at the operating temperature in the range 77–120° K, and the value should not exceed

10^{-9} amps cm^{-2} at a bias of 300 volts if the current noise is not to contribute appreciably to the energy resolution.

(c) *Capacitance*

The incremental capacitance of the junction is directly related to the depletion layer thickness and to the resistivity of the silicon, so that a measurement of capacitance can show what the resistivity of the silicon is after the processing of the counter, and can predict what is the maximum energy of a charged particle for complete absorption. The simplest method of

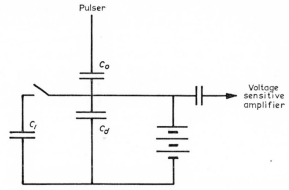

FIG. 6.12 Measurement of capacitance

measuring capacitance is with the circuit shown in Fig. 6.12. A voltage pulse of known amplitude, v, is fed from a pulser through a small test capacitance C_0 on to the capacitance of the depletion layer C_d at a d.c. bias V. This puts a charge vC_0 on C_d so that the voltage amplifier sees a pulse of amplitude $v\dfrac{C_0}{C_d}$. A knowledge of v and C_0 and the sensitivity of the amplifier will determine C_d, or alternatively the value of capacitance C_1, may be found which, when connected in parallel with C_d, halves the voltage signal. Then $C_1 = C_d$. The second method is capable of greater accuracy than the first, since C_1 may be calibrated with considerable accuracy in a separate experiment on an a.c. bridge, and since no knowledge of v is required. The depletion layer thickness x is given by

$$C_d = \frac{\varkappa A}{4\pi x} \tag{6.2}$$

where $\varkappa$ is the dielectric constant of the semiconductor, and A is the area of the junction. (x is necessary for the calculation of space charge generation current in the previous section.)

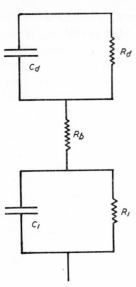

In a semiconductor with a fixed concentration of fully ionized impurities it is expected that C_d should be proportional to $V^{-\frac{1}{2}}$, and in many cases this is found to be the case, but departures from this law are found not infrequently and are worthy of comment. Sometimes a capacitance proportional to $V^{-\frac{1}{3}}$ is found reminiscent of the behaviour of junctions made with low resistivity crystals, where the depletion layer width is controlled by the (non-uniform) concentration of the diffusant. Such behaviour in a high resistivity junction may indicate the presence of a second unintentional diffusant which has penetrated further into the crystal than the main one, or of an impurity which is uniformly distributed in the original material and whose ionization probability varies with the electric field in the junction. This effect has been discussed earlier in Section 5.3.

FIG. 6.13 The effective circuit of a junction counter

Another possibility is a fault in the measurement arising from an incomplete knowledge of the effective circuit of the device. In its complete form this is depicted in Fig. 6.13, where C_d and R_d are the capacitance and resistance of the depletion layer, R_b is the bulk resistance of that part of the crystal not included in the depletion layer and C_1 and R_1 are the capacitance and resistance of the back contact. The resistances in this circuit are strictly incremental values dv/di. In a good counter R_b and R_1 would both be small, so that the effective circuit reduces to R_d and C_d in parallel. However, R_1 is not always completely negligible, and then the effective capacitance will be a function of C_d, C_1, R_d and R_1 and the frequency of measurement. To assume that only C_d and R_d

are important would then lead to unexpected values being deduced from a simple measurement. Bridge measurements of the impedance of the device as a function of frequency can, of course, be used to determine the values of the separate components in the effective circuit.

Lithium ion drifted detectors show a much smaller variation of capacitance with bias, indeed if the compensation of the acceptors by lithium were perfect there would be none at all. The measurement of the capacitance variation with bias is therefore valuable because it reveals the departure from perfect compensation. For example a high current flow during the drifting process can lead to a marked departure from exact compensation because of the space charge of the current carriers. Capacitance measurements give a check on this and other factors in the drift process. Good lithium drifted detectors show very little change of capacitance above a bias of 10 volts.

(d) Noise

There may be more noise generated than that predicted by the shot noise and current noise equations of Chapter 4 if there is a large amount of surface conductivity or if a contact is noisy. It is quite simple to display the noise from a counter on an oscilloscope and to compare its amplitude with that of noise generated in a circuit consisting of a resistor and capacitor in parallel, the values of which equal those found for the depletion layer and with the resistor passing the same current as the counter. If a variable bandwidth amplifier is used a rough determination of the frequency spectrum is possible. Comparisons between different methods of making contacts and a study of the effects of surface cleaning treatments on the observed noise can quickly show what its origin is. Also if the residual noise proves to be mainly at low frequencies it can be eliminated during subsequent experiments by using suitable amplifier time constants.

6.6 Testing with radiation

(a) Energy resolution

The simplest direct test of a particle counter's performance is to measure its energy resolution with a low activity alpha particle source, using a low noise (preferably charge sensitive) amplifier and a pulse height analyser. A thin source is needed so that the alpha particle spectrum is not broadened by absorption; for the same reason the space between the counter and

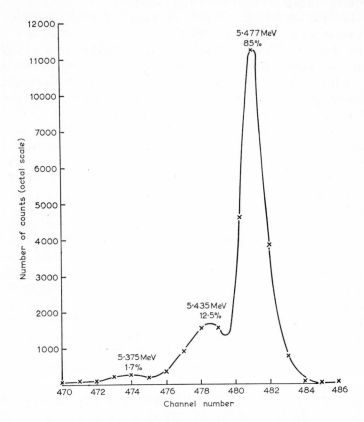

FIG. 6.14 Energy resolution of a junction counter for alpha particles

the source should be evacuated. The actual counting rate needs to be fairly low, because the random arrival times result in a fluctuating d.c. component to the signal. This would normally be lost in the a.c. coupled amplifier, and if the mark-space ratio of the pulses is more than about 10^{-3} this can affect the energy resolution of the system. The best kind of alpha particle source is one with several nearby energy maxima such as Americium 241 or Plutonium 239.

A fairly good result for a counter of under 1 cm² in area is that shown in Fig. 6.14. The main alpha particle groups are resolved, and the resolution measured on the main one is about 15 keV full width at half maximum. When the alpha particle energies are accurately known it is possible to measure the charge collection efficiency of the counter by injecting known quantities of charge at the input of the amplifier, using a small known test condenser connected to the input, and hence in series with the capacitance of the counter and the amplifier. A voltage pulse of amplitude v charges the test condenser C_0 with a charge $C_0 v$, and the same charge will also appear across the input of the amplifier. By finding the voltage v which gives an output equal to that due to an alpha particle one can determine the charge collection efficiency as $wC_0 v/We$ where W is the alpha particle energy, and w the mean energy per ion pair.

Usually this kind of measurement merely confirms that the energy resolution is that expected from the electrical measurements, and that the charge collection efficiency is near 100 per cent, but it may reveal various characteristic faults which could not be found by other methods. For example, the charge collection efficiency may be low, indicating a high concentration of recombination centres or traps, which might be too far from the centre of the energy gap to have a serious effect on the reverse current. Another kind of fault which occurs fairly often is 'double peaking', where monoenergetic particles give rise to two quite separate peaks in the pulse height spectrum. This results from a non-uniformity of some kind in the counter, which may be due to the back contact giving a non-uniform field in the depletion layer, or to the diffused layer having a finite sheet resistivity and causing a non-uniform field. It could equally be due to a non-uniform lifetime, which might be a property of the starting material, could be caused by the diffusion, particularly if this is not of uniform depth, or could be due to irradiation of part of the device. Any non-uniformity of lifetime would give different charge collection efficiencies at different points on the surface, and could be detected by probing experiments with a small area alpha particle source. A patchy diffusion would also show as a non-uniform window thickness which could be detected in the way described in Section 6.6(c). Irradiation effects would normally occur only after large doses of radiation (see Chapter 10).

Non-uniform fields would cause the pulses coming from different parts of the counter to have slightly different shapes. After shaping in the amplifier these would become pulses of different amplitude. Such a fault can be identified by using a wide-band amplifier to observe the true pulse shapes, or by varying the voltage applied to the counter (this latter method is hard to use in an unambiguous way, as changes in field might also change the charge collection efficiency).

Any one of these defects would make the energy resolution worse, and in extreme cases would give double peaking by making two parts of the counter behave as two different units.

Thin beta particle sources are also of value in testing detectors, and in certain circumstances it may be impossible to use α-particles at all. For example, the window thickness of lithium drifted detectors may exceed the alpha particle range so that beta sources (or gamma sources in the case of germanium) have to be used. A further difference is that the specific ionization of beta particles is low, and therefore trapping and recombination effects are less serious than with alpha particles. Beta particles provide a better way of assessing current noise and are a more realistic test of those counters which will be used for beta and gamma radiation only. The experimental procedure is essentially the same as that for testing with alpha particles.

(b) Depletion layer thickness

It is easy to check the thickness of the depletion layer and its variation with voltage by measuring the linearity of response to charged particles of various energies and determining the limit of the linear regime. This has been done with surface barrier detectors by Dearnaley and Whitehead,[3] whose results are reproduced in Fig. 6.15. The pulse height is a linear function of proton energy up to some value which is a function of applied voltage. A knowledge of the range-energy relations for protons in silicon shows that the counter thickness increases as $V^{\frac{1}{2}}$, and has the value predicted by the capacitance measurements. In fact this particular measurement does very little apart from confirming previous estimates and is not a valuable method of diagnosing defects in performance.

(c) *Window thickness*

The diffused layer of the *p-n* junction, and the evaporated gold of the surface barrier counter constitute a dead layer or

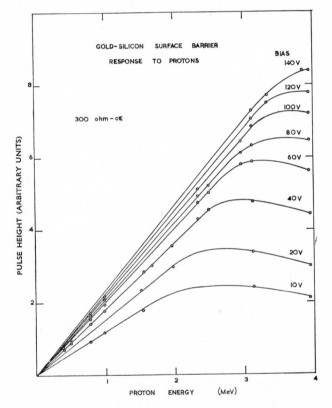

FIG. 6.15 The response of a surface barrier counter to protons (After DEARNALEY and WHITEHEAD[3])

window, in which energy lost by the ionizing particle does not contribute to the signal. This layer will be less than the thickness of the diffused layer, since the field in the junction penetrates into it somewhat, so that some charge collection can occur. Williams and Webb[40] describe two methods of determining this thickness, and of finding several other properties of the diffused layer as well.

Their first method is to use a collimated alpha particle beam and to determine the variation of pulse height with

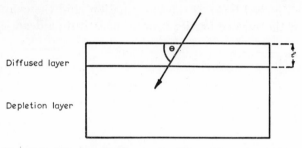

Diffused layer

Depletion layer

FIG. 6.16 Window thickness of a diffused junction (After WILLIAMS and WEBB[20])

angle of incidence. They assume that the specific energy loss of the alpha particles, dE/dx, is in fact dE_o/dx, that for the incident particle of energy E_o. Then, as can be seen from Fig. 6.16, when the particles are incident normal to the surface the energy lost in the dead layer of thickness l is $l\dfrac{dE_o}{dx}$. The output pulse from the counter is therefore proportional to $\left(E_o - l\dfrac{dE_o}{dx}\right)$. At any other angle θ to the surface it will be proportional to $\left(E_o - l\dfrac{dE_o}{dx}\cdot\dfrac{1}{\sin\theta}\right)$. The difference between these two signals is $l\dfrac{dE_o}{dx}\left(\dfrac{1}{\sin\theta} - 1\right)$ and the fractional change in pulse height, η, defined as this quantity divided by the maximum signal, is

$$\eta = \frac{E_o}{\left(E_o - l\dfrac{dE_o}{dx}\right)}\left(\frac{1}{\sin\theta} - 1\right) \tag{7.3}$$

By plotting η against $\left(\dfrac{1}{\sin\theta} - 1\right)$ and assuming a value of

dE_0/dx of 140 keV per micron Williams and Webb derived a value of l from the slope of the resulting line. Over a range of diffusion depths from 4 to 0·3 microns, as calculated from the time and temperature of diffusion and the known diffusion constant of the impurity (phosphorus), they find window thicknesses almost exactly half the diffusion depth in each case. They confirm these values by measuring the spectral dependence of the photoresponse of the diodes in the wavelength range 4000-6000 Å, and plotting it against the absorption constant at each wavelength. They conclude from their measurements that the main reason for the existence of this dead layer is the rapid drop in carrier lifetime in the heavily doped material near the surface. At about half the diffusion depth it falls sharply to 10^{-12} or 10^{-13} seconds.

Surface barrier counters have the advantage of very much thinner windows, which have only been detected with fission fragments. An estimated thickness is 0·01 microns.

6.7 Carrier recombination and fission defect

As explained in Section 3.3 recombination processes are only strictly defined by the carrier lifetime for small departures from the equilibrium carrier concentrations. These conditions are not satisfied near the track of an ionizing particle, so that the carrier lifetime can only be used as a guide to assess the importance of recombination in a particular material. The rate of recombination which actually takes place in a real situation depends not only on the recombination centre density, but also on the numbers of electrons and holes available for recombination. The implications are worked out in Section 3.3, and are, briefly, that recombination is relatively more important where the densities of holes and electrons are high and where the applied electric field in the counter is low. A number of cases where these predictions are borne out may be noted here. Firstly, it is invariably the case that energy resolution, expressed in keV, is better for beta particles than for the more densely ionizing alpha particles, and this is particularly true for lithium ion drift counters where the applied fields are low. Resolutions of 6 keV FWHM have been reported[21] for beta particles with counters which are worse than diffused or surface barrier counters for alpha particles. This results in part from the extra recombination centres produced by the heavier particle.

The most pronounced effects are obtained with fission fragments,[41] as might be expected. Early results showed a pronounced departure from linearity when pulse height was plotted against energy, and it appeared that the extrapolation of the results would cross the energy axis at about 10 MeV – hence the name 'fission defect' which has been applied to this effect. It was shown that this was not a window effect, but only recently has it become clear that its origin lies partly in elastic nuclear collisions and partly in the very high recombination rate around the tracks of low energy (high specific ionization) particles. For this reason the charge collection efficiency is lowest for heavy, slow fragments.

6.8 The effects of temperature, magnetic field and light

It may not always be possible to operate counters in ideal conditions as regards temperature, magnetic field, and ambient light level, so brief consideration is given here to the effects that these parameters might have on the performance of junction counters.

Changes of temperature will alter the generation rate and mobility of carriers, so affecting the noise and the charge collection time in the counter. By far the most important of these changes is the increase in current noise, given by equations (5.13) and (5.21). In each of these n_i varies as $\exp(-E_g/2kT)$ where E_g is the energy gap of the semiconductor (equation (3.1)) and τ_r, given by equation (5.11), also varies exponentially with temperature through n_1 and p_1. The net result is a very rapid increase in current with temperature, and a corresponding increase in current noise, as given by equations (5.25) and (5.27). The same equations explain why low-energy gap semiconductors will never be satisfactory at room temperature, for it is the ratio E_g/kT which is important. Clearly, then, such materials might be useful if cooled, and this is the logic for operating germanium counters between 4° K and 150° K. Reduced temperatures will change the carrier mobilities, generally increasing them, and thereby reducing the charge collection time. This might be important for some applications, but so far it has apparently received little attention. Mobility changes will not directly affect the resolution of a counter. Finally, it should be noted that temperature does not affect the depletion layer thickness in a very marked way, since this depends on the ionized impurity concentration in the semiconductor (equation (5.7)), and all impurities are normally ionized in the depletion layer.

A magnetic field will change the electron and hole trajectories between successive scattering events in the depletion layer; when parallel to the electric field it will cause the carriers to spiral, and when perpendicular to the electric field it will deflect carriers by giving them a component velocity perpendicular to both fields. In either case the recombination probability is increased, in the first case by increasing the path length necessary for complete collection, and in the second by deflecting carriers sideways into a surface region where recombination is more rapid. The second of these two effects is likely to be the larger.

Shockley[42] has discussed this situation, and shows that no appreciable effect should be observed at fields less than H, where

$$\mu H = 10^8 \qquad (6.4)$$

with both quantities expressed in practical units. Thus, in silicon at room temperature magnetic fields below 5×10^4 oersteds should not matter. In germanium at 78° K, however, the electron mobility is about 3×10^4 cm^2 volt^{-1} sec^{-1} and at 4° K it is about 10^6 cm^2 volt^{-1} sec^{-1}, so that fields above 3×10^3 oersteds and 10^2 oersteds respectively should have an effect. This has been confirmed by Walter, Dabbs and Roberts[43] who observed changes in pulse height in germanium surface barrier detectors at liquid helium temperatures in fields of a few hundred oersteds, and were able to suppress signals due to 5 MeV alpha particles completely at fields of a few thousand oersteds.

Light of quantum energy greater than the energy gap is strongly absorbed in semiconductors, with absorption constants in the range 10^4 to 10^6 cm^{-1}, and generates electron-hole pairs. Any light absorbed in the depletion layer of a counter therefore contributes to the dark current and to the noise in the counter. A counter with a thick insensitive window (thicker than the absorption depth for the light) will obviously have greatly reduced photosensitivity, and for that reason diffused junctions are less sensitive than surface barriers, as a general rule. It is, indeed, possible to make diffused junctions with such thick windows that their photosensitivity is negligible, but this normally involves such high diffusion temperatures that the carrier lifetime τ_r and, hence, the counter performance, deteriorate seriously.

Surface barriers with very thin gold coatings show the greatest photosensitivity, and measurements reported by Tuzzolini, Hubbard, Perkins and Fan[44] showed a sensitivity of 0·13 μamps per μwatt at a wavelength of 5461 Å for a counter coated with 50 Å of gold. The response was uniform to within a few per cent over the surface. Whilst this is not as high as the cathode sensitivity of a photomultiplier it certainly requires the detectors to be mounted in near darkness for good energy resolution. In some cases an aluminium foil in front of the detector will prove satisfactory, but it has been found that evaporated aluminium over the normal gold coating results in very poor performance because the aluminium affects the properties of the junction, even through the gold. Rather strangely, Amsel[45] reports that surface barriers, made with evaporated tin oxide (transparent) instead of gold, show very little photosensitivity.

6.9 A comparison between types of junction counter

It is possible to summarize much of the information in this chapter in the form of a table bringing out the points of difference and similarity between diffused junctions, surface barriers, and lithium ion-drift devices. Table 6.1 also amplifies the later sections of this chapter where measurements on counters have been described in general terms, since they apply equally to all types of junction. Some of the figures given will undoubtedly be improved upon by the time this book is published, but they nevertheless give a fair basis of comparison between the three types.

TABLE 6.1

	Raw material	Sensitive Thickness	Best known Resolution	Limitations	Most suitable Applications	Comments
Diffused Junctions	Ge or Si. High resistivity. Long lifetime. (Available commercially)	up to 1 mm	20 keV for 5 MeV alphas	Thickness limited by resistivity. Resolution limited by current noise in small area devices and inhomogeneity in large ones	Monitoring Health Physics Medical work etc. where robustness is more important than resolution	More robust and more readily encapsulated than surface barriers.
Surface Barriers	Ge or Si. High resistivity. Long lifetime. (Available commercially)	up to 2 mm	3·8 keV for Cs^{137} betas. 11 keV for 6 MeV alphas	Thickness limited by resistivity. Resolution limited by current noise in small area devices and inhomogeneity in large ones.	High resolution charged particle spectrometry and applications involving special geometry.	Main problems are obtaining a low noise, stable back contact and the selection of good material. Encapsulation is possible only with epoxy resins.
Lithium Ion-drift Devices	Ge or Si. Medium resistivity. Long lifetime. (Available commercially)	up to 10 mm	*Silicon* 3·8 keV for Cs^{137} betas. 15 keV for 6 MeV alphas. *Germanium* 3·5 keV for Cs^{137} betas 2·8 keV for Co^{57} betas	Thickness limited by experimental technique. Resolution limited by current noise for betas and gammas but by recombination for alphas and heavy ions.	*Silicon* High resolution charged particle spectrometry at high energies. *Germanium* Gamma ray spectrometry.	Main problems are in control of drift process and, for germanium, the stability of the finished device.

N.B.—All germanium counters require cooling to liquid air temperature. Resolution figures include amplifier contribution

Such a table as this cannot hope to be comprehensive, and as a result is liable to be controversial. Obviously the broad generalization must often be wrong, and the opinions are sometimes the personal ones of the authors. What it should show in this case is that there are jobs for each of the kinds of junction counter described, and that their basic similarity does not mean that two of the types will soon be redun‧dant.

As a final illustration of the kind of performance which has been achieved in the field of charged particle spectrometry

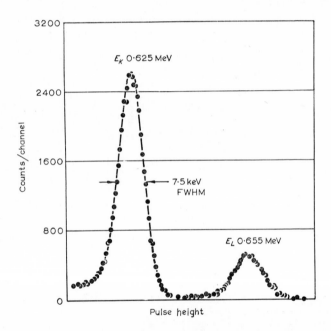

FIG. 6.17 Cs^{137} beta particle spectrum (After Fox and BORKOWSKI[16])

Fig. 6.17 reproduces the results of Fox and Borkowski[16] using a high voltage silicon counter to resolve the internal conversion beta-ray spectrum of Cs^{137} showing almost complete separation of the K and L shell electrons.

REFERENCES

For this chapter

1. Donovan, P., *Proceedings of Asheville Conference, NAS-NRC Publication No.* **871**, 268 (1961).
2. Moncaster, M. E., Northrop, D. C. and Raines, J. A., *Nucl. Instr. and Methods*, **22**, 157 (1963).
3. Dearnaley, G. and Whitehead, A. B., *Nucl. Instr. and Methods*, **12**, 205 (1961).
4. Archer, R. J., *J. Electrochem. Soc.*, **104**, 619 (1957).
5. Andreyeva, V. V. and Shishakov, N. A., *Zh. Fis. Khim*, **35**, 1351 (1961).
6. Klema, E. D., *Nucl. Instr. and Methods*, **26**, 205 (1964).
7. Siffert, P., Coche, A. and Laustriat, G., *Mem. Soc. Roy. des Sci. de Liège*, X, No. 2., (1964).
8. Amsel, G., *Rev. Sci. Instr.*, **32**, 1253 (1961).
9. Fox, R. J. and Borkowski, C. J., *I.R.E. Trans. Nucl. Sci.*, **NS-9**, No. 3, 213 (1962).
10. Andrews, P. T., *Proceedings Nuclear Instrument Symposium, Harwell*, Heywood & Co. (London 1962).
11. Mayer, J. W., *I.R.E. Trans. Nucl. Sci.*, **NS-9**, No. 3, 124 (1962).
12. Pell, E. M., *J. Appl. Phys.*, **31**, 291 (1960).
13. Chasman, C. and Allen, J., *Nucl. Instr. and Methods*, **24**, 253, (1963).
14. Dearnaley, G. and Lewis, J. C., *Nucl. Instr. and Methods*, **25**, 237 (1964).
15. Goulding, F. S. and Hansen, W. L., *I.E.E.E. Trans. Nucl. Sci.*, **NS-11**, No. 3, 186 (1964).
16. Ammerlaan, C. A. J. and Mulder, K., *Nucl. Instr. and Methods*, **21**, 97 (1963).
17. Siffert, P., Rougeot, H. and Coche, A., *Mem. Soc. Roy. des Sci. de Liège*, X, No. 2, 95 (1964).
18. Backenstoss, G., *B.S.T.J.*, **37**, 699 (1958).
19. Sullivan, M. H. and Eigler, J. H., *J. Electrochem. Soc.*, **104**, 226 (1957).
20. Miller, G. L., Pate, B. D. and Wagner, S., *I.E.E.E. Trans. Nucl. Sci.*, **NS-10**, No. 1, 220 (1963).
21. Blankenship, J. L. and Borkowski, C. J., *I.R.E. Trans. Nucl. Sci.*, **NS-9**, No. 3, 181 (1962).
22. Norgate, G. and McIntyre, R. J., *I.E.E.E. Trans. Nucl. Sci.*, **NS-11**, No. 3, 291 (1964).
23. Gibbons, P. E., *Nucl. Instr. and Methods*, **16**, 184 (1962).

24. Reiss, H., Fuller, C. S. and Morin, F. J., *B.S.T.J.*, **35**, 535 (1956).
25. Freck, D. V. and Wakefield, J., *Nature*, **193**, 669 (1962).
26. Hansen, W. L. and Jarrett, B. V., *U.C.R.L. Report*, **11589** (1964).
27. Carter, J. R. and Swalin, R. A., *J. Appl. Phys.*, **31**, 1191 (1960).
28. Palms, J. M. (private communication).
29. Tavendale, A. J., *I.E.E.E. Trans. Nucl. Sci.*, **NS-11**, No. 3, 191 (1964).
30. Palms, J. M. and Greenwood, A. H., *Bull. Amer. Phys. Soc.*, **10**, 124 (1965).
31. Williams, R. L., *Proceedings of Asheville Conference*, NAS-NRC Publication No. **871**, 202 (1961).
32. Buck, T. M., Wheatley, G. H. and Rodgers, J. W., *I.E.E.E. Trans. Nucl. Sci.*, **NS-11**, No. 3 (1964).
33. Statz, H., *Proceedings of Asheville Conference*, NAS-NRC Publication No. **871**, 202 (1961).
34. Llacer, J., *Brookhaven Report*, No. B.N.L. **7853** (1964).
35. Hansen, W. L., Goulding, F. S. and Lothrop, R. P., *J. Appl. Phys.*, **34**, 1570 (1963).
36. Hansen, W. L. and Goulding, F. S., *Nucl. Instr. and Methods*, **29**, 345 (1964).
37. Goulding, F. S. and Hansen, W. L., *Nucl. Instr. and Methods*, **12**, 249 (1961).
38. Madden, T. C. and Gibson, W. M., *I.E.E.E. Trans. Nucl. Sci.*, **NS-11**, No. 3, 154 (1964).
39. Goulding, F. S., *Proceedings of Asheville Conference*, NAS-NRC Publication No. **871**, 202 (1961).
40. Williams, R. L. and Webb, P. P., *I.R.E. Trans. Nucl. Sci.*, **NS-9**, No. 3, 160 (1962).
41. Joyner, W. T., Schmitt, H. W., Neiler, J. H. and Silva, R. J., *I.R.E. Trans. Nucl. Sci.*, **NS-8**, No. 1, 54 (1961).
42. Shockley, W., *Electrons and Holes in Semiconductors*, p. 214, Van Nostrand (Princeton, N.J., 1950).
43. Walter, F. J., Dabbs, J. W. T. and Roberts, L. D., *Oak Ridge National Laboratory Report*, ORNL **2877** (1960).
44. Tuzzolino, A. J., Hubbard, E. L., Perkins, M. A. and Fan, C. Y., *J. Appl. Phys.*, **33**, 148 (1962).
45. Amsel, G., *Rev. Sci. Instr.*, **32**, 1253 (1961).

CHAPTER 7

INSTRUMENTATION FOR SEMICONDUCTOR COUNTERS

7.1 Introduction

The capabilities of semiconductor junction counters can be fully realized only if the ancillary electronic equipment is designed to suit their characteristics. This is particularly true with regard to their energy resolution and speed of response. Over the past decade or more the majority of nuclear radiation measurements have involved scintillation, proportional or Geiger counters, none of which call for an amplifier of particularly low noise performance. Only for the small signals from gaseous ionization chambers have amplifiers of appreciable gain, low noise and good stability been required. The number of users of such a system has been small, but now that similar requirements are being met in increasing numbers for semiconductor counters the principles of low-noise amplifier design are receiving much wider attention.

In radiation monitoring and space research the great advantage of compactness in the counter is lost if a bulky amplifier is also necessary. In such cases a transistorized amplifier has obvious virtues. In studies of nuclear reactions with a particle accelerator the compactness and simplicity of semiconductor detectors make it possible to use numbers of them simultaneously for measurements of the angular distribution of yield from the target. Even greater numbers of small detectors could be mounted in a linear array along the focal plane of a magnetic spectrometer, replacing the nuclear emulsions at present employed. In such cases, however, the problems of amplifying signals from many detectors and handling the quantity of data which they could provide are considerable.

Adequate pulse height analysis of an energy spectrum extending over an energy range of 6 MeV with even a single detector of 30 keV energy resolution, for instance, requires at least 500 channels for the display. Simultaneous measurements at several angles would render even greater numbers of channels desirable; multi-dimensional pulse height analysers of 20 000 channels capable of division into many two-dimensional matrices are being designed in the U.S.A. for this purpose. Magnetic tape pulse-storage systems present another way of coding and handling large quantities of data. Computers are being increasingly used for the handling and immediate reduction of data in experiments of ever-growing complexity. The need for such powerful methods has stemmed to no small extent from the sophistication of experiments which have become possible with the use of semiconductor detectors. The operating cost of an average nuclear particle accelerator justifies extensive measures to avoid the wastage of information that results from repeating lengthy measurements with a single counter moved to different angles, or the risk of losing touch with the experiment owing to the high rate at which data can be accumulated.

In this chapter we shall discuss some of the new problems in electronics which have been raised by the requirements of semiconductor counters. Some ideas as to future trends in experimental arrangements will also be put forward. Equipment commonly in use already with other types of detectors, for instance pulse-height analysers, coincidence units, and scalers, will not be discussed here.

Unless otherwise stated, noise figures throughout this chapter are expressed in terms of the equivalent particle energy in silicon. For germanium the corresponding figures are lower by about 20 per cent owing to the lower energy loss per electron-hole pair in this material.

7.2 Pulse amplifiers

(a) Voltage-sensitive and charge-sensitive amplifiers

The signal from a semiconductor counter, as in a gaseous counter, consists of a pulse of electrical charge collected into the capacitance between the detector electrodes. The charge released by a 1 MeV particle stopped in the depletion layer is about $5 \cdot 10^{-14}$ Coulomb; in a typical detector capacitance of 100 pF this produces a voltage signal of 0·5 mV. A voltage amplifier can be designed with an r.m.s. noise level at the input only 1 per cent of this, *i.e.* 5 μV, but a stability of 1 per cent in the output is achieved only if the input capacitance varies by less than this amount, *i.e.* 1 pF in this instance. The detector capacitance varies with bias voltage, while the input capacitance of the amplifier can also change with the filament temperature of the first tube, since this affects the space charge layer around the cathode. As a matter of practical convenience it is a further disadvantage in the voltage amplifier that each change in detector bias changes the pulse height–energy calibration although the charge collected is very nearly constant. For these reasons a different amplifier configuration is generally to be preferred; this is the charge-sensitive or integrating amplifier. In this a capacitative feedback loop creates a very large effective input capacitance; this capacitance is stable and outweighs the small variations mentioned above. The charge-sensitive amplifier configuration was first proposed by Cottini, Gatti, Giannelli and Rossi[1] for use with ionization chambers. Figure 7.1(*a*), (*b*) shows schematically the two types of amplifier with relevant input circuit parameters. In these diagrams C_d is the detector capacitance, R_d the leakage resistance and R_s the series resistance of undepleted silicon and of the electrodes. R_l is the detector load resistance and R_a the amplifier input resistance. C_a is the amplifier input capacitance and includes stray capacitance to earth from the connecting lead. In the voltage amplifier, Fig. 7.1(*a*), feedback through resistor R_f to the cathode resistor of the first stage, R_k, determines the gain. The output voltage V_o for charge Q released in capacitance C_d is given by

$$V_o = (Q/C_d)(R_f/R_k) \qquad (7.1)$$

In the other configuration feedback takes place through a small capacitance C_f to the grid of the first tube so that the input capacitance is $(A + 1)$ C_f for an amplifier open loop gain of A. If the loop gain is sufficiently large that $A \gg C/C_f$,

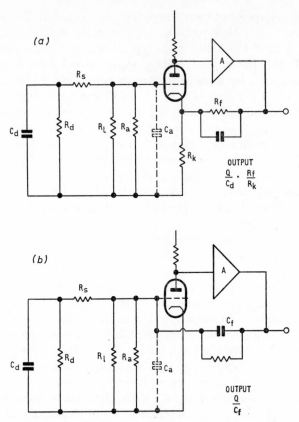

FIG. 7.1 Input circuit parameters for (a) a voltage-sensitive and (b) a charge-sensitive amplifier configuration; from DEARNALEY, G., *Journ. Brit. I.R.E.*, 24 153 (1962)

where C is the total input capacitance ($C_a + C_d$), the output voltage signal is

$$V_o = Q/C_f \qquad (7.2)$$

Under these conditions V_o is independent of C_a and C_d. C_f is made very small, typically a few picofarads, in which case the gain of the pre-amplifier corresponds to some 20 to 50 mV for each MeV of particle energy dissipated in the counter. It is important to note that since these two configurations differ only in the manner by which negative feed-

back is applied, no significant difference results in the signal
to noise ratio which can be achieved with a given detector and
input tube. There is a small effect in practice owing to the
increased input capacitance caused by the presence of a feedback capacitor C_f in the charge-sensitive circuit.

(b) *Low-noise pre-amplifier design*

The noise level of the amplifier is essentially the same for
the two configurations discussed above since feedback does
not affect the signal to noise ratio. The amplifier noise arises
principally from fluctuations in grid current and anode current
(shot noise) in the input tube. When a low noise level is important the input stage is generally a pair of triodes, 'cascode
connected' as in the circuit of Fig. 7.2. This arrangement

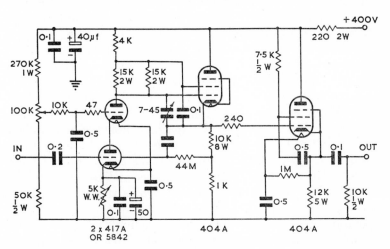

FIG. 7.2 Charge-sensitive pre-amplifier circuit, due to CHASE, HIGIN-
BOTHAM and MILLER[2]

combines the features of a low amplification factor, μ, a high
mutual conductance, g_m, and high gain in one stage. The low
μ permits low voltage operation which results in a low grid
current, while the high g_m leads to low shot noise. Suitable
tubes should also have low microphony and a stable cathode
emission, and types E83F, 417A, E88CC and EC1000 are
particularly good for this application. Triodes are preferable to

multi-electrode tubes since they are free from partition noise. Figure 7.2 shows the circuit of a cascode charge-sensitive pre-amplifier designed by Chase, Higinbotham and Miller.[2] It consists of an input stage, an amplifier and an output cathode follower. The top of the cascode load resistor and the amplifier screen are 'bootstrapped' from the output stage in order to assist in achieving an open loop gain of over 10^3 without excessive phase shift at high frequencies. Besides ensuring true charge-sensitivity this high gain gives a fast rise time, since the latter is equal to the open loop rise time divided by the reserve gain, which is defined as AC_f/C. The open loop rise time of this circuit is 2 μsec. In such circuits the input stage is generally screened and the layout arranged so that negative feedback does take place predominantly through the small feedback capacitor rather than through stray capacitance. Similar circuits have been published by Blankenship,[3] Goulding and Hansen,[4] and Goulding.[5]

Goulding[5] has stressed the fact that there is a mutual dependence between the characteristics of pre-amplifier and detector for optimum performance. A wide variety of semi-conductor detectors is now in use with leakage currents which may range between 10^{-9} and 10^{-5} amp and capacitance between about 2 and 2000 pF. No single design of preamplifier can give the best performance which is possible over these ranges. A low-leakage, low-capacitance detector calls for a pre-amplifier with low input capacitance and low grid current, while in the case of high-leakage, high-capacitance detectors of large area it is advantageous to use in the input stage a pentode, such as the 7788, having a high mutual conductance despite the accompanying high input capacitance and grid current. Goulding[5] has designed a set of three pre-amplifier input stages to meet these different conditions, each being used with a common output circuit.

When compactness as well as good energy resolution is required with small capacitance detectors, R.C.A. 'Nuvistor' tubes are available with overall dimensions little greater than those of transistors and an anode dissipation of about 1 watt. A compact low-noise charge sensitive pre-amplifier with type 7586 Nuvistor triodes has been designed by Chase, Higin-botham and Miller.[2] This circuit has an r.m.s. equivalent noise charge of 1200 electronic charges for an input capacitance of 12 pF, corresponding to a 10 keV line width. However, recent developments in field-effect transistor pre-amplifiers have enabled better performance to be achieved with even greater compactness and lower power dissipation. These and other transistor preamplifier circuits are discussed in Section 7.2(d).

The pre-amplifier gain can be calibrated by feeding in a small charge at the input. The fast pulse from a relay with mercury-wetted contacts is fed through a small capacitance to the input grid. In practical cases the charge collection efficiencies of detectors vary a little but the signal from a given detector exposed to an alpha test source can be compared with the pulser signal. The most convenient arrangement is to be able to preset the pulse output control potentiometer so as to correspond to the particle energy in MeV. It is subsequently very easy to calibrate the entire electronic arrangement, and, for instance, to set discriminator levels by means of pulser signals. Chase[6] has used such an input charge calibration together with an amplitude to digital conversion system to provide a sampled servomechanical control of the stability of an entire detector and amplifier assembly to better than one part in $4 \cdot 10^3$.

It is often desirable to examine in detail a small part of an energy spectrum, for instance in the study of a few groups of particles of closely similar energy. It is then an advantage to be able to bias out, in the main amplifier, some part of the amplitude of pulses from the pre-amplifier in order to spread the residual pulse height over a wide dynamic range. This must, of course, be done without introducing the likelihood of a drift in bias level with time, or changes in bias level with variation of counting rate under normal circumstances. These problems have been solved in an unpublished circuit of Fairstein, while Gatti[7] has put forward a design in which each pulse from the pre-amplifier triggers a precision charge generator which subtracts a fixed quantity of charge from the input circuit.

(c) *The optimization of signal to noise ratio*

Besides providing additional gain the main amplifier should also carry provision for control of the pulse shape in order to obtain an optimum signal to noise ratio consistent with the rate of counting. By consideration of the frequency spectrum of the noise it is possible to choose an amplifier bandwidth and mid-band frequency so as to minimize the component of noise in the output. In the combined system of detector and amplifier there are essentially four distinguishable noise contributions, two determined by detector characteristics and two by the input tube. These are the two types of detector noise arising from bulk and surface leakage currents, together with amplifier shot noise and grid current noise. Of these, all but surface leakage in the detector can be studied theoretically and have a predictable frequency dependence for the noise spectrum. By eliminating surface leakage current in a detector with a guard-ring structure Goulding and Hansen[4] have been able to analyse the remaining noise contribution and test the conditions for maximum signal to noise. Similar considerations have also been studied by Fairstein[8] for both resistance-capacitance (RC) and delay-line pulse shaping circuits.

The signal amplitude is best expressed in terms of the charge released within the detector by ionization, and hence it is logical, in a discussion of signal to noise ratio, to consider the various noise contributions also in units of charge. Fairstein defines the 'equivalent noise charge', in root-mean-square Coulombs, as that quantity of charge which, if applied to the input of the amplifier in a time short compared with the amplifier response time, would produce an output voltage pulse of amplitude equal to the observed r.m.s. noise voltage. He also describes practical methods of measuring the equivalent noise charge in a detector and amplifier.

Throughout the following discussion of RC pulse shaping, it will be assumed that the amplifier has single integrating and differentiating circuits with equal time constants, τ, since this is close to the optimum for signal to noise ratio, as shown by Gillespie[9]. It will also be assumed that τ is long compared with both the detector rise time and the input time constant due to the product of the total input capacitance and series resistance.

Under these conditions the amplifier bandwidth is proportional to the low-frequency cut-off. It is found experimentally that detector surface noise approximates to an inverse frequency dependence of mean square noise charge. Thus the level of noise at the output due to this source is independent of the time constants, τ. The presence of detector surface noise will then not influence the choice of time constant. Goulding and Hansen[4] have listed the formulae for the magnitude of the other sources of noise, which we shall now consider in turn.

For a triode the shot noise within a bandwidth Δf is equivalent to a mean square input voltage

$$\overline{v_s^2} \simeq \frac{10\ kT}{g_m} \Delta f \tag{7.3}$$

in which k is Boltzmann's constant, T is the absolute temperature and g_m the triode mutual conductance. The input tube grid current, i_g, is subject to fluctuations with a mean square amplitude given by

$$\overline{i_g^2} = 2ei_g\Delta f \tag{7.4}$$

where e is the electronic charge. Since the load on the grid circuit is capacitative the mean square noise voltage is

$$\overline{v_g^2} = \frac{2ei_g}{4\pi^2 f^2 C^2} \Delta f \tag{7.5}$$

The detector bulk leakage current, i_d, introduces a corresponding term

$$\overline{v_d^2} = \frac{2ei_d}{4\pi^2 f^2 C^2} \Delta f \tag{7.6}$$

After multiplying these terms by the amplifier gain, which is a function of frequency, and integrating over the amplifier bandwidth Goulding and Hansen[4] obtain the terms listed in Table 7.1. Two other sources of noise which we have not so far considered are tube flicker noise, due to fluctuations in cathode emission, and thermal noise in the input shunt resistance, R. As can be seen from the formulae in Table 7.1 these are generally much smaller than the other terms, assuming that R is made greater than 10 MΩ. Since the shot noise varies as $1/\tau$ while the other major contributions are proportional to τ, the sum of all the noise contributions at the amplifier output can be minimized by a suitable choice of τ. For increasing values

TABLE 7.1

Noise source	Equivalent mean square noise at the input, in (electron charges)²
Input tube shot noise	$1600\ C^2/g_m\tau$
Grid current noise	$12i_g\tau \times 10^6$
Detector leakage current	$12i_d\tau \times 10^6$
Input resistance thermal noise	$6\cdot10^5\ \tau/R$
Input tube flicker noise	$16\ C^2$

C = total input capacitance in pF
g_m = input tube mutual conductance in milliamp/volt
τ = amplifier time constant in μsec
i_g = input tube grid current in μA
i_d = detector leakage current in μA
R = total input shunt resistance in MΩ

Noise contributions from various sources, adapted from the paper of Goulding and Hansen.[4] To obtain the line width in keV measured as full width at half maximum of the pulse height distribution, multiply the square root of the sum of the contributions by $8\cdot10^{-3}$.

of the detector current this optimum will lie at smaller values of the time constant, τ. This can be seen in Fig. 7.3, adapted from Goulding and Hansen's paper.[4] The calculated values assume a tube grid current of $2\cdot10^{-9}$ amp, a mutual conductance, g_m, of 16 mA/volt, and an input shunt resistance of 5 MΩ. It can be seen from this figure that the amplifier should be designed to allow variation of the time constants in small steps over the range 0·1 to 3 μsec.

When detectors are operated at high bias voltages in order to obtain deep depletion layers the detector current and noise become relatively large. Lithium-drifted detectors also show a fairly large reverse current, principally arising from the large volume in which space charge generation occurs. Grid current in the amplifier input tube is, under these circumstances, negligible compared with the detector current, which may be several μA. The capacitance of the detector can, however, be very small; in a silicon counter with a 3 mm depletion layer thickness the capacitance is only about 3 pF per cm². A good signal to noise ratio can be achieved if the

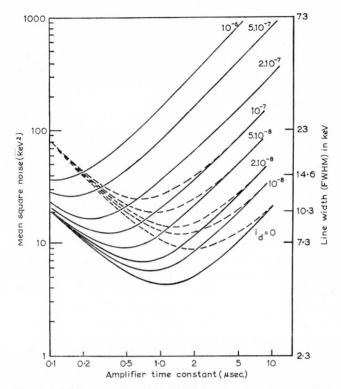

FIG. 7.3 Noise variation with amplifier time constant, τ, and detector current, i_d. The input tube g_m is taken as 16 mA/volt and the smooth curves are for 40 pF total input capacitance, while the dotted curves are for 80 pF capacitance; from GOULDING and HANSEN[4]

total amplifier input capacitance, C, is made as small as possible, so minimizing the shot noise term in Table 7.1. The time constants for optimum signal to noise ratio are then quite short, of the order 0·1 μsec or less. By consideration of such factors Blankenship[10] has obtained a line width due to noise of only 3 keV in an amplifier and a small lithium-drifted detector of about 1 pF capacitance. It is generally very difficult to obtain linear pulse height analysis of such fast-rising pulses, and Gibbons (priv. comm.) has drawn attention to the need for an accurate pulse-stretching circuit to overcome this problem. Such a circuit should be, as far as possible, free from pulse height changes due to counting rate variation over a reasonably wide range.

Ammerlaan[11] has pointed out another effect of using short RC time constants in the amplification of pulses from lithium-drifted silicon counters of appreciable thickness. The charge collection time can be as much as a few tenths of a micro-second in such cases, which is comparable with the amplifier pulse-shaping time-constants for optimum signal to noise ratio. The energy of the particles determines the range of the ionized track in the detector and thereby influences the distance over which charge carriers are collected. Thus the shape of the pulse becomes a complex function of the energy, and non-linearities are introduced when this pulse is shaped in the amplifier. Ammerlaan[11] has published calculations which enable the degree of non-linearity to be derived fairly simply in a given case. He points out that where good linearity is required, at the expense of a reduced signal to noise ratio, it is preferable to use a delay-line shaping network, which can easily be arranged to give no distortion of the energy scale as it responds to the peak excursion of the signal.

Fairstein,[8] and Gatti and de Martini[12] have considered the effect of more complex types of pulse shaping on the signal to noise ratio. Double delay-line clipping with single RC integration results in a relatively poor signal to noise ratio, but is necessary if a high counting rate and good recovery from overload pulses are required. When high counting rates must be tolerated but the overload problem is not serious, Fairstein[8] recommends double RC differentiation. The double differentiated waveform, shown in Fig. 7.4, has the advantage that the time of cross-over from a positive to a negative signal may be used for accurate timing. The cross-over time is defined to a much better degree than the rising edge of the pulse, and is less dependent upon pulse amplitude. Thus in an unpublished circuit of Fairstein the cross-over time allows a timing accuracy of about 10^{-8} sec although the double differentiated waveform has a duration of about 10^{-6} sec.

Fairstein has recently introduced an amplifier of high stability and with double RC differentiation (Tennelec Instrument Co., Inc., model TC 200). In the case of low-capacitance, high-leakage detectors the first differentiation time-constant

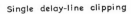

Single delay-line clipping

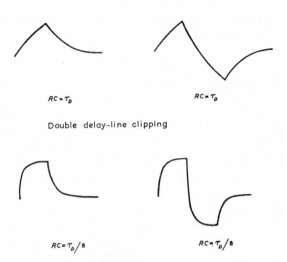

$RC = T_D$ $RC = T_D$

Double delay-line clipping

$RC = T_D/8$ $RC = T_D/8$

FIG. 7.4 Waveforms for single and double delay-line clipping, with single RC integration. The delay-line length is assumed constant throughout (After FAIRSTEIN[8])

can be set very short for optimum signal to noise ratio. In order to obtain a longer output pulse, suitable for linear pulse height analysis, the second differentiation time-constant may be set much larger than the first. This same arrangement is also valuable in the case of very high pulse rates when pile-up becomes more a serious consideration than signal to noise ratio. A biased amplifier is then connected between the two stages of amplification to remove unwanted small signals which are the most common source of pile-up.

In making count-rate measurements of the activity of a source, as in radioisotope tracer work, it may be more useful to know the rate of amplifier noise pulses which exceed a given discrimination level rather than the r.m.s. noise level. Since the noise spectrum depends on the type of noise source (grid-current or shot noise) it is necessary to be aware as to which contribution is dominant. Fairstein[13] has published a useful graph of the noise count rate as a function of the ratio of discrimination level to r.m.s. noise. However, certain types of detector contact, for example silver paste, can introduce detector noise pulses which are in excess of the values calculated for the amplifier noise spectrum.

(d) Low-noise transistor pre-amplifier design

The compact size and low power requirements of transistor amplifiers are obvious advantages in equipment where space and weight are to be minimized. This is true in portable radiation detectors, in the use of multiple detector arrays and of course in space research. The low heat dissipation in most transistors enables them to be mounted in vacuo, close to a charged-particle detector, so as to minimize stray capacitance in the input circuit. Until recently, however, the transistor pre-amplifier could not match the signal to noise performance of a good vacuum-tube system, at least in the most common situations. Since 1963 the position has changed, and some field-effect transistors are available which, when cooled, can compete with the best vacuum tubes in terms of noise, while possessing the advantages listed above. At present their cost is rather high and selection is necessary because of the variability of characteristics, but these features are likely to be improved in the future.

The earlier transistor pre-amplifiers were built using junction transistors. The base current of this type of transistor is analogous to the vacuum-tube grid current but exceeds it by a factor of at least thirty under conditions of equal noise contributions from base and collector. For small values of input capacitance this leads to an r.m.s. noise charge which is expected to be at least five times greater for the transistor amplifier, and this is borne out in practice. The best pre-amplifiers using junction transistors show some 20 keV of noise, measured as the particle energy equivalent to the full width at half maximum of the pulse height distribution for a well defined pulse input. This is to be compared with about 3 keV noise in a good vacuum tube amplifier under similar conditions of small input capacitance. However, the conditions for optimum signal to noise ratio depend greatly upon the input capacitance, C (see Table 7.1). In junction counters with shallow depletion layers, the capacitance may be as much as

500 pF/cm^2, and the shot noise, being proportional to C^2, is very high indeed especially if the area is large. The balance between shot noise and grid current noise cannot then be reached without exceeding the anode dissipation of most tubes. The transistor amplifier is then no longer at a disadvantage, and the position of equivalence is reached for an input capacitance of about 700 pF. A low-noise charge sensitive pre-amplifier using junction transistors, designed by Emmer[14] is shown in Fig. 7.5. This circuit gives an equivalent line width of 30 keV for 30 pF input capacitance.

Jonasson[15] has studied the application of tunnel diodes for the input stage of a voltage-sensitive pre-amplifier, followed by a stage of high input impedance. The theoretically attainable noise performance of the input stage is very good, but there is a large contribution from the second stage. Jonasson obtained an equivalent line width of 12 keV, for an input capacitance of 18 pF, using an IN 3561 tunnel diode. This is appreciably better than can be achieved with a junction transistor, but it was found necessary to select the diode carefully because of their variability. It was also found necessary to regulate the tunnel diode bias voltage very closely.

The unipolar field-effect transistor was first described by Shockley[16] in 1952. Its action is based on voltage control of majority carrier flow through a semiconducting channel, the width and conductance of which are varied by the reverse-bias potential of a p-n junction. As shown schematically in Fig. 7.6, it consists of a silicon crystal to which are made two ohmic contacts, source and drain, with a rectifying contact termed the gate applied between them. The width of the conducting channel between source and drain is governed by the extent of the depletion layer of the reverse-biased gate junction. When the depletion regions on opposite sides of the crystal merge, the device is said to saturate or 'pinch off'. The current flow is then virtually independent of the drain voltage. Because the gate is a reverse-biased junction its input impedance is very high ($\sim 10^8 \, \Omega$) and the input capacitance (gate-source or gate-drain) is small, of the order of a few pF. The characteristics of the field-effect transistor, or FET, have been described in detail by Radeka,[17] and the noise sources of the FET have been discussed in several papers by van der

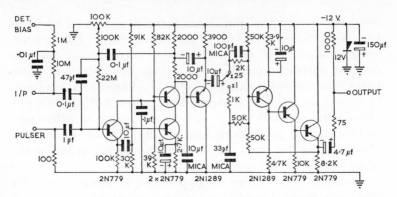

FIG. 7.5 Transistor charge-sensitive pre-amplifier for semiconductor counters; from EMMER[14]

Ziel.[18] The major contributions are thermal noise in the conducting channel, shot noise in the gate-channel junction, and flicker noise. The thermal noise, $\overline{i_d^2}$ within a band-width Δf is given by

$$\overline{i_d^2} = 4KT\Delta f . g_m . Y \tag{7.7}$$

where g_m is the saturated transconductance and Y is a function of the operating conditions and may be taken to equal about 0·7 in practical cases. This thermal noise is equivalent to that in a resistance R_n in series with the gate, where

$$R_n = Y/g_m \tag{7.8}$$

In a good FET, R_n may be only about 500 ohms compared with 250 ohms for the low noise E88CC tube under working conditions. Coupling between the channel and the gate introduces a noise current in the input circuit which increases the equivalent noise resistance somewhat, the extent depending upon the input capacitance.

Shot noise introduces a mean square gate current

$$\overline{i_g^2} = 2e . i_g . \Delta f \tag{7.9}$$

when the gate-source current can be assumed negligible. This contribution usually seems to be less significant than the flicker noise, which is characterized by a $1/f$ frequency dependence. This introduces a mean square channel voltage

$$\overline{v_f^2} \propto \Delta f/f \tag{7.10}$$

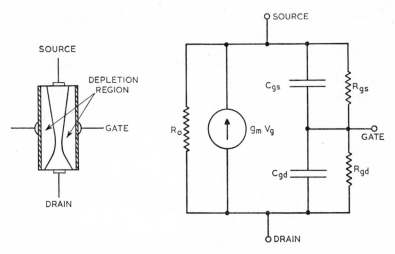

FIG. 7.6 Schematic diagram of a field-effect transistor, and its equivalent circuit

and arises from carrier-density fluctuations due to trapping in the space-charge region of the device. It is a variable quantity, depending as it does on defect centres in the crystal and conditions at its surface.

Since thermal noise decreases with temperature there is an advantage in cooling the FET. However, at very low temperatures the carrier density in the channel decreases and statistical fluctuations in the current increase. Blalock[19] has verified this behaviour by measurements of the noise line-width of an FET pre-amplifier as a function of main amplifier RC time-constants at four temperatures, $78°$, $125°$, $195°$ and $295°$ K. (See Fig. 7.7). He found the best performance was obtained at $125°$ K. The preamplifier circuit designed by Blalock is shown in Fig. 7.8 and gave an equivalent line width of less than 3 keV at room temperature and 1·6 keV at $125°$ K, for zero input capacitance. The slope of line-width against capacitance was less than 0·06 keV per pF. Other FET pre-amplifier designs have been published by Radeka[17], Smith[20] and Wintenberg and Pierce.[21] The best field-effect transistors from the point of view of noise appear to be the 2N2500 and 2N2608. As Radeka points out, it is desirable to have a range of low-noise FETs with gate input capacitances which match the various detector capacitances which are to be met.

At present, therefore, the FET pre-amplifier can give, at least when cooled, a signal to noise performance comparable with that of the best vacuum-tube circuits, for low input capacitances below about 100 pF. Since the detector itself is often cooled in order to improve its resolution this suggests

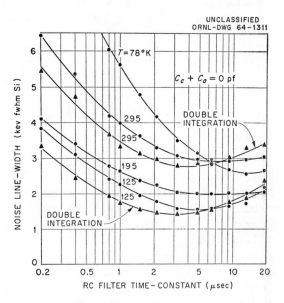

FIG. 7.7 Noise line-width as a function of temperature and R.C. filter time-constant for a field-effect transistor pre-amplifier; from BLALOCK[19]

that at least the first stage of the FET pre-amplifier should be mounted close to the detector so that both may be cooled together. Lithium-drifted germanium detectors are usually operated at around 100° K and have a very high intrinsic resolution for gamma rays. They also have a relatively low capacitance so that it is advantageous to keep the stray capacitance to a minimum by mounting the amplifier input stage close to the detector. The low input capacitance of the FET makes it unsuitable for use with detectors of high capacitance. In this case a junction transistor pre-amplifier is likely

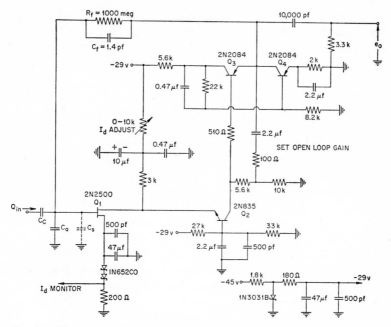

FIG. 7.8 Charge-sensitive pre-amplifier with a field-effect transistor in the input stage; from BLALOCK[19]

to be preferable, and there is little point in reducing stray capacitance by short leads.

(e) Fast pulse amplification

It is often necessary to sacrifice some signal to noise ratio for accuracy of timing the response, for instance, in the detection of coincident pulses in the presence of a high background counting rate. One method, mentioned above, is to use a double-differentiated wave-form, the cross-over time being determined quite accurately by the centroid of the pulse before clipping. A less satisfactory method is to use short amplifier time constants so as to obtain a fast pulse rise which can be utilized for timing. In this case the timing will generally shift with the pulse amplitude. In both cases the conditions for optimum signal to noise ratio are lost. In considering fast pulse operation, a significant difference between voltage-sensitive and charge-sensitive pre-amplifiers must be pointed out. The effective input capacitance, C_a, of a charge-sensitive amplifier is made very large by negative feedback through capacitance C_f, so that

$$C_a = (A + 1)\, C_f \qquad (7.11)$$

where A is the open loop gain. Thus C_a can greatly exceed the detector capacitance, C_d. As charge flows round the grid circuit these two capacitances act in series and the rise time of the signal on the input grid is governed by the smaller. Thus the pulse rise time is given by $R_s\, C_d$, where R_s is the detector series resistance; in a large area detector with a shallow depletion layer and a few hundred Ω series resistance this rise time may approach 1 μsec. In the voltage sensitive amplifier the input capacitance C_a is small and limits the pulse rise time at the input grid to $R_s\, C_a$. Thus charge sensitive amplification should not be used for even moderately fast pulse requirements without consideration of this effect. Since the rise time is inversely proportional to the reserve gain, AC_f/C, the open loop gain, A, should be large when fast-rising pulses are required.

A third configuration which is sometimes useful in high counting-rate experiments is the current-sensitive pre-amplifier in which the input stage is arranged to have a very low input impedance. By using a junction transistor in the emitter-input mode an input impedance of less than 10 Ω can be obtained. Such an amplifier can give a rise-time of a few nanoseconds and handle extremely high pulse rates, up to 10^8 per second. The signal to noise ratio is, however, governed by the charge collection time and this mode of amplification is therefore useful only for thin fully-depleted detectors which have short collection times. It can be valuable in applications which call for fast gating of a few selected events from a large background of unwanted pulses. One commercially available model is the Solid State Radiations, Inc., type 112.

A system with greater potentialities results from providing simultaneous fast and slow amplification by means of a dual amplifier arrangement, consisting of a wide band amplifier for the fast timing signal and a narrow band low-noise amplifier for good energy resolution. In this way the best advantage is made of the fast response and good resolution of most semiconductor detectors. Several methods have been proposed for splitting the signal pulse in order to feed two amplifier chains. Dearnaley and Whitehead[22] proposed a capacitative pick-off to the input of a series of distributed amplifiers, a method which has been used successfully in experiments at A.E.R.E., Harwell.

Williams and Biggerstaff[23] have described a transformer pick-off circuit which provides better performance and is shown in Fig. 7.9. A small transformer, the primary of which is in series with the detector, feeds a fast signal to the input of a wide-band amplifier. The output is used to trigger a tunnel-diode discriminator, and provision is made for the discrimination level to be set remotely. Satisfactory triggering is claimed for input signals corresponding to an equivalent particle energy of 200 keV (in silicon). Fast timing with a jitter of less than 1 nano-second and a shift with particle energy of less than 0·2 nanosec. per MeV can be achieved with such a system, while introducing only about a 2 keV increase in noise line-width into the low-noise amplifier system. Such a time pick-off circuit is now available commercially (ORTEC model 260).

A system such as this has obvious applications in coincidence studies of nuclear reactions, and in time of flight measurements. It may also be used to eliminate pile-up of successive pulses in high-counting-rate experiments. If two fast timing pulses should arrive within a predetermined time an 'inhibit' pulse can be generated which prevents the entry of the delayed linear signal into a pulse-height analyser.

In these fast pulse applications it is always necessary to ensure that the pulse rise time of the detector itself is adequately short. Thus it may be necessary to minimize the series resistance of the detector by avoiding the presence of an undepleted layer of silicon, as can be done by appropriate choice of voltage and wafer thickness. This is particularly important at very low temperatures where the resistivity of the undepleted semiconductor may be far greater than its value at room temperature. The effect of a detector pulse rise time which exceeds that of the amplifier is to give a reduced output signal, as was observed by Dodge and his collaborators[24] in experiments on silicon detectors at around 20° K. The detector

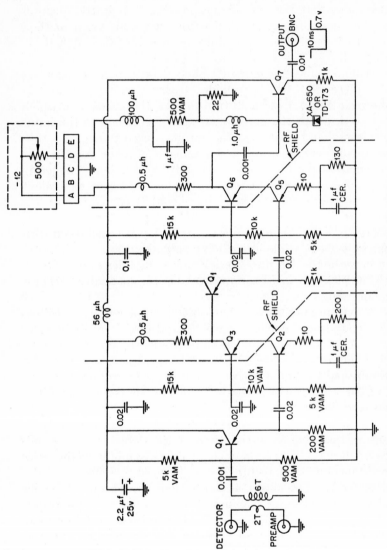

Fig. 7.9 Time pick-off circuit due to WILLIAMS and BIGGERSTAFF [23]

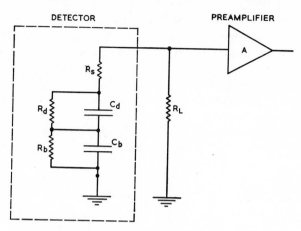

FIG. 7.10 Equivalent circuit of a junction detector

equivalent circuit originally proposed by Walter[25] in order to explain such effects is shown in Fig. 7.10 and is important when considering the fast pulse response of semiconductor detectors.

In minimizing the series resistance of the detector, R_s, it is necessary to ensure a low sheet resistance over the detector front face, and a low forward resistance in the base contact of the detector. At the present time these requirements are best met by a surface-barrier at the front face and a diffused contact at the rear.

Finally, of course, we must consider the charge collection time of the detector. Effectively there is an upper limit to carrier velocities in silicon and germanium, at around 10^7 cm/ sec. The change of carrier velocity with applied field is very small above this value.[26] Thus a lower limit to the charge collection time in a 1 mm thick depletion layer is 10^{-8} sec. Tove and Falk[27] have published convenient nomographs for obtaining the charge collection time in a given detector (Fig. 5.5). Of course, the carriers which are temporarily trapped at defect sites in the crystal contribute a slow tail to the signal. It is important in fast pulse applications that the detector is of good quality material, showing a negligible change of signal with collecting field when using a charge-sensitive amplifier. Radiation damage to the detector increases the probability of trapping of carriers and has been observed to increase the slow-rising component of the signal. Radiation damage, discussed in Chapter 10, has therefore to be considered in fast-pulse experiments.

Fast amplification with a good signal to noise ratio can be achieved by employing a narrow bandwidth, as for instance in parametric amplifiers. Chase[28] has considered the applicability of this form of amplifier for semiconductor counters. If, as is shown in Fig. 7.11(a), a rapidly variable capacitor C_p is

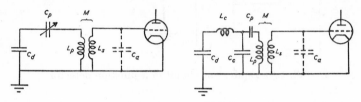

FIG. 7.11 (a) and (b) Parametric amplification of junction detector signals; from CHASE[28]

connected in series with the detector capacitance C_d an a.c. voltage will appear across it when a charge q is released in the detector. If the ratio of the maximum to the minimum value of C_p is r, the peak-to-peak a.c. voltage across C_p is

$$V_p = q(r - 1)/r(C_d + C_p) \qquad (7.11)$$

Owing to the magnitude of the detector series resistance it is necessary to decouple the detector from the high Q primary circuit by means of L_c and C_c as shown in Fig. 7.11(b). The problem is then to match this signal into an RF amplifier. By consideration of the losses to be expected in the transformer, in the parametric capacitor and in the detector together with the loading associated with electron transit time in the amplifier input tube. Chase concluded at this time (1960) that parametric amplification was unlikely to give any advantage over a conventional method of amplifying signals from semiconductor detectors. However, work has since progressed further and it is understood that the parametric amplifier is at last showing promise of becoming superior to all other types of amplifier in terms of signal to noise ratio. All that can be said at present (1965) is that this work by Chase and his group may soon prove to be leading the way to future low-noise amplifier design.

7.3 Electronics for particle identification

(a) *Pulse shape discrimination for junction counters*

It is often desirable to record only those particles which are stopped within the depletion layer of a junction counter and to discriminate against more penetrating particles which produce an ill-resolved background. A method of achieving such discrimination was first described by Amsel[29] and a circuit has since been published by Funsten.[30] The method is based on

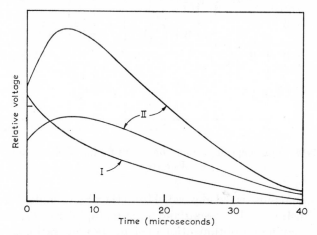

FIG. 7.12 Oscilloscope traces of two types of pulse: I, due to particles stopping within the junction depletion layer, and II, due to those which penetrate beyond the depletion layer; from FUNSTEN[30]

the fact that short-range particles produce only a fast rising pulse, whereas those that penetrate the depletion layer give also a slow component due to diffusion of carriers to the field region. This slow component extends to times of the order of tens of microseconds, as can be seen in Fig. 7.12, which shows pulse shapes for the two cases after RC differentiation with a 15 μsec time constant.

The discriminator circuit due to Funsten[30] is shown in Fig. 7.13 and is used following a fast rise time pre-amplifier.

The pulse is differentiated by $R_1 C_1$ and delay line clipped in the first stage, the clipping time being 3 μsec. Fast-collection pulses return sharply to the base-line while slow pulses give a long tail. After limiting in the next stages, differentiation by $R_2 C_2$ gives a larger trailing edge pulse for the fast signals. The fourth stage limits the leading edge and the output is fed through the final emitter follower stage to an amplifier which provides a suitable gating pulse for a pulse height analyser.

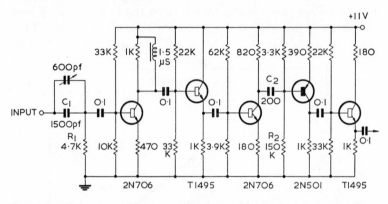

FIG. 7.13 Pulse shape discrimination circuit for junction detectors; from FUNSTEN[30]

The signal pulse is fed in parallel from the pre-amplifier through an adjustable delay circuit and a main amplifier incorporating pulse shaping for optimization of signal to noise ratio. Funsten notes that the circuit was unsatisfactory for small pulses owing to non-limiting in the second stage, and was marginal for particles which stop only just beyond the depletion layer.

Scheer[31] has described a method of pulse shape discrimination which makes use of an oscilloscope display with a masked photo-multiplier to provide a triggering signal. This method requires rather more equipment than in Funsten's arrangement.

A second application of pulse shape discrimination is to distinguish between different types of particles when all are stopped within the depletion layer of a detector. This is possible because the rise time of the signal at the detector electrodes depends upon the distance over which charge carriers are collected, and this in turn depends on the particle range. The time differences so introduced are greatest for relatively long-range particles in lithium-drifted detectors several millimetres in thickness, in which collecting fields are relatively low. Ammerlaan, Rumphorst and Koerts[32] have described a successful experiment on these lines, by which deuterons and alpha-particles with energies in the range of 8 to 26 MeV were distinguished. The pulse height at a fixed time after the start of the signal pulse was used as a measure of the particle range, while the final pulse height depends only on the total energy lost in the detector. In their experiment these two pulses were applied to an oscilloscope X-Y display and the results were recorded photographically. Protons, deuterons and alpha particles gave points whose loci were distinguishable over a wide range of energies. This group also published calculations of the expected pulse shape which are in agreement with their experimental data.

Pulse rise times in this work were of the order of 0·5 microseconds. It is much more difficult to apply this method to short-range particles in surface-barrier or diffused-junction counters, but Seagrave[30] has been able to distinguish between 3 MeV protons and 3 MeV alpha-particles incident on the rear face of a 0·5 mm thick silicon detector, fully depleted by a bias of 190 V.

In both these experiments it is preferable to have the incident particles enter the detector through the n-type electrode. Under these conditions the holes make a somewhat longer transit than the more mobile electrons, so that differences in pulse rise time are exaggerated.

(b) Particle identification by simultaneous dE/dx and E measurements

The most precise discrimination between different types of particles requires the use of a pair of detectors in series. The first of the pair, which may be a thin semiconductor counter or a thin-windowed gaseous proportional counter, is used to give a measure of the rate of energy loss, dE/dx, for particles which pass through it. The second detector should have a sensitive depth adequate to absorb the residual energy of the particle. The sum of the pulses in the two detectors is then proportional to the particle energy E (if the dE/dx detector is of the gaseous type its signal will require additional gain in order to match the pulse height-energy calibration of the semiconductor detector). If the thin detector has a thickness Δx its signal, ΔE, will be given approximately by

$$\Delta E = (dE/dx)_0 \times \Delta x \qquad (7.13)$$

where $(dE/dx)_0$ is the initial rate of energy loss of the particle.

We see from equation (1.2) that, to a first approximation,

$$dE/dx \propto (Mz^2/E).(\log_e[E/I] + \text{const.}) \qquad (7.14)$$

and as the logarithmic term varies slowly with energy the product $E \times dE/dx$ is roughly constant for a given type of particle. Thus, forming the product of the pulse height, ΔE, from the transmission detector with the sum of pulse heights from both detectors gives us an output which depends only upon the mass and charge of the particle and not upon its energy. This signal may be used to gate the response of a pulse height analyzer, or may be separately recorded so that events due to different types of particles may be distinguished.

A rather better approximation to equation (1.2) may be shown to be

$$(dE/dx) (E + \text{const.}) \propto Mz^2 \qquad (7.15)$$

and this product is easily formed by adding a fixed, though adjustable, pulse height to the sum pulse, E.

This method of particle discrimination was first applied to the use of semiconductor detectors by Wegner[34] who constructed the first successful thin dE/dx detector of silicon (see Section 6.4(c)). The earlier circuits for performing the analogue multiplication (see, for example, the paper by Stokes[35]) utilized Raytheon QK-329 squaring tubes, but these often suffered from a change of characteristics with time, and were sometimes noisy. A system based on a chain of diodes in a logarithmic attenuator circuit has been described for this application by Vincent and Kaine.[36] The most recent development has been the use of circuits based on field-effect transistors for pulse height multiplication as described in the paper by Radeka.[37] The multiplication is obtained through the proportionality of the channel conductance to the gate voltage.

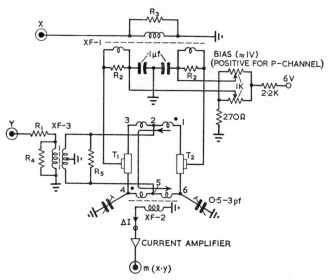

FIG. 7.14 Pulse amplitude multiplying circuit; from RADEKA[37]

In the circuit published by Radeka (Fig. 7.14) two F.E.T.'s
are arranged in a balanced bridge configuration. By transformer coupling, one input signal is applied with opposite
polarity to the two gates, increasing the conductance of one
channel and decreasing that of the other. The second input is
applied as a voltage to the channels and the difference in
channel currents is then proportional to the product of the
two pulse heights. The maximum speed of operation is limited
by the FET charging time to about 10–20 $n$sec. Radeka describes two current amplifier circuits to follow the circuit of
Fig. 7.14 for different speeds of operation, and the performance figures of these systems are listed in Table 7.2.

For more accurate particle discrimination such as is required for distinguishing between He^3 and He^4 ions over a
wide range of energies, it is necessary to make a close approximation to the true energy-loss formula. An empirical study of
the range-energy relations for protons and alpha particles in
silicon (Fig. 1.2) shows that they are well approximated by a
power law. Several circuits have now been designed which
allow analogue multiplication of pulse heights raised to a
variable exponent. Deighton and Sayle[38] have designed a

TABLE 7.2

Pulse Amplitude Multiplier Performance

Multiplier design	*A*	*B*
Solution time	0·1 sec.	20 nsec
Pulse length range	0·1–2 sec.	20–100 nsec
X-input maximum	1·5 V	1·5 V
Y-input maximum	0·6 mA	1·5 V
Output to current amplifier (max.)	125 μA	250 μA
Residual signal, for $x = x$ max, y = 0.	<0·3%	<3%

From Radeka[37]

small computer capable of producing an output signal V_0 from up to four input pulse amplitudes, W, X, Y and Z such that

$$V_0 = (W \pm aX \pm b)^\alpha (cY \pm dZ \pm e)^\beta \qquad (7.16)$$

where a, b, c, d, e, α and β are independently variable. This circuit requires 3 μsec input pulses and can handle about 3000 operations per second. It has been successfully used[39] for particle discrimination with a silicon dE/dx and E combination, setting $W = Y = \Delta E$, $X = (E - \Delta E)$, $Z = 0$, $\beta = 1$ and adjusting a and α until a constant output was obtained for particles of a wide range of energies. It was found very convenient to store the output signals in an X-Y storage oscilloscope in order to accumulate data over a period of time and be able to inspect it visually.

Goulding and his collaborators[40] have published a rather more simple circuit, similarly based on logarithmic elements for producing the expression

$$V_0 = E^{1·73} - (E - \Delta E)^{1·73} \qquad (7.17)$$

which gives an output, V_0, characteristic of the particle type. This formula is derived from the empirical range-energy relation: range proportional to $E^{1·73}$. Their circuit requires pulses 3 μsec wide and is capable of handling up to $5·10^4$ pulses per second.

(c) Particle identification by time of flight

A method of particle identification which is in some ways complementary to the methods described above is by measurement of the time of flight of the particles over a fixed path. Such a method is most accurate for low energy heavy ions, for which it may be very difficult to obtain a suitably thin dE/dx detector.

For non-relativistic velocities the relation between flight time and energy is

$$t = 71 \cdot 92(M/E)^{\frac{1}{2}} . d \qquad (7.18)$$

where t is the flight time in $n$sec, M is the particle mass, E is the energy in MeV and d is the flight path in metres.

Mass and energy determination using the time of flight method has been described by Gemmell[41] and by Williams, Kiker and Schmitt.[42] A typical arrangement of the electronics is shown in Fig. 7.15. A pulsed accelerator beam is required

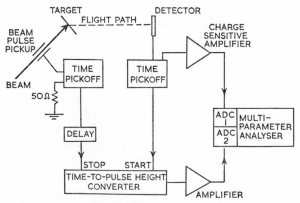

FIG. 7.15 A typical time-of-flight arrangement for semiconductor detectors used by WILLIAMS, KIKER and SCHMITT[42]

and for optimum results a pulse duration of less than 1 $n$sec is desirable. A timing signal is derived either from the arrival of the beam itself, using an electrostatic pickup cylinder, or from the r.f. system which deflects the beam. Simultaneous fast-slow amplification (see Section 7.2(e)) provides the time signal for the arrival of the particle at the detector and a measure of its energy. The difference in time between the two time signals is a measure of the particle velocity and is converted to a voltage output signal by means of a fast time-to-pulse-height converter (such as the ORTEC model 263). The energy and velocity signals may be fed to a pair of analogue-to-digital converters in a two-parameter pulse height analyser. Alternatively the time pulse can be squared and multiplied by the energy pulse in an analogue multiplier such as those described in Section 7.3(b). The resulting pulse would then be proportional to the particle mass and could be used as a gating signal for the energy spectrum.

Gemmell[41] showed that it is possible to separate B^{10}, C^{12} and C^{13} ions using a flight path of only 63 cm. Since the separation depends only upon mass and not upon charge, particles of the same mass, such as He^3 and tritons, are not separated. As a rule, however, they would emerge with widely different energies from most reactions and could be distinguished in the energy spectrum.

7.4 Electronics for complex systems

(a) *Small arrays*

A number of applications call for the use of up to ten detectors simultaneously, either in a close linear array, for instance with a magnetic spectrometer, or spaced apart for measurements of the yield at different angles to the beam in experiments with a particle accelerator. In such cases it is necessary to record both the pulse height and position of the detector and sometimes also the time of arrival of the signal. The electronics and recording system can then become relatively complicated, although there are several ways in which unnecessary duplication can be avoided.

Separate pre-amplifiers, which may be transistorized for compactness and low power consumption, may be used with a single main amplifier, pulse shaping network, and calibration system. Provision should be made for each pre-amplifier to give, in addition to the amplified pulse, a coding signal which governs the storage of the information. With a multidimensional pulse height analyser this coding signal controls the section of the memory in which the digitized pulse height information is stored.

In order to minimize the counting rate which reaches the pulse height analyser a biased amplifier is desirable for each detector channel so that unwanted small pulses can be rejected. Background pulses due to long-range particles can then be largely eliminated by using relatively thin fully-depleted detectors. Unwanted pulses due to short range particles can, of course, be removed by suitable absorbers in front of each detector. Those pulses which are of interest can then be mixed and fed to the pulse height analyser without introducing an excessive dead time. Pulses which arrive simultaneously at two detectors must be rejected. A routing signal generated in each detector channel provides the appropriate address signal for the storage of spectra in separate sections of the analyzer memory. Such a system for up to 16 detectors, has been built by Hiebert and Gallagher,[43] adapting for the purpose the transistorised biased amplifier design of Goulding and Landis of Lawrence Radiation Laboratory at Berkeley, California. The temperature stability of gain and bias control in this circuit has been tested and found to be excellent. A coincidence condition can be imposed with a further detector, such as a gamma-ray counter, so that only the coincident particle spectra will be recorded. With minor modification this system will allow eight separate dE/dx and E detector combinations to be operated simultaneously, the mixed signals being multiplied using a single fast analogue multiplier of the type designed by Radeka (Section 7.3(b)).

Bilaniuk, Hamann and Marsh[44] have described an alternative system which uses only two fast amplifiers for a number of detectors. The detectors are linked by small inductances so as to form a lumped parameter delay line with a delay of the order 10^{-7} sec between adjacent stages. The difference in time of arrival of the signals at the two ends of the line can be used to determine the position of the counter from which they originated. Figure 7.16 shows their arrangement schematically. Since fast amplifiers are required in this method the signal to noise ratio and therefore also the energy resolution are relatively poor.

For a small number of closely-spaced surface barrier detectors, conveniently prepared by simultaneous evaporation of gold or to a single silicon wafer, Dearnaley has found a simple

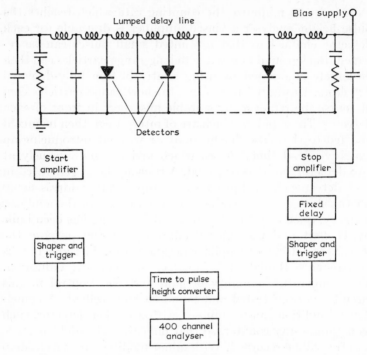

FIG. 7.16 Schematic diagram of the lumped delay-line circuit used by BILANIUK, HAMANN and MARSH[44] for a 20-unit array of semiconductor detectors

method of distinguishing pulses from separate counters involving the use of only one low-noise amplifier. This is connected to the end detector of the group, while use is made of the slight surface conductance between adjacent detectors to provide coupling to the others. With typical spacings of about 0·1 mm between detectors 1 cm in length this coupling resistance is of the order 10MΩ. The pulse rise time is thus governed by the total series resistance together with the small detector capacitance, which is typically a few pF. The pulse shaping network of the main amplifier, which will have time constants near 1 μsec, will then disperse the pulse heights according to the position of the detector relative to the end one. Since the array is designed for use with a magnetic spectrometer only a few small bands of energy, corresponding to different particle types, are possible for particles which arrive at the focus. Different types of particle can thus be distinguished and in this system good energy resolution is retained. In the case of separated counters, for instance in an angular distribution experiment, the same method can be applied if the counters are linked by appropriate resistances.

The storage of data from an array of semiconductor detectors presents new problems. In the case of only one or two detectors it may be feasible to have the data read out of the pulse height analyser to an electric typewriter for notebook storage. When we have eight or sixteen detectors, each capable of yielding a spectrum occupying 100 to 256 channels in as little as three minutes of experiment time some other means of recording is required.

For up to four detectors, punched paper tape offers a relatively economic solution. It is easy to feed this to a computer for data reduction, but the total number of events which may be stored on a single tape is limited.

The use of magnetic tape greatly improves the speed of recording and allows much greater storage capacity. The first magnetic tape storage systems for nuclear data used analogue recording, but the poor resolution of this method (of the order of 6 per cent) limits its potentiality. Digital recording overcomes this objection, and a typical arrangement of the system might be as follows. The one or more signals associated with a given detection event are reduced to binary numbers by analogue to digital converters (see Section 7.4(d)) and these numbers are grouped into a single binary 'word' which is fed into a buffer store. The purpose of this is to accept information which arrives in a random manner and supply it to the tape recorder at a more nearly uniform rate so as to give a good packing density. When large fluctuations in input rate occur it is possible to match the tape speed continuously to the mean input count rate. The tape itself may be narrow ($\frac{1}{4}$ in.), or wide (1 in.) in which case as many as 25 recording tracks are possible, corresponding to 25 bits of information for each word. The system employed at A.E.R.E., Harwell, makes use of 7200 foot reels of 1 in. 16-track tape with a maximum density of 200 words per inch giving a maximum capacity of over 10^7 words (or events).

The analysis of recorded information is carried out by playing back the tape at high speed (50–150 in./sec) and sorting the events in a magnetic core memory, typically of about 1000 channels capacity. The contents of the store can then be displayed on a cathode-ray tube, transferred to punched cards, or fed directly to a computer (see Section 7.4(d)). Since the replay time will usually be much shorter than the record time the analyser and computer are in use for the minimum time, and can accept tapes from a variety of experiments. The tape forms a convenient permanent storage of the information.

It is not possible in this method to inspect all the information which is being recorded during the course of the experiment, and it is customary to use a small pulse-height analyser to monitor part of the data from the detectors and so check that the experiment is proceeding satisfactorily.

(c) Large arrays

Of the methods mentioned above only the lumped delay line system of Bilaniuk et al.[17] is practicable for numbers of detectors between 20 and 100. Operation near the upper end of this range is likely to be difficult owing to the effect of a long line on the pulse rise time and amplitude, which would probably make it difficult to retain adequate signal to noise ratio in the system. However, such large detector arrays are often required for applications in which accurate energy determination is not essential, for instance in the focal plane of a broad-range magnetic spectrometer. Here the position of the detector determines the particle momentum and relatively poor energy resolution then suffices to identify its mass. A good deal of energy resolution and stability in the amplification system can thus be dispensed with, in order to simplify the requirements. Transistor detectors, each with a gain of about 100, would be valuable in these circumstances. The counting rate in each detector is likely to be very low so that a long output pulse is acceptable; cadmium sulphide detectors have been prepared with a charge multiplication factor of nearly 10^3, and an output signal duration of around 10^{-3} sec. Both these types of detector would produce output signals of nearly a volt in amplitude for particles of a few MeV and with such magnitudes a number of scanning and pulse storage systems are feasible. One is to connect each detector output to a small unit in a matrix of secondary electron emitting surfaces which can be scanned by an electron beam. The rapid discharge of the potential to its equilibrium value under electron bombardment provides an output signal through the capacitance to a common back-plate, as in an iconoscope. The random arrival of signals at the detectors is thereby converted to a sequential form related to the position of each detector in the array. Thus the signals from 500 detectors could be displayed linearly on a 500 channel pulse height analyser in a manner simply related to the energy spectrum of the particles being studied. Alternatively, pulse coding and magnetic storage methods can be devised.

A related problem is that of a two-dimensional array, or mosaic, in which it is required to know the spatial distribution of charged particles over an area. This may arise, for instance, in the focussing of a very weak beam of particles. Here no energy resolution is called for in the detection system, though the signals must of course be distinguishable from background noise and pickup from the accelerator. Valentin[45] has used a matrix of 100 semiconductor junction detectors, each with a transistorized pulse amplifier which stores the pulses in a low-capacitance integration capacitor. A high impedance commutator scans the capacitors and the amplified commutator output is fed to the bright-up of a cathode ray tube. Tepper, Miller and Kycia[46] have described a somewhat similar beam profile indicator for a high energy accelerator. Their device makes use of an array of 32 lithium-drifted silicon detectors arranged in the form of a cross of dimensions 2·5 in. The counts from each detector are fed continuously to a multi-channel scaler which provides a live analogue display of the beam which is of great value in setting up an experiment. A large number of counts were anticipated and so each detector was connected to a separate transistorised charge-sensitive preamplifier. Signals above the noise and background level trigger a discriminator, the output of which opens a gate to allow a fixed amount of charge to be deposited on a low-leakage capacitor. A commutator periodically connects a common analogue-to-digital converter to each tempory storage capacitor in turn, discharging it and generating a train of digital pulses corresponding to the number of counts received in that detector. These pulses are routed into a conventional pulse-height analyser, with an appropriate address advance signal applied between each successive train. A similar electronic system could be used with a much large detector array for a broad-range magnetic spectrometer if detectors with a high charge-multiplication factor could be prepared in quantity, and if almost all energy discrimination could be sacrificed. Broad[47] has suggested an alternative and simpler system for indicating the profile of more intense beams of relatively smaller dimensions. An etched slice of n-type silicon has at its surface acceptor states. Thus, in 5000 Ω cm n-type silicon the intrinsic potential difference of 0·6 volt between surface and interior will produce a depletion layer about 25μ in thickness. In the absence of any conducting deposit the surface has a very high sheet resistance. Following ionization in the shallow depletion layer, positive charge will accumulate at a small local area on the surface and only slowly leak away. It is feasible that this charge could be detected by a conventional orthicon electron scanning process and the amplified signal could then be used to display the distribution of ionization on a cathode ray tube. Charge will be collected at the surface until the surface potential is appreciably reduced. The spatial resolution is governed by the surface sheet resistance and capacitance, and the scanning frequency. If the sheet resistance is 10^8 Ω per square and the scanning frequency 10 kc/s, a point accumulation of charge may spread to an area of the order 0·1 mm². Roughly 10^6 electrons are necessary to raise the potential of such an area by 0·1 volts so that the method is restricted to beams of a fairly high ionization density.

(d) Data handling by computer

The handling of data from even a pair of semiconductor detectors in a time-of-flight arrangement can be very formidable. Accurate energy determination may require 1000 channels of information, and velocity determination from the time of flight probably requires 100 channels, so for the two detectors we need 2.10^5 channels. The experiment may call for the detection of coincidences between the emission of different combinations of particles which therefore involve different intervals in their times of arrival at the detectors. It is almost impossible to devise a system to handle such a mass of data without 'on-line' or immediate reduction by automatic computer. The alternative would be storage of the information on magnetic tape for subsequent analysis by repeated passes through a programmed read-out and computation system. This would not allow the results to be inspected during the course of the experiment and could easily lead to a waste of expensive accelerator time.

Present day acceleration costs are so high (£100 to £500 per hour) and the experiments being devised are becoming so complex that notebook data storage and desk calculator computation are no longer efficient means of handling the information. The course of the experiment may depend on the result of a computation made from the initial data, or in other words, feedback from the data to the experiment is required. Magnetic tape storage is then unsuitable, and on-line computers are increasingly coming into use as the most efficient means of conducting experiments. Coupled with a wide variety of display facilities such a system can allow a close control of a complex experiment and allow the experimenter freedom from routine operations so that he can attend to the unexpected. The possibility is presented of providing feedback from the computer to the accelerator, for instance to alter the beam energy in response to a command based on the on-line reduction of initial data, or from the computer to the experiment, for example to change the angle between a pair of detectors in order to search for coincident particle groups.

Pulse-height analysers have simultaneously been developed to carry out simple arithmetical operations on stored data, such as background subtraction, integration of counts within a peak, etc., these operations being brought about by switches on the front panel. The important difference between such a facility and a computer lies in the fact that the analyser stores only data in its memory whereas the computer can store instructions as well, so that operations on the data and their sequence can be made very flexible and numerous simply by alteration of the control programme. It is also possible to share time in a computer between two or more experiments if the rate of data input is not too large or between experimental data-handling and mathematical computation.

A typical computer system for the multi-parameter analysis of data will comprise analogue-to-digital converters (ADC's), time identifying or coincidence circuits, the memory or store, the control system and the input and output system to which are linked various display devices. It may clarify the description if we consider some of these elements in further detail. The input pulse height is converted to a digital pulse train by the ADC and the most common method, due to Wilkinson,[48] is to charge a capacitor to a voltage proportional to the maximum of the pulse height. This capacitor is then discharged linearly using a constant current while regular 'clock pulses' are counted until the capacitor voltage reaches zero. Clock frequencies of several megacycles are commonly used, leading to conversion times of the order of some tens of microseconds. The maximum number of channels feasible by this method is about 4000 (2^{12}) and a corresponding number of 'words' is required in the computer memory. Time digitizing is usually more difficult as the time intervals to be measured may be only a few nanoseconds. Time 'expansion' can be effected by rapidly charging a small capacitor at a linear rate during the time interval to be measured, and then discharging it very slowly, again with a constant current, while clock pulses are counted. Alternatively a 'time vernier' can be made by starting one train of short clock pulses on arrival of the first signal and a second train of slightly different frequency on arrival of the second. The time that elapses before a coincidence of the clock pulses gives a measure of the time interval between the start of the two trains. Present computer memory systems are mostly of the magnetic core or magnetic thin film variety, and typical speeds of computation are between 3 and 40 μsec for memory sizes of 4000 to 64,000 words. Control programmes are usually fed in by punched paper tape or cards. Input and output systems provided may comprise an electric typewriter, line-printer, magnetic tape recorder and replay system, card-punch and a cathode-ray tube (CRT). The visual display which the last facility allows is most valuable and many different types of representation of the contents of the memory are feasible, such as isometric display of a three-dimensional array of data points, representing pulse-height, number of counts and time for example. A useful facility in conjunction with the CRT display is a 'light-pen' which is a hand-held photo-electric device which can be placed in contact with the visible display in order to feed back information to the computer. The pen can recognize a given channel by the time synchronization of the display sweep and thus the experimenter may define that region of a displayed spectrum which is to be integrated, or hold the pen against a peak of the spectrum and, on the appropriate instruction, the corresponding particle energy can be displayed, being computed from an earlier calibration. One form of CRT display sometimes used is termed a 'twinkle box'. In this the dead time of the system, arising from the time required to scan the memory, is minimised by recording briefly each event as it is stored. The display appears as a succession of bright points in the appropriate positions of the CRT.

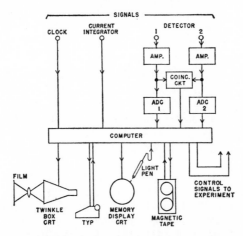

Fig. 7.17 A typical on-line computer facility[49] used with a pair of semiconductor detectors

A typical on-line computer system[49] for two-parameter analysis of data is shown schematically in Fig. 7.17 and has been in use at Brookhaven National Laboratory for several years. Such systems together with their control and display equipment allow more imaginative use to be made of the potentialities of semiconductor detector arrays. Unexpected results of an experiment can be rapidly investigated and the flexibility of the control makes it less likely than with fixed-programme analysis that an unforeseen behaviour of the experiment could be overlooked. It seems likely that most groups using or planning large particle accelerator installations will find the need for a computer-based data handling system in order to make effective use of the machine.

REFERENCES

For this chapter

1. Cottini, C., Gatti, E., Giannelli, G. and Rossi, G., *Il Nuovo Cimento*, **3**, 473 (1956).
2. Chase, R. L., Higinbotham, W. A. and Miller, G. L., *I.R.E. Trans. Nucl. Sci.*, **NS-8**, No. 1, 147 (1961).
3. Blankenship, J. L. and Borkowski, C. J., *I.R.E. Trans. Nucl. Sci.*, **NS-8**, No. 1, 17 (1961).
4. Goulding, F. S. and Hansen, W. L., *Nucl. Instr. & Methods*, **12**, 249 (1961).
5. Goulding, F. S., *I.E.E.E. Trans. Nucl. Sci.*, **NS-11**, No. 3, 177 (1964).
6. Chase, R. L. and Kane, J. V., unpublished work described by Bromley, D. A., *I.R.E. Trans. Nucl. Sci.*, **NS-9**, No. 3, 135 (1962).
7. Fabri, G. and Gatti, E., *Nucl. Instr. & Methods*, **15**, 237 (1962).
8. Fairstein, E., *I.R.E. Trans. Nucl. Sci.*, **NS-8**, No. 1, 129 (1961).
9. Gillespie, A. B. *Signal, Noise and Resolution in Nuclear Counter Amplifiers*, Pergamon Press (London, 1953).
10. Blankenship, J. L. and Borkowski, C. J., *I.R.E. Trans. Nucl. Sci.*, **NS-9**, No. 3, 181 (1962).
11. Ammerlaan, C. A. J., *Mem. Soc. Roy. Sci. de Liège*, X, No. 2, 211 (1964).
12. Gatti, E. and de Martini, F., *Nuclear Electronics*, II, 265, I.A.E.A. (Vienna, 1962).
13. Fairstein, E., *Nucleonics*, **20**, No. 8, 148 (1962).
14. Emmer, T. L., *I.R.E. Trans. Nucl. Sci.*, **NS-9**, No. 3, 305 (1962).
15. Jonasson, L. G., *Nucl. Instr. & Methods*, **26**, 104 (1964).
16. Shockley, W., *Proc. I.R.E.*, **40**, 1365 (1952).

17. Radeka, V., *I.E.E.E. Trans. Nucl. Sci.*, **NS-11**, No. 3, 358, (1964).
18. van der Ziel, A., *Proc. I.R.E.*, **50**, 1808 (1962) and *Proc. I.E.E.E.*, **51**, 461 and 1670 (1963).
19. Blalock, T. V., *I.E.E.E. Trans. Nucl. Sci.*, **NS-11**, No. 3, 365 (1964).
20. Smith, A. J., *A.E.R.E. Harwell Report* No. **R 4379** (1963).
21. Wintenberg, R. E. and Pierce, J. F., *Univ. of Tennessee Elec. Eng. Dept. Report*, No. **11**, Oct. 1963.
22. Dearnaley, G. and Whitehead, A. B., *Nucl. Instr. & Methods*, **12**, 205 (1961).
23. Williams, C. W. and Biggerstaff, J. A., *Nucl. Instr. & Methods*, **25**, 370 (1964).
24. Dodge, W. R., Domen, S. R., Hirshfield, A. T. and Hoppes, D. D., *I.E.E.E. Trans. Nucl. Sci.*, **NS-11**, No. 3, (1964).
25. Walter, F. J., *Proc. Asheville Conf.*, NAS-NRC Publication No. **871**, 237 (1961).
26. Prior, A. C., *J. Phys. and Chem. of Solids*, **12**, 175 (1959).
27. Tove, P. A. and Falk, K., *Nucl. Instr. & Methods*, **29**, 66 (1964).
28. Chase, R. L., *NAS-NRC Publication* **871**, 221 (1961). Ed. Dabbs, J. W. T. and Walter, F. J.
29. Amsel, G., Baruch, P. and Smulkowski, O., *Nucl. Instr. & Methods*, **8**, 92 (1960).
30. Funsten, H. O., *I.R.E. Trans. Nucl. Sci.*, **NS-9**, No. 3, 190 (1962).
31. Scheer, J. A., *Nucl. Instr. & Methods*, **22**, 45 (1963).
32. Ammerlaan, C. A. J., Rumphorst, R. F. and Koerts, L. A. Ch., *Nucl. Instr. & Methods*, **22**, 189 (1963).
33. Seagrave, J. D., *private communication*.
34. Wegner, H. E., *I.R.E. Trans. Nucl. Sci.*, **NS-8**, No. 1, 103 (1961).
35. Stokes, R. H., *Rev. Sci. Instr.*, **31**, 768 (1960).
36. Vincent, C. H. and Kaine, D., *I.R.E. Trans. Nucl. Sci.*, **NS-9**, No. 3, 327 (1962).
37. Radeka, V., *I.E.E.E. Trans. Nucl. Sci.*, **NS-11**, No. 1, 302 (1964).
38. Deighton, M. O. and Sayle, E. A., *Proc. I.E.E.* (to be published).
39. Morrison, G. C., Gale, N. H., *et al.*, *Proc. Conf. on Direct Interactions and Nuclear Reaction Mechanisms*, Padua 1962, ed. Clementel E. and Villi C., Gordon and Breach, New York, (1963).
40. Goulding, F. S., Landis, D. A., Cerny, J. and Pehl, R. H., *I.E.E.E. Trans. Nucl. Sci.*, **NS-11**, No. 3, 388 (1964).

41. Gemmell, D. S., *I.E.E.E. Trans. Nucl. Sci.*, **NS-11**, No. 3, 409 (1964).
42. Williams, C. W., Kiker, W. E. and Schmitt, H. W., *Rev. Sci. Instr.*, **35**, 116 (1964).
43. Hiebert, R. D. and Gallagher, J. D., *private communication*.
44. Bilaniuk, O. M., Marsh, B. B., Hamann, A. K. and Heurtley, J. C., *Nucl. Instr. & Methods*, **13**, 906 (1961)
45. Valentin, F., *Nuclear Electronics*, III, 249, I.A.E.A. (Vienna, 1962).
46. Tepper, L., Miller, G. L., and Kycia, T., *I.E.E.E. Trans. Nucl. Sci.*, **NS-11**, No. 3, 431 (1964).
47. Broad, D. A. G., *private communication*.
48. Wilkinson, D. H., *Proc. Camb. Phil. Soc.*, **46**, 508 (1950).
49. Kane, J. V. and Spinrad, R. J., *Nucl. Instr. & Methods*, **25**, 141, (1963).

For general reading

Gillespie, A. B., *Signal, Noise and Resolution in Nuclear Counter Amplifiers*, Pergamon Press (London, 1953).
Elmore, W. C. and Sands, M., *Electronics*, National Nuclear Energy Series, Div. 5, 1, McGraw-Hill (New York, 1949).
Lewis, I. A. D. and Wells, F. H., *Millimicrosecond Pulse Techniques*, Pergamon Press (London, 1954).
Chase, R. L., *Nuclear Pulse Spectrometry*, McGraw-Hill (New York, 1961).

CHAPTER 8

APPLICATIONS OF SEMICONDUCTOR
DETECTORS IN NUCLEAR PHYSICS

8.1 Introduction

Having now considered in some detail the performance which can be expected from various types of semiconductor detector and the ancillary electronics, we are in a position to discuss how they may best be applied to a variety of measurements. The purpose of this chapter is to guide the user in assessing the potential advantages of semiconductor counters and in deciding which detector structure will be the most suitable. The material is therefore classified according to the types of measurement which can be made. In each case factors which render semiconductor counters preferable or inferior to other types of counter will be stressed, while specific experiments will be described only in so far as they illustrate the points under discussion. Already any full account of experiments which have been carried out with semiconductor detectors would be both lengthy and tedious.

Throughout this chapter the term 'junction detector' will be used generally for both surface barrier and diffused junction detectors, as distinct from conduction counters. Most of the applications described in this chapter are for silicon junction counters, although the most striking new developments are taking place in the field of gamma-ray studies with lithium-drifted germanium detectors. These give every indication of revolutionizing gamma spectrometry just as silicon detectors have done in the case of charged-particle spectrometry over the past few years.

8.2 Alpha-particle spectrometry

Owing to the very strong dependence of the nuclear potential barrier penetrability on the energy release in alpha decay the energies of alpha particles from radioactive sources always lie between about 4 and 10 MeV. The range of such particles in solids is very low and therefore well suited to detection by a shallow *p-n* junction counter of silicon.

Two types of measurement are generally important; these are energy determination and flux measurement, possibly for weak groups of particles in the presence of large numbers of others with closely similar energy. The two chief purposes of such measurements are the determination and quantitative analysis of alpha-active elements, and the study of the nuclear properties of heavy nuclei by elucidation of their alpha-particle and gamma-ray decay schemes. To quote from a recent paper by a group[1] with much experience in these fields: 'Until some years ago, the ionization chamber was the instrument that best fitted the above-mentioned requirements. The recent development of solid state detectors with an improvement of the sensitive area of the detectors from some mm^2 to some cm^2 and with optimum resolution (1 cm^2–17 keV, 4 cm^2–40 keV, and 9 cm^2–80 keV) together with their relative simplicity of construction and operation limit the application of the ionization chamber to the field of measurement of elements with half-life higher than 10^6 years or in general to radioactive alpha sources of very low specific activity. In the field of measurements in which the timing of the detectors is important, like half-lives of excited levels or angular correlation measurements, semiconductor detectors are superior.' For weak sources spread over an extended area the ionization chamber retains a great advantage.

Two of the factors determining the energy resolution which can be achieved with a semiconductor detector are electrical noise, in both detector and amplifier, and trapping effects in the silicon. Since a higher bias voltage causes increased detector noise but reduces trapping effects, owing to a decrease in transit time, it is necessary to find a compromise. This compromise will vary from one detector to another, depending on the leakage current and the density and type of trapping centres. Signal to noise ratio in the amplifier can be optimized as discussed in Chapter 7. So as to obtain the maximum collecting field and the minimum volume of depletion layer for space-charge generation it is necessary to use silicon of relatively low resistivity. Thus 100 Ω cm n-type, or 300 Ω cm p-type silicon with an applied bias of 50 V gives a depletion layer of about 50 microns in which the mean collecting field is 10^4 V/cm. This depth is roughly twice the range of 5 MeV alphas in silicon. Too shallow a depth in large-area counters must, however, be avoided since the capacitance may then become too high for a good signal to noise ratio to be obtained. In order to minimize the density of trapping and recombination centres, silicon of high and uniform minority carrier lifetime should be used.

The excellent linearity of the output of junction counters with particle energy makes calibration of the equipment simple and accurate. This is, however, not true if the counter has an appreciable window thickness; surface barrier counters or shallow-diffused junctions should be used.

In measurements of the intensities of close groups of alpha particles it is important that the low-energy tail of the pulse-height spectrum should be as low as possible. It is necessary to mask off the edge of the detector, where an irregular collecting field leads to output pulses of reduced amplitude. This collimation must not introduce scattering from the edge of the defining aperture. Effects due to the 'pile-up' of pulses in the electronics must be minimized. Chetham-Strode, Tarrant and Silva[2] have studied these and other factors in detail and obtained a ratio of peak to background in the Cm[244] spectrum of 700:1, measured 200 keV below the main peak. Little change in the background was observed over a range of voltages and for different resistivities of silicon. This is surprising, since a likely cause of background near the peak is trapping of carriers for a time comparable with the amplifier response time. The amount of this effect will vary with the collecting field. Dearnaley did observe a significant improvement in peak:background with increasing bias voltage in a surface barrier detector, and obtained a value of 1200:1 at 300 volts bias measured 200 keV below the main peak of a Cm[244] spectrum. At greater separations from the peak the ratio is higher and values of 8000:1 were obtained in several detectors in the region 1 MeV below the peak energy. In measurements with very weak sources the alpha activity on the chamber walls must be minimized by suitable choice of material. The high purity of silicon is an advantage here compared with the material of, for instance, an ionization chamber.

Applications of energy and flux measurements for alpha particles include the assay of suitably thin samples of alpha-active material, for instance from reactor fuel elements. The effect of a high gamma-ray background from the specimen is minimized again by using a shallow depletion layer in the

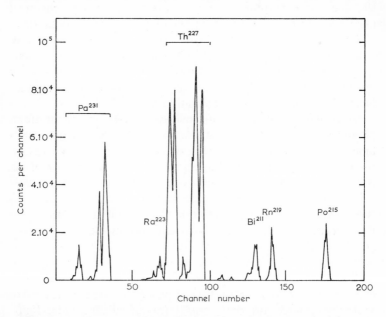

FIG. 8.1 Actinium series alpha-particle spectrum from an aged sample of Pa^{231}, observed with a 0·25 cm^2 silicon surface barrier detector; from CHETHAM-STRODE, TARRANT and SILVA[3]

detector. As an example, Fig. 8.1 shows the spectrum of an aged sample of Pa^{231} in which various daughter activities can be identified. In other cases the activity may be induced in an accelerator experiment; a spectacular instance of this has been the discovery of element 103, Lawrencium, produced by the capture of accelerated boron ions by californium (Ghiorso *et al.*[3]). After bombardment the target was rapidly conveyed to a silicon junction detector which enabled identification of the new element by its unique alpha spectrum and rate of decay.

Since junction detectors give a fast signal they may be used in a fast coincidence arrangement for alpha-gamma coincidence studies of radioactive sources in order to study the decay scheme. The gamma-ray energies are generally low so that the gamma detector may be either a second junction counter or a scintillation counter. In either case good counting geometry can be employed. The fast signal of the solid counter is here an advantage in comparison with an ionization chamber, while a magnetic spectrometer would generally have too small an acceptance angle. Scintillation counters would give insufficient energy resolution for this application.

If the nuclei of a radioactive target are aligned magnetically at low temperatures junction counters may be used to study the variation in yield of alphas, or of fission fragments, in different directions. The first application of junction counters, of germanium, was in fact made by Walter, Dabbs, Roberts and Wright[4] for this purpose, in 1958. Germanium surface-barrier detectors are well suited to low-temperature operation and the compactness, good energy resolution, fast response and relative insensitivity to magnetic fields are all valuable in this work.

8.3 Charged-particle spectrometry

Most of the measurements on charged-particle reactions in low-energy nuclear physics are carried out with electrostatic generators of the Van de Graaff type. These are commonly used to accelerate protons, deuterons, tritons, He[3] or alpha particles and a few machines have been adapted for lithium ion acceleration. Accelerated particle energies lie mainly between 0·5 and 6 MeV but in recent years the two-stage or Tandem Van de Graaff has doubled this range while three-stage machines are now under construction. These multistage machines can also accelerate heavy ions such as carbon, oxygen and nitrogen. For higher energies linear accelerators and cyclotrons are in use for both light and heavy particles. Most applications require a linear response with particle energy in a detector. Since the maximum depletion layer depth in a simple p-n junction counter is about 1 mm its useful range is to about 12 MeV for protons, 16 MeV for deuterons, 48 MeV for alphas and nearly 200 MeV for oxygen ions (see equation (1.6)). This covers most requirements in experiments with the lower energy machines. Lithium-drifted detectors have intrinsic layers of up to about 5 mm thickness, extending the range of linear response by over a factor of two in energy. Counters may, of course, be set at an angle to give a greater effective depth, while counters of sufficiently wide sensitive volumes may be used with particles incident parallel to the electrodes to obtain an effective depth of 1 cm or more. Alternatively, counters which are sensitive throughout their thickness may be stacked together in series. Silicon conduction counters, at low temperatures, have some applications for particles of range approaching 1 cm but these counters show at present rather too low an energy resolution. The range of operation of semiconductor counters is therefore much greater than that of gaseous counters, but less than that obtainable with a scintillator, which, therefore, is more useful for long-range particle experiments. In comparison with the scintillation counter there is, however, little or no dependence of the response on the type of particle detected: the scintillation counter shows severe saturation of response for heavy ions. Fig. 8.2 shows data from measurements by Halbert and Blankenship[5] and by Williams, Kiker and Schmitt[6] on the pulse-height from silicon surface-barrier detectors as a function of particle type. Bromine and iodine ions show a departure from the extrapolated alpha-particle calibration, but nitrogen ions do not. Some of the departure is due to the greater effect of the surface dead layer or window for short-range ions; some is due to a larger fraction of the energy loss being taken up by recoiling silicon nuclei, which at their low energies do not ionize very effectively, and some is due to a reduced collection efficiency for electron hole pairs from a region of dense ionization. The energy resolution of semiconductor detectors for heavy ions is worse than it is for lighter particles because of fluctuations in these three effects.

We have already seen that the high energy resolution is an

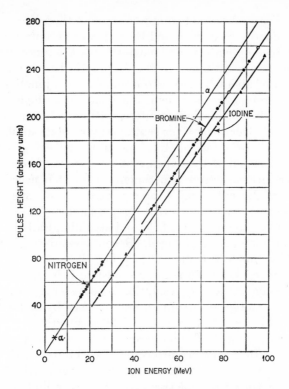

Fig. 8.2 The response of silicon surface-barrier
detectors to He⁴, N¹⁴, Br⁸⁰ and I¹²⁷ ions as a function
of energy

outstanding feature of the performance of junction detectors.
In particle accelerators the highest energy definition is provided by Van de Graaff generators, from which the spread in
particle energies rarely exceeds 1 part in 10³. An energy resolution approaching this can therefore be useful, though in many
cases a compromise must be made between the counting rate
required and the target thickness which can be tolerated
because of the energy spread introduced for both incident and
emerging particles. Unlike the case of a radioactive source,
the particles emitted at different angles from the target in an
accelerator experiment have different energies owing to
'kinetic spread', resulting from the forward momentum of the

incident beam. A second compromise must therefore be made between energy resolution and the detector acceptance angle. A slit-shaped detector in a plane normal to the beam direction gives the best counting geometry. In practical cases an energy resolution of about 30 keV is obtainable[7] with junction counters. This resolution is generally a great advantage in comparison with scintillation counters, with which it is difficult to achieve better than 4 per cent energy resolution. Magnetic analysis, as for the case of alpha-spectrometry, can give better energy resolution at the expense of solid angle of acceptance. However, in accelerator experiments it is often necessary to study particles extending over a wide range of energies. In most magnetic spectrometers this must be done by slow scanning, varying the magnetic field and assuming that the target condition remains unchanged. Recent broad-range instruments have made this unnecessary but these involve instead the optical scanning of a nuclear emulsion. It is far preferable, where the highest energy resolution is not essential, to display the whole energy spectrum simultaneously by pulse height analysis. Figure 8.3 shows a typical spectrum from a thin target mainly of Ca^{40} bombarded with 9.5 MeV protons, observed with a silicon surface-barrier counter. The linear response of junction detectors with energy, for particles which do not penetrate the depletion layer, makes calibration of the equipment both accurate and simple. This is a further advantage in comparison with methods involving magnetic analysis, in which hysteresis effects and a non-linear dependence of field or magnet current on particle energy are troublesome.

In accelerator experiments it is important to minimize the background of particles scattered from the walls of the target chamber or from the frame that supports the target, which will usually be prepared on a thin backing foil. It is necessary that the beam should enter through a well-designed collimator and, equally, the detectors should be collimated so as to observe particles from only the direction of the target. The beam, most of which will pass through the thin target with a certain amount of small-angle scattering, should be allowed to travel on down a long tube to avoid back-scattering. Figure 8.4 shows the design of a scattering chamber in which a number of junction counters can be set at different angles

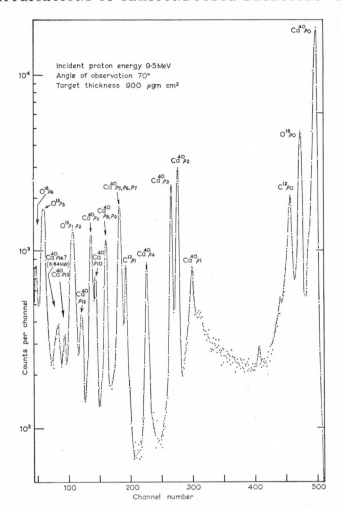

FIG. 8.3 Particle spectrum observed by POLETTI and THOMAS in
the bombardment of a thin Ca⁴⁰ target with 9·5 MeV protons. The
upper three peaks are due to elastic scattering from C¹², O¹⁶ and
Ca⁴⁰, and most of the remaining peaks are due to protons inelastic-
ally scattered from Ca⁴⁰. The spectrum was obtained in a time of
about 3 min. (From POLETTI, A. and THOMAS, M., priv. comm.)

around a target. Detector holders and collimators are mounted
in radial grooves and the whole upper plate of the chamber
may be rotated in order to study the reaction at other sets of

angles. The compactness of semiconductor detectors is an obvious advantage in the design of such equipment; only the nuclear emulsion has this virtue to a comparable degree. Despite precautions in beam collimation it is difficult to obtain a background appreciably less than 0·1 per cent of the intensity of a strong peak which is at a higher energy.

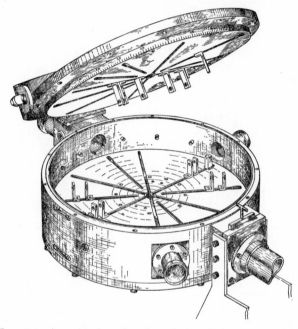

FIG. 8.4 A scattering chamber designed for use with an array of semiconductor detectors (reproduced by permission of ORTEC, Oak Ridge, Tenn., U.S.A.)

In measurements of inelastic scattering or Coulomb excitation the strong flux of elastically scattered particles can give a troublesome background. Here semiconductor detectors are inferior to methods using magnetic analysis, though it is possible to use a compact magnetic analyser of large solid angle of acceptance followed by a junction detector. This arrangement ensures that particles of the intense group do not enter the detector.

Junction detectors can in most cases replace with advantage the existing detectors used with magnetic spectrometers for heavy charged particles. Compared with scintillation counters they are simpler and essentially unaffected by magnetic fields, against which a photomultiplier tube must be shielded with iron. A linear array of counters can be used in place of a nuclear emulsion, if the problems of providing amplification and data handling for the output signals can be solved. Some methods of accomplishing this were described in Section 7.4.

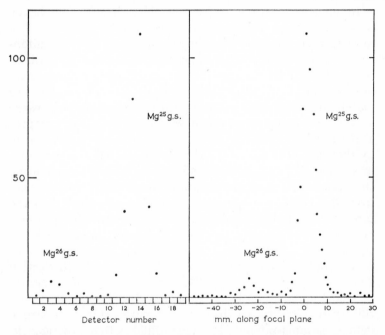

FIG. 8.5 Spectrum of protons from the Mg (d, p) reaction measured (on the left) with a 20-unit array of silicon junction detectors and (on the right) with a nuclear emulsion. In each case the detector was mounted at the focal plane of a magnetic spectrometer (After PARKINSON and BILANIUK[8])

In Fig. 8.5 the output of an array of 20 germanium surface barrier detectors, each 1 mm wide, is compared with the conventional nuclear emulsion in the focal plane of a magnetic spectrograph. In this work, by Parkinson and Bilaniuk,[8] an array of gold-doped germanium conduction counters was also tested; in both systems the detectors were cooled with liquid nitrogen. Silicon surface-barrier detectors may be used at room temperature for this application; a simple method[9] of preparing such an array is by evaporation of gold through a comb of wires on to an etched silicon wafer. Since a large signal is more important than good energy resolution in this application, transistor detectors or cadmium sulphide conduction counters giving charge amplification have a considerable advantage.

In nuclear reactions, especially those induced by heavy ions, a rich variety of particle types may be produced. The most powerful method of distinguishing them is by simultaneous measurement of dE/dx and E; discussion of this will be reserved until the next section, but simpler methods may often be sufficient. Adjustment of the depletion layer depth to match the range of a particle group under study will cause particles of longer range but lower ionization density to give a lower pulse height. An example of the use of this is given by the work of Cedarlund, Horn and Scolnick.[10] The neutron-producing H^3 (d, n) He^4 reaction was monitored by counting the associated alpha particles; protons of comparable energies from the H^2 (d, p) H^3 reaction, which also occurred in the target, were distinguished by operating the detector at a bias voltage sufficient only to give a depletion layer thickness equal to the alpha range. In other cases it may be necessary to use pulse shape discrimination, as described in Section 7.3(a), in order to cut out those particles which penetrate beyond the depletion layer. It should also be possible to use this system to remove background pulses due to a strong beta- or gamma-ray flux. It is more difficult to remove a background due to particles of higher energy but shorter range than those under study, for instance to observe 6 MeV protons in the presence of an alpha continuum extending to 20 MeV. This can, however, sometimes be accomplished with an appropriate absorber foil in front of the detector. Thus 0·007 in. of aluminium will reduce the maximum alpha energy to 2 MeV but leave the protons with 3 MeV in the above example. A judicious combination of absorber foil thickness and counter depletion layer depth can enable a group to be counted without background due to other radiations. Figure 8.6 shows a 7·5 MeV deuteron group from the B^{11} (Li^6, d) N^{15} reaction

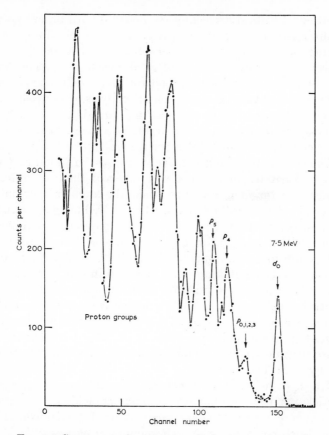

FIG. 8.6 Spectrum of protons and deuterons from the $B^{11} + Li^6$ reaction observed in a 15 000 ohm cm silicon surface barrier counter operated at 30V bias. Particles entered the detector through a 0.004 in. aluminium absorber which excluded alpha particles of up to 18 MeV. (From MORRISON, G. C., MILLER, P. D., GALE, N. H. and DEARNALEY, G., unpublished)

observed in a silicon surface-barrier counter of 15 000 Ω cm resistivity. The absorber foil of 0·004 in. of aluminium excludes scattered lithium ions and alphas, while the detector bias voltage, 30 V, was chosen to cut off the proton spectrum at 6·5 MeV. Such methods can, of course, allow the various groups in a complex spectrum to be identified. Simple control of the effective counter thickness by means of the bias voltage is often a great advantage in comparison with other types of counter. This control can be carried out remotely, for example during observation of the pulse-height spectrum from the detector. The three features of good energy resolution, linearity of response and simple control of the effective counter thickness enable, with pulse-height analysis, a very clear and rapid observation to be made of a charged-particle reaction and the suitability of a given target. This in itself can result in appreciable saving of accelerator time.

The compactness and relatively low cost of junction detectors make it feasible to use a number of them at different angles to a target in order to study the angular distribution of yield of charged particles. Besides reducing accelerator time in comparison with repeated measurement at different angles with one detector, the conditions of target and beam energy are uniform. Some of the difficulties of pulse amplification and data handling were discussed in Chapter 7.

The fast signal from junction detectors allows, with suitable electronic equipment, a high counting rate of the order 10^5 pulses per sec to be counted without gain shift[11]. This is an advantage compared with gaseous or scintillation detectors. Pulse shaping systems for high counting rates were considered briefly in Section 7.2(c).

The fast rise-time of junction detectors is also useful in particle-particle or particle-gamma coincidence measurements; here one or both detectors may be of the semiconductor type. Such coincidence measurements are necessary to elucidate nuclear decay schemes and to reduce background from other processes. Thus particle-gamma coincidence measurement can greatly simplify a complex gamma-ray spectrum and Fig. 8.7, from a paper by Almqvist, Kuehner and Bromley,[12] shows this very clearly. In this figure (a) shows the alpha spectrum from the Al^{27} (p, a) Mg^{24} reaction while (b) is the gamma-ray spectrum observed in a 5 in. by 4 in. NaI(Tl) scintillation crystal. By gating on the a_1 group to the first excited state of Mg^{24} the coincident gamma-ray spectrum (c) was obtained; this corresponds to a pure 1·37 MeV gamma ray to the Mg^{24} ground state.

When a timing signal alone is required, without energy resolution, contoured junction detectors of the type described

FIG. 8.7 The upper spectrum (*a*), shows the Al^{27} (p, α) Mg^{24} reaction observed with a silicon junction detector, while (*b*) shows the complex gamma spectrum resulting from the Al^{27} + p reactions, observed with a 5 in. x 4 in. NaI(Tl) scintillator. When the gamma spectrum was gated in coincidence with the $α_1$ group in the particle spectrum the pure 1.37 MeV gamma-ray spectrum (*c*) was obtained; from ALMQVIST, KUEHNER and BROMLEY[12]

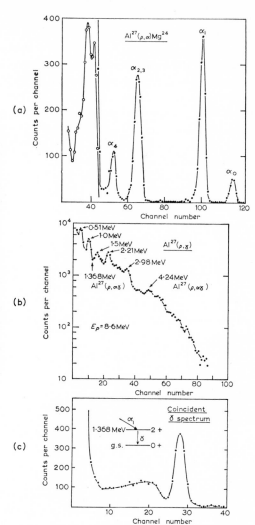

by Huth and his colleagues[13] offer a spectacularly fast response. Internal pulse amplification by factors of between 10 and 100 have been achieved with such detectors, when operated with a collecting field approaching that which causes avalanche breakdown ($1 \cdot 2 \times 10^5$ V/cm). The depletion layer thicknesses of the units studied by Huth have been about 200μ so that the rise time of the signal pulse may be expected to be of the order 1 $n$sec, assuming a carrier velocity of 4×10^7 cm/sec in p-type silicon at this field strength. Owing to the internal amplification no fast amplifier is required, and the detector output is capable of triggering a tunnel diode directly.[14]

The compact form of semiconductor detectors makes it simple to mount them for angular correlation studies, in

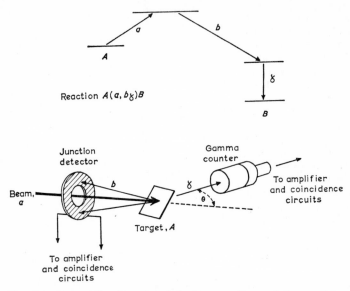

FIG. 8.8 An annular junction detector may be used for particle-gamma angular correlation studies. In the reaction A (a, b γ) B the (b, γ) correlation takes a very simple form if particle b is detected close to 180° to the incident beam; (After BROMLEY[15])

which the coincident yield is measured for different angles between two detectors (see Fig. 8.4). The analysis of such experiments is greatly simplified if one of the two detectors is set close to 0° or 180° to the incident beam. This is generally difficult, but Bromley[15] has described the application of an annular surface barrier detector to angular correlation experiments. In the arrangement illustrated in Fig. 8.8 the beam is directed through a hole at the centre of the silicon detector so that the latter receives particles emerging from the target at an angle close to 180° to the incident beam direction.

Thus for coincidence measurements junction counters have the advantages, in comparison with scintillation counters, of compactness and a better energy resolution. They have the disadvantage of producing a small output signal which requires amplification before it will operate a coincidence circuit. Amplifier arrangements for fast coincidence work were described in Section 7.2(e).

In general it may be said that nuclear spectrometry has two chief aims. The first is the collection of data about particular excited states of nuclei: their energies, angular momenta, parities, lifetimes, isotopic spin and so on. The hope of this study is that such information can eventually, as in the case of atomic spectroscopy, be fitted into a comprehensive theory of nuclear structure. The second aim is the study of nuclear reaction mechanisms: whether a given reaction proceeds by a direct interaction between single nucleons, by compound nucleus formation involving many nucleons, or by some intermediate process.

The range of bombarding energies made possible by the recent development of multistage electrostatic accelerators is much greater than was earlier available. As a result the Coulomb potential barrier can be overcome for all nuclei and excitation energies of up to about 30 MeV can be induced. In the heavier nuclei vast numbers of closely-spaced levels can be excited and if they are to be distinguishable very high detector energy resolution is required, matching that of the accelerator. Nuclear spectrometry under such conditions is practicable only if the data can be accumulated rapidly by means of a number of detectors operated simultaneously. Measurement of the lifetimes of excited states and analysis of complete decay schemes involve fast coincidence techniques; the potentially fast response of semiconductor counters is an important advantage here.

In much of the region of excitation now attainable nuclear levels are not well-separated, but overlap to a considerable degree. Fluctuations in reaction cross-sections then arise from statistical interference between the overlapping states, sometimes cumulative, sometimes destructive. Detailed analysis of the fluctuation about the mean can yield the average behaviour of a single level in that region. Study of the distribution of cross-section values can reveal the relative proportion of direct reaction and compound nucleus formation. Statistical analysis of cross-sections integrated over all angles can show the presence of intermediate structure. In all this type of work several hundred cross-section determinations are required, and at a variety of angles, in order that a statistical analysis may be accurately made over a representative sample. Here again the potentialities of semiconductor detectors can be well utilized; it would scarcely be practicable to use any other form of detector.

Thus the present trend in low-energy nuclear physics owes as much to the development of these detectors as it does to the newer types of accelerator. Together with the application of the electronic computer to on-line data processing, these factors have given a considerable impetus to experimental nuclear physics, likely to broaden considerably our understanding of nuclear processes and structure.

8.4 Identification of particle type

With the heavier bombarding particles and higher beam energies now available from nuclear accelerators many different types of particle may simultaneously be produced in an experiment. Thus, under lithium-ion bombardment, protons, deuterons, tritons, He^3 and He^4 particles are all likely to emerge from the target. The problem is then to identify the type of particle as well as the energy and flux, in cases for which the simple methods outlined in the previous section are inadequate. The simultaneous measurement of the rate of energy loss, dE/dx, and energy, E, in a compound system of a thin transmission counter and a counter which gives full absorption has been developed into a valuable technique for such requirements. Equation (1.2) shows that the product

$$E \times dE/dx \propto Mz^2[\log_e E + \text{const}] \qquad (8.1)$$

and therefore varies only slowly with energy, in the energy region in which charge-exchange effects are slight. The pulse height product from the two detectors can thus be used as a gating signal to discriminate between particles which differ in mass, M, or charge, z. The electronic instrumentation by which this operation may be carried out has been described in Section 7.3(b).

Two systems have been developed which employ semi-conductor counters; in one the counters are both of the semi-conductor type, and in the other dE/dx measurement is made by a thin-windowed gas proportional counter or ion chamber. In the first case, because the semiconductor transmission counter is very thin and can be close to the second counter, few particles are scattered so that they fail to be detected in both. Also, nearly ten times as many ionization events are produced in the solid counter compared with a gaseous one, for a given small energy loss; better resolution is therefore possible in the dE/dx pulse. Finally, the solid detector can be made with a negligible 'window' thickness.

Methods of fabricating thin fully-depleted silicon detectors for this type of work are described in Chapter 6. The difficulties lie mainly in the handling of very thin silicon wafers and in the provision of a suitably low-injecting electrode at the rear face. It is also important to avoid the channelling effects described in Section 1.2(a), since these may cause an appreciable spread in the transmission spectrum (see Fig. 1.4). The residual-energy detector in the combination may be either a p-n junction or a lithium-drifted device, depending upon the range of the particles to be detected. Figure 8.9 shows the combination of dE/dx and E detectors designed by Wegner.[16] Wegner[17] has demonstrated that channelling effects may govern the capability of such a system for resolving particles which are close in mass, and his results confirm the importance of avoiding the likelihood of channelling as far as possible by choosing an appropriate crystal orientation. Detector manufacturers are exhorted to follow this advice. The crystal orientation of the E detector, on the other hand, is of no importance.

In the second type of system a thin-windowed gas counter is used as the transmission counter, with a silicon detector operating inside the gas-filled volume. This type has the merit that the energy loss in the transmission counter can be adjusted by control of the gas pressure. In the proportional counter gas multiplication provides useful amplification of the small signal. The signal is not as fast as that from a solid counter, and now that fast pulse multiplication circuits have been developed (Section 7.3(b)) the semiconductor dE/dx

detector has a powerful advantage in this respect. Compound gaseous and solid detector systems for particle identification have been described by Chasman and Bromley,[18] Halbert,[19] and Anderson, Bromley and Sachs[20]; Fig. 8.10 shows the counter designed by Halbert.

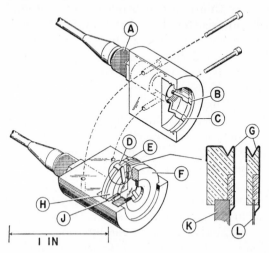

FIG. 8.9 Semiconductor dE/dx and E detector assembly. (A) miniature connector, (B), (C), (D), (E) gold foil junction contacts, (F) gold aperture assembly, (G) detail showing gold foil contacts, (H), (K) E detector, and (J), (L) dE/dx detector; from WEGNER[16]

The excellent particle separation which can be achieved by such means is well illustrated by Fig. 8.11, from the paper by Chasman and Bromley[18]; in this work the transmission detector was a gridded gas ionization chamber. By gating on separate peaks in the multiplier output spectrum different ions can be distinguished.

The conditions for optimum performance in a system of two junction detectors have been considered in detail by Wegner.[16] The presence of an absorbing layer in front of the energy detector increases the difference in pulse height between a given pair of groups, since dE/dx decreases with E. At the same time the peaks are broadened due to the statistical fluctuation in ionization in the absorber, discussed in Section

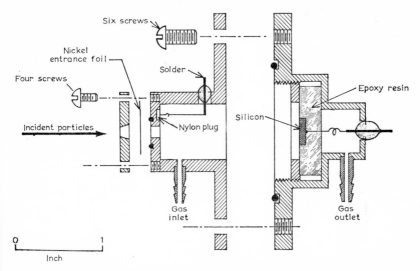

FIG. 8.10 dE/dx and E detector system used by HALBERT[19] for heavy ion identification. The dE/dx detector is here a thin-windowed gas proportional counter operating with an argon-CO_2 mixture at 6 cm Hg pressure. (An improved version with a longer anode wire is now in use)

1.4. When the pulse heights in the two detectors are added these fluctuations cancel for the total energy signal, but they remain for the dE/dx signal and therefore affect the product. The noise level is, of course, increased when signals from two detectors are added. The broadening due to statistical fluctuations in ionization in the transmission detector can be calculated from the formulae in Section 1.4. A useful approximate formula for thin silicon detectors has been given by Mollenauer, Wagner and Miller[21]; the resolution, R, as a percentage of the energy loss ΔE (in MeV) and measured as full width at half maximum of the distribution is given by

$$R = 7 \cdot 35 x z^{\frac{1}{2}}/\Delta E \tag{8.2}$$

where z is the charge of the particle and x is the detector thickness in thousandths of an inch. The line width for 8·78 MeV alphas in a 0·0017 inch thick detector cannot be less than 5 per cent, and in practice was found to be 7 per cent.

As an illustration of the value of particle discrimination systems such as have been described, Fig. 8.12 shows the gated

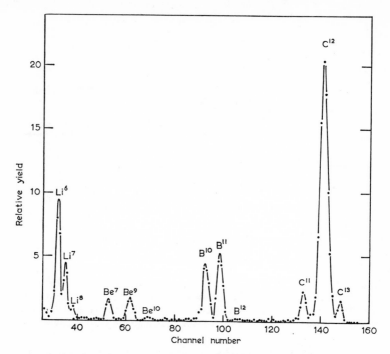

FIG. 8.11 The multiplied $E \times dE/dx$ pulse-height spectrum observed in studies of $C^{12} + C^{12}$ reactions at 125 MeV by CHASMAN and BROMLEY[18]. In this case the dE/dx detector was a gridded gaseous ionization chamber, with a silicon junction counter for energy measurement. Energy spectra for the individual isotopes are obtained by setting gates on the peaks of this spectrum

proton, deuteron and triton spectra observed simultaneously in one detector, by Wegner.[16] The reactions were induced by the bombardment of Be^9 with alphas of 28 MeV. Without discrimination of particle type it would clearly be almost impossible to interpret the charged-particle spectrum. In a similar way Chasman and Bromley[18] have been able to investigate several modes of break-up following the bombardment of a C^{12} target with energetic C^{12} ions.

In the case of lower energy heavy ions, for instance C^{12} and O^{16} ions of only a few MeV, it is impossible to make a suitably thin dE/dx detector as the range of such ions in silicon is only a few microns. Gemmell[22] has demonstrated the possibility of

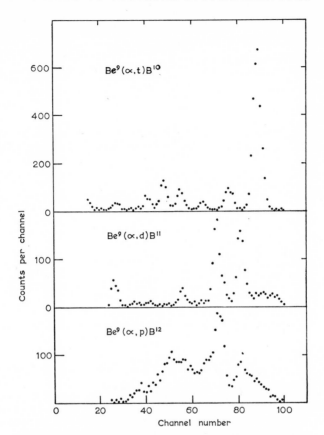

Fig. 8.12 Gated proton, deuteron and triton spectra in the $Be^9 + \alpha$ reactions observed using a semiconductor dE/dx and E particle identification system; from WEGNER[16]

a time-of-flight method for determination of particle mass in such cases. For a given energy the particle velocity is inversely proportional to the square root of the mass, so that simultaneous energy and velocity measurements allow the mass to be derived. Details of the electronic arrangement for such measurements have been given in Section 7.3(c). Using a flight path of 63 cm, an overall time resolution of 2 nsec and a 4 cm² silicon surface-barrier detector, Gemmell was able to distinguish particles of mass 1, 2, 4, 10, 12 and 13 with energies between 1 and 6 MeV, produced by the bombardment of a C¹² target with 7 MeV deuterons. This technique is a valuable complement to the method of identifying particle type by a two-detector telescope.

8.5 Polarization measurements

The investigation of the spin polarization of the products of a nuclear reaction is rapidly becoming more widely used as

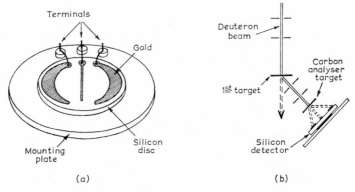

(a)   (b)

FIG. 8.13 A triple surface barrier detector for measurements of the polarization of charged particles from nuclear reactions, for example in C¹² (d, p) (MINGAY and DEARNALEY)

a particularly sensitive method for determining nuclear properties. The experiment is usually carried out by measurement of the asymmetry produced in a second scattering of the particles by an 'analyser' target of material for which the spin polarization properties are well known, such as helium or carbon. Detectors are placed symmetrically to left and right of this analyser and in the plane of the first reaction or scattering process. A triple silicon surface-barrier detector was constructed for this application by Dearnaley and Mingay, and is shown schematically in Fig. 8.13. In use, this detector is mounted 1-2 cm behind a carbon analyser foil, so that the two side counters accept particles scattered through 40°-60° while the centre counter acts as a monitor for the unscattered particles. Any asymmetry in the detector itself is measured by rotation about its axis through 180°, and also by substitution of a gold scatterer for the carbon film; since gold gives essentially pure Coulomb scattering no spin polarization is introduced.

Junction detectors possess several advantages for this application which make them preferable to the scintillation counters or nuclear emulsions previously employed. Surface barrier detectors prepared by gold evaporation are self-collimating and require no defining apertures which could introduce unwanted scattering. Their good energy resolution enables the study of separate groups of particles from the initial reaction. A strong background of neutrons and gammas is generally present from this initial reaction; effects of this can be minimized in the detector by operating it with a depletion layer no greater than is necessary for the particles under study.

Evans, Kuehner and Almqvist[23] have used large area junction counters to measure left-right asymmetry of protons scattered by a carbon analyser. A magnetic spectrometer in front of the analyser selects the proton group to be studied so that a relatively thick analyser foil may be used. Figure 8.14 shows the performance of a junction counter in this arrangement in comparison with a thin CsI scintillator, for the study of polarization in the C^{12} (d, p) C^{13} reaction leading to the excited state of C^{13} at 3·85 MeV. Only the significant improvement in background and energy resolution achieved with junction detectors makes the experiment possible.

In preliminary studies of the polarization of He^3 ions of about 25 MeV scattered from various light nuclei, Flynn and Rosen[24] have found it essential to use a dE/dx and E particle identification system of silicon detectors. So many He^4 ions result from (He^3, He^4) reactions that detection of the scattered He^3 ions by nuclear emulsions proved impracticable owing to the impossibility of distinguishing He^3 from He^4.

8.6 Fission studies

Despite the importance of the fission process as a source of nuclear power many features of the division and prompt neutron emission of fissioning nuclei are understood only qualitatively. Semiconductor detectors are being used in a number of important and elegant experiments in this field, for which they are well suited.

Electronic, as distinct from radiochemical methods of studying fission fragments, have employed pairs of ionization chambers or a time-of-flight system with scintillation detectors. A scintillation counter alone is useless because of poor energy resolution and saturation effects which result from the very high ionization density caused by fission fragments. Time-of-

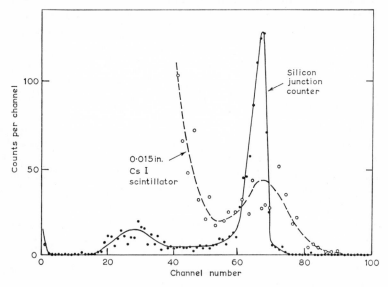

FIG. 8.14 Spectra observed in a study of polarization in the C^{12} (d, p) reaction leading to the 3·09 MeV state of C^{13}, at a deuteron energy of 8·6 MeV. The background is very much lower with a silicon junction counter than with a thin caesium iodide scintillator (After EVANS, J. E., Ph.D. Thesis, 1962)

flight methods are capable of giving excellent energy resolution at the great expense of poor geometrical efficiency. Semiconductor detectors can give very good energy resolution together with a large solid angle of acceptance, which is a valuable feature in this application since the targets or sources used must be very thin indeed. The problem of supporting a thin, active source between a pair of back-to-back ionization chambers is avoided with solid detectors since the fissile material can be deposited on the face of one of a pair of junction counters which are mounted to face each other. Surface barrier or shallow-diffused junction counters have a very thin 'window' and are therefore well suited to the detection of fission fragments, which have a short range. The fast signal from junction counters is also an advantage for coincidence measurements of correlated fragment pairs. Observations are often made over a long period and the stability of silicon junction detectors is a good feature.

The response of silicon junction detectors is not linearly dependent on the fission fragment energy. There are several reasons for this: the window, although thin, can cause a detectable loss of response; nuclear recoils account for most of the energy loss by fragments and the low energy silicon ions produced do not ionize very effectively, while, finally, carriers may not all be collected from the densely ionized track of the fragment. Carrier recombination is especially large in that vicinity since the passage of the fission fragment itself causes damage to the crystal. Thus there is a defect[24] in pulse height for fission fragments in comparison with the value extrapolated from the response for particles of lower ionization density, such as alpha-particles, and the effect was revealed when a comparison of the pulse-height spectra of semiconductor counters was made with the mean energies known from time-of-flight data.

The simplest detector calibration function to describe this behaviour is of the two-parameter form:

$$E = Kx + \delta \qquad (8.3)$$

where x is the pulse height and δ is called the pulse-height defect, which has a value of about 10 MeV. Wegner, Britt and Shlaer[25] found δ to be independent of the type (p or n) of silicon and its resistivity, but to be about 2·5 MeV greater for the heavy mass group than for the lighter one. The defect decreased by a factor of two as the average electric field in the detector was raised from $2 \cdot 10^3$ to $2 \cdot 10^4$ V/cm, in agreement with the idea that part of the defect arises from trapping and recombination of carriers before collection.

For even higher collection fields two distinct types of distortion effect have been observed in fission fragment spectra.

Wegner, Britt and Shlaer[25] and also Schmitt *et al.*[26] found an effective decrease in the energy per electron-hole pair in at least part of the detector. This is almost certainly an internal amplification effect similar to that observed by Huth and his colleagues[13, 14] near the onset of avalanche breakdown, which takes place in a field of the order 10^5 V/cm. Some, though not all, surface-barrier detectors show a second effect, described by Walter,[27] in which only the higher energy fragments showed an enhanced pulse height. This type of distortion occurred in relatively low collecting fields and could be influenced by surface treatment of the detector. Gibson and Miller[28] suggested that the multiplication process is due here to tunnelling injection through the oxide layer of the detector. The large flux of holes which reaches the front electrode after passage of a high-energy fragment sets up an electrical double layer across the silicon oxide zone, in which carriers have a low mobility. The field in this layer may cause electrons to tunnel through the oxide and, rather as in a triode, cause an amplification of the total charge crossing the depletion layer. Similar effects have been observed in some surface-barrier detectors exposed to an intense pulse of protons, in experiments by Hemmendinger, Silbert and Moat,[29] while diffused junction counters showed no such behaviour.

The choice of a detector for fission studies is therefore guided by several factors, some of which have been summarized by Walter and his colleagues[30] as follows:

1. The resistivity should not be too low or the electric field may exceed that for breakdown in a depletion depth equal to the fragment range. The resistivity must therefore exceed 25 Ω cm.

2. If the counter area is large, a higher resistivity must be used in order to reduce the detector capacitance and thus improve the signal to noise ratio, as discussed in Section 7.2(c).

3. If the resistivity is too high, the field will be insufficient to ensure good charge collection; about 10^4 V/cm is a desirable value, and higher values may result in charge multiplication.

4. High resistivity material leads to an excessive depletion

layer thickness and therefore excessive noise as well as undue sensitivity to gamma rays and background due to fast neutrons (see Section 8.12).

5. Some surface-barrier detectors exhibit multiplication by tunnelling injection at relatively low fields, and should be rejected. Walter[27] notes that a more strongly p-type surface gives less likelihood of injection and detectors in which this has been intentionally brought about are now commercially available. Diffused junction detectors do not show this effect but generally have a thick window (0·5 to 1 μ) which is undesirable.

Returning to the point of detector calibration, we realize that since the pulse-height defect δ, was found[25] to be dependent on the particle mass, equation (8.3) is inadequate. Schmitt, Kiker and Williams[31] proposed instead the four-parameter equation

$$E = (a + a'M) x + b + b'M \qquad (8.4)$$

where M is the fragment mass and a, a', b, b' are constants. The pulse-heights of bromine and iodine ions of known energies were used to determine these constants, since their masses are reasonably close to those of a typical light and heavy fission fragment, respectively. In an experiment in which the fission fragments from Cf^{252} a spontaneous fission source, were studied by the time-of-flight method and their energies were deduced by the calibration formula (8.4) above, good agreement was found with previously known data for the average number of prompt neutrons emitted as a function of fragment mass. However, Stein[32] has found that although this calibration procedure can be fitted accurately to the case of Cf^{252}, the same calibration constants lead to inaccuracies when extended to the thermal fission of U^{235}. It seems that for accurate work over a series of fission experiments an even more elaborate calibration procedure will be necessary. A better understanding of the processes which give rise to the empirical constants above is of great importance. Studies of the response of silicon and germanium detectors to heavy ions, and measurement of the window thickness will help to separate the contributing factors.

Let us turn now to consider briefly some experimental arrangements which have been used in fission measurements and which illustrate the advantages and limitations of semiconductor detectors. Since fragment velocities can be determined by a time-of-flight arrangement and energies can be found by a suitable pulse-height calibration, so that particle masses can be deduced, the experiments can be described in terms of the number of energy and velocity determinations that can be made simultaneously.

A triple energy determination has been made by Williams, Schmitt, Walter and Neiler[33] with the equipment shown in

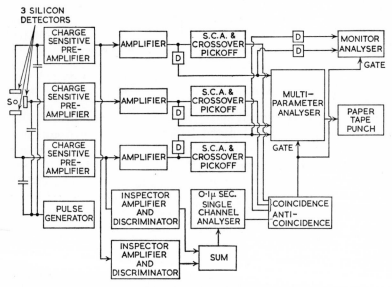

FIG. 8.15 Triple energy determination equipment used by WILLIAMS, SCHMITT, WALTER and NEILER[33] for fission studies

Fig. 8.15. The energies of correlated fragments can be measured in coincidence with the energy of a third emitted particle, usually a long-range alpha particle. Large-area silicon surface barrier detectors are used and the counting rate is therefore high. Pile-up pulses are rejected in the following manner: the preamplifier output pulses are clipped with a 20 $n$sec line and used to trigger a pair of fast disciminators, the outputs of which are summed and fed to a fast single-channel analyser. An anti-coincidence signal is generated if the sum pulse-height falls outside the narrow range corresponding to two coincident signals. The three-parameter output data is stored on punched paper tape. With this equipment mass and energy distributions, mass-energy correlations and total kinetic energy-mass correlations may be investigated, in both spontaneous and neutron-induced fission.

A single-velocity, single-energy determination arrangement has been described by Williams, Kiker and Schmitt[6] (Fig. 8.16). A 4 cm² silicon surface-barrier detector is used at the

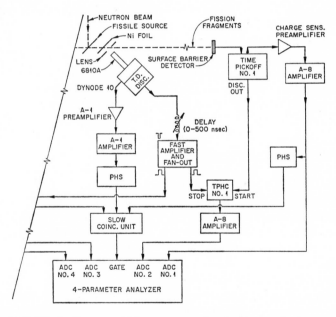

Fig. 8.16 Block diagram of the energy and velocity correlation system used by Williams, Kiker and Schmitt[6] for fission fragments

end of a 2 metre flight path. A transformer coupling (see Section 7.2(e)) allows a fast timing signal to be obtained as well as the slow, high-resolution energy signal. A time-zero pulse is obtained by mounting a very thin nickel foil near the fissile source; each fragment causes about 70 slow electrons to

be 'splashed' out of this foil, and these are accelerated electro-
statically into a scintillation counter. The measured time
resolution of this system is about 0·4 nsec. The initial momentum equality governs the fragment velocity; measurement of
this allows the initial mass to be deduced. The final energy is
governed by the final fragment mass, which is typically lower
than the initial mass owing to the emission of a few prompt
neutrons on the way to the detector. Thus with such equipment the number of neutrons emitted can be studied as a
function of fragment mass, and the fine structure (due to
nuclear shell effects) which appears in the final fragment mass
distribution can be investigated. The lines drawn on the left
of Fig. 8.16 are intended to indicate how the equipment could
be extended to make double-energy, double-velocity measurements on correlated fragment pairs.

W. E. Stein[32] has made use of a pair of large-area surface-
barrier detectors in a double-velocity, single-energy measurement. A thin foil and electron detection system again provide
the time-zero signal, as in Fig. 8.16. In this experiment, however, capacitive coupling is made between the fast amplifier
and the fission detector. The overall time resolution is measured to be about 0.5 nsec. By measurements of the fragment
masses before and after neutron emission and by timing their
flight, the final energies can be deduced. Thus the pulse height
can be plotted as a function of energy for a range of particle
masses between 90 and 150. Some of the results of this work
by Stein are shown in Fig. 8.17, and it may be shown by plotting the slopes and intercepts of the straight lines on this
figure that the results are consistent with a function of the
form given in equation (8.4). The slope varies only slightly,
and the intercept varies linearly with mass. It remains to be
seen whether this calibration procedure is universal for all
surface-barrier detectors and all ranges of fragment mass.

Reaction cross-sections and angular distributions of fission
fragments have been measured with junction detectors for
fission induced by charged particles. Huizenga, Vandenbosch
and Warhanek[34] bombarded U^{233} and U^{238} with carbon ions of
energies between 60 and 120 MeV. The cross-sections observed
in such reactions are often small and the good geometrical
efficiency which can be achieved with junction counters is an

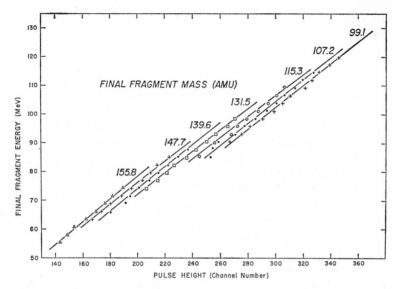

FIG. 8.17 Pulse-height as a function of fission fragment mass and energy in a silicon surface-barrier detector; from STEIN[32]

advantage here. The chief difficulty lies in distinguishing the fission fragments from scattered carbon ions.

A further and very novel type of experiment by which fission cross-sections can be investigated in a most powerful way has been developed by a group at Los Alamos Scientific Laboratory. A nuclear detonation is used as a source of neutrons and semiconductor detectors operated in a current mode[35] respond to the flux of fission fragments from a foil. This method, first carried through in 1964, shows great promise as a means of measuring fission cross-sections over a wide energy range in materials which, owing to a high rate of spontaneous fission or a high alpha activity, would be extremely difficult to study by conventional means. Owing to the generality of this method, further details are reserved until Section 8.12 in which neutron-induced reaction studies are considered.

8.7 Photonuclear experiments

The ejection of charged particles from a nucleus by gamma radiation occurs when the gamma energy exceeds the particle binding energy. This process is part of an important field of nuclear physics, the interaction of nuclei with electromagnetic radiation. The gamma radiation for these experiments is generally produced as *bremsstrahlung* in the slowing down of electrons from a linear accelerator or a betatron, and the range of charged particle energies most often studied lies below 20 MeV. This is a region in which semiconductor detectors can give a linear response with particle energies and have other potential advantages. The principal one for this application is the relatively low response to a high gamma flux, which is due in part to the short pulse length which can be obtained, and which minimizes the pile-up of electron pulses. Thus Schultz[36] found that a silicon diffused junction counter would operate in a mean gamma flux of 4 R/hour, with a peak pulse gamma flux no less than $3 \cdot 10^4$ R/hour. Despite this background the detector was able to count 5 MeV alpha particles, the gamma-induced pulse pile-up corresponding to a particle energy of only about 2·5 MeV. Schultz remarks that under such conditions all other ionization-based detectors were completely inoperative. The limited detector area is a disadvantage in comparison with scintillation counters, however.

The simplest reactions to study are those induced in silicon itself, since in this case the detector can act simultaneously as target and detector. If a separate target is used it must necessarily be thin so that the charged products emerge with only a small energy loss, and furthermore the detection efficiency is reduced by geometrical considerations. Several studies have been made[37, 38, 39] of the Si^{28} (γ, p) and (γ, a) reactions. The pile-up of electron pulses constitutes a major problem: Lokan and his collaborators[38] assumed that the spectrum of the background due to electrons was exponential; Ullrich[39] used an electronic method for eliminating pulse pile-up and was able to measure proton spectra down to 1·5 MeV proton energy without distortions.

Not all the protons emitted from the Si^{28} (γ, p) reaction leave the residual Al^{27} nucleus in its ground state; by measurements with *bremsstrahlung* radiation with several different endpoint energies Ullrich[39] was able to reduce branching ratios for some of the resonances and derive the cross-section for the ground-state transition. Since the Si^{28} (γ, a) reaction yields alpha particles with energies higher than those of the protons, the small number of alpha particles can be measured. In all these experiments so far the effects of the small admixtures of Si^{29} (4 per cent) and Si^{30} (3 per cent) in natural silicon are neglected.

The O^{16} (γ, p) reaction has also been studied with silicon detectors. This is a well-known reaction but the method can be extended to other target materials now that the technique has been demonstrated. Scheer, Schlüpmann and Triantafyllidis[40] made use of a double detector telescope in order to suppress the background due to electrons and to photoprotons produced within the detectors. A 90 μ thick fully-depleted detector was mounted close to a 2 mm thick lithium-drifted silicon detector; pulses in the latter were recorded only if the energy loss in either detector exceeded the maximum value possible for an electron. The coincidence condition between the two detectors eliminated most of the background due to (γ, p) reactions in the silicon, and furthermore the detectors were surrounded by 10 cm of lead as shielding. In this way protons of between 4 and 30 MeV could be measured with an energy resolution of about 100 keV.

The same group[41] has measured the spectra of alpha-particles emitted from titanium, nickel, copper and niobium targets irradiated with 32·5 MeV *bremsstrahlung*. Background problems are less serious in the case of (γ, p) reactions since the detectors may have a shallower depletion layer.

8.8 High-energy physics

In this section we consider the use of semiconductor detectors for very high energy charged particles. Such particles travel with only a small energy loss through the largest semiconductor detectors so far prepared, so that measurements are restricted to the rate of energy loss, dE/dx. As was discussed in Section 1.2, dE/dx changes only slowly with energy in the relativistic region, passing through a minimum of about 1·5 MeV/gm/cm² for energies near the particle rest mass. The detectors therefore have poor energy resolution, further impaired by statistical fluctuations in ionization—the Landau effect—which introduces a spread of about 30 per cent in the

energy loss through a thin detector. Since the energy loss
depends on particle mass, the detectors may be useful in distinguishing heavy and light particles, and their fast output
signal can be utilized for coincidence measurements. However,
the signal is small, less than 1mV in amplitude, so that a high
gain amplifier is necessary. Miller[42] and his group at Brookhaven found appreciable difficulties owing to electrical and
acoustical interference in the pre-amplifiers when used near a
high-energy accelerator, the Cosmotron. They point out that
since good energy resolution is impossible, a detector which
incorporates amplification, such as the transistor detector,
would avoid this problem. If vacuum-tube amplifiers are to
be used, the miniature 'Nuvistor' triodes are well-shielded
and are preferable to other types as regards microphony.

The energy loss of high-energy particles is small so that it
is necessary to use deep sensitive volumes. High resistivity
and lithium-drifted silicon junction counters have been tested
for this application, while Van Putten and Vander Velde[43]
have used gold-doped silicon conduction counters. With the
first of these types, Miller and his co-workers[42] were able to
distinguish protons and π^+-mesons of momentum 750 MeV/c,
following magnetic analysis of the accelerated beam. Koch,
Messier and Valin[44] used lithium-drifted counters with an
intrinsic volume 0·8 mm deep and 5 mm wide. In such a case
it is possible to allow particles to impinge parallel to the plane
of the junction, so that a much greater depth of silicon is
traversed at the expense of useful area. Fig. 8.18 shows
protons and π^+ mesons distinguished, after magnetic analysis,
in such a detector; the particle momentum was 615 MeV/c.
The π^- mesons selected by reversal of the magnetic field are
shown in the same figure. The most probable energy loss in
silicon for protons and π-mesons is shown in Fig. 8.19.
Results obtained by Yuan, Miller and Wagner for protons and
mesons of momentum 3 BeV/c using a lithium-drifted silicon
junction counter are shown in Fig. 8.20.

Conduction counters often show an inferior energy resolution to junction counters but this is masked in this application
by the statistical effects. Van Putten and Vander Velde[43]
used gold-doped silicon counters with an area of 3·2 cm^2 and
a thickness of 2·5 mm, and they were operated at 140° K.

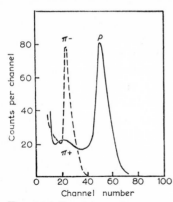

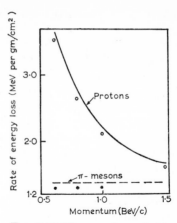

FIG. 8.18 Spectrum of protons and π-mesons of momentum 787 MeV/c observed in a lithium-drifted silicon counter. The particles traversed the counter in a plane parallel to its surface; from KOCH, MESSIER and VALIN[44]

FIG. 8.19 The most probable energy loss of protons and π-mesons in silicon. The points are experimental results and the lines are calculated theoretically; from KOCH, MESSIER and VALIN[44]

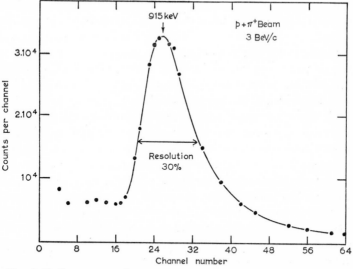

FIG. 8.20 Spectrum of protons and π-mesons of momentum 3 BeV/c observed in a 2 mm thick, 1 cm diameter lithium-drifted silicon detector, operated at 400 V bias. The points are in excellent agreement with the theoretical Landau curve, also shown; from YUAN, L.C.L., MILLER, G. L. and WAGNER, S., *Proc. Conf. on Nucl. Instr. for High Energy Physics*, CERN, July 1962

The fluctuations in energy loss were studied for π^- mesons of 1500 and 2500 MeV/c and compared with theoretical predictions of Rossi[45] and Sternheimer.[46] Sun[47] has described a plan to use 680 such detectors to form a matrix 340 square inches in area to trigger a liquid hydrogen bubble chamber on suitably selected events. Blumenfeld and Pandolfi,[48] continuing work on this project, have prepared conduction counters of suitably high resistivity by irradiating n-type silicon of about 2000 ohm cm resistivity with the order of 10[7]R of Co[60] gamma rays. The contacts were of nickel, applied by a chemical plating process. 2·5 mm thick wafers gave pulse heights of about 300 mV when exposed to minimum-ionizing particles; the signal-to-noise ratio observed was greater than ten and pulse rise-times were of the order of 100 $n$sec.

Since the energy resolution obtainable with semiconductor detectors of sizes which are at present available is severely limited owing to the Landau spread, these detectors are of little use in energy determination for minimum-ionizing particles. They can be used for spatial resolution, for momentum determination in conjunction with magnetic analysis, and they can give a fast response. Huth and his collaborators[13, 14] have prepared contoured junction counters in which internal amplification takes place under the high collecting field of about 10[5] V/cm. They have shown that it is possible to obtain sufficient internal gain that even minimum-ionizing particles will give a detector output signal large enough to trigger a tunnel diode discriminator directly. In this way a signal is obtained with a rise time of a fraction of a nanosecond, without any need for a fast amplifier.

Semiconductor detectors have also been found useful in an array for indicating the profile of a beam of high-energy particles from an accelerator. Tepper, Miller and Kycia[49] describe an array of 32 lithium-drifted silicon counters, arranged in the form of a cross 6.4 cm by 6·4 cm. Each counter has a sensitive volume 2 mm cube in which a minimum ionizing particle gives up an energy of about 800 keV. The electronics for handling the output of this array is described in Section 7.4(c); it provides a continuous visual display of the beam profile, of great value in setting up a high energy beam for an experiment. Radiation damage is, however, likely to limit the useful life of these detectors to about 10^{12} particles per cm^2, or about one year of operation.

8.9 Beta spectrometry

Most of the work on beta spectrometry is carried out by means of magnetic analysis in conjunction with a scintillation or Geiger counter. As Berényi and Fényes[50] have shown, the semiconductor counter is preferable to the scintillation counter owing to its insensitivity to magnetic fields, and superior to the Geiger counter in possessing a good energy resolution. Goulding[51] has further pointed out that the low inherent background of semiconductor counters can be an advantage in the case of weak sources.

Despite the lower energy resolution which can be achieved by the use of a semiconductor detector alone for beta spectrometry a few advantages remain. The compact size of the detector allows simpler apparatus in the study of $\beta-\gamma$ angular correlations, and the geometrical efficiency of detection can exceed that of the magnetic spectrometer.

One problem in the case of energy measurement for beta particles is that of obtaining an adequate sensitive depth in the counter. The range of a 1 MeV beta in silicon may be as much as 1·6 mm (see Fig. 1.5). The development of lithium-drifted counters, with sensitive volumes as deep as 5 mm, has eased this problem. Difficulties which arise from poor charge collection in the detector are less serious for beta detection than for heavier particles, owing to the low density of ionization. It has therefore been possible to achieve better energy resolution for betas than it has for alpha particles. A second problem is that of backscattering of the electrons, causing them to leave the detector and so contributing a low-energy tail on the spectrum for monoenergetic betas. Corrections can be made to the spectrum for both resolution and backscattering effects: Bertolini, Cappellani, Fantechi and Restelli[52] describe how this may be done. Casper and Thompson[53] used a similar method to derive beta endpoint energies to a precision of 3 keV.

McKenzie and Ewan[54] studied the response of a 12,000 Ω em

diffused silicon counter to monoenergetic electrons of 100 to 1200 keV energy, with the results shown in Fig. 8.21. The depletion layer thickness was equivalent to the range of 350 keV electrons, so that at higher energies than this the total energy absorption peak diminishes and a second peak corresponding to the most probable energy loss appears at a pulse height equivalent to about 180 keV. The energy resolution was 15-20 keV but with an improved amplifier an energy resolution of 7·5 keV was achieved for 55 keV electrons.

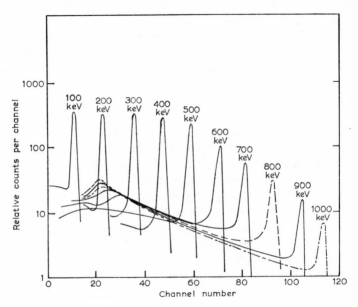

Fig. 8.21 The response of a 12 000 ohm cm diffused junction silicon counter to equal numbers of monoenergetic electrons in the range 100 keV to 1 MeV. At a detector bias of 200 V the thickness of the depletion layer corresponds to the range of an electron of energy 350 KeV; from McKenzie and Ewan[54]

Borkowski and Fox[55] used a guard-ring structure and special surface treatments in high-resistivity surface barrier detectors in order to operate them at bias voltages over 1000 V, giving depletion layers up to 1·5 mm thick. An energy resolution of 7·5 keV was achieved for 625 keV betas from the Cs[137] conversion spectrum, while Fig. 8.22 shows the outstanding per-

formance of such a detector to betas of nearly 1 MeV from
Bi²⁰⁷. The K-, L- and M- conversion lines are observable for
the first time, since magnetic analysis involves a geometrical
efficiency which is far too low for use with a thin source of
low activity.

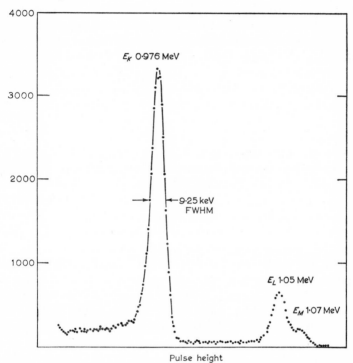

FIG. 8.22 The response of a 6000 ohm cm guard-ring surface
barrier detector, of area 20 mm², to Bi²⁰⁷ internal conversion
electrons. The detector bias was 1200 V and the detector was
cooled to 0° C; from BLANKENSHIP and BORKOWSKI[56]

Lithium-drifted detectors give even deeper depletion layers,
though the increased volume of the field region leads to an
increase in detector noise. This can be reduced by cooling,
and Blankenship and Borkowski[56] have obtained slightly
better performance than in Fig. 8.22, for Bi²⁰⁷ conversion
electrons in a detector used at 77° K. Mann, Haslett and
Janarek[57] have obtained a resolution of 26 keV at room temperature in a lithium-drifted junction.

The fast signal and compact form of junction counters make them valuable in coincidence measurements of betas with charged particles or gamma rays. It is easy to record the passage of a fast beta even when its range is too great for energy determination. Heavier charged particles can be eliminated with absorber foils. In this way short beta half-lives can be measured in a pulsed accelerator experiment.

Since semiconductor counters are little affected by magnetic fields they can be used in conjunction with magnetic analysis for beta spectrometry. Rae and Bowey[58] have designed a beta spectrometer for use with Compton recoils as a gamma mono-chromator. An array of ten surface barrier detectors is used at the focus of a sector magnet with a 0·01 cm thick detector at the entrance slit, operated in coincidence.

An interesting application of semiconductor detectors to the measurement of certain ultra-short nuclear lifetimes has been made by Tove and Jonasson.[59] When a nuclear state is fed and decays through gamma-ray transitions with high internal conversion coefficients a sensitive measure of the time interval between formation and decay of the state is obtained by passing the emitted particles through a high-frequency electric field. If both electrons are detected the sum pulse-height will show a spread which is governed by the time interval between the emissions. Tove and Jonasson allowed the emitted betas to pass through a microwave cavity operated at 2500 Mc/s and be detected in a silicon junction counter. Lifetimes of around 10^{-11} sec can be measured with good accuracy in this way, and with a 10 kMc/s cavity lifetimes as short as 10^{-12} sec would be measurable.

Lithium-drifted germanium detectors seem unlikely to have any special advantages for beta spectrometry. They require cooling to about $100°$ K or below in order to give good energy resolution, and at present it is less easy to obtain a thin entrance window in such a detector than in the case of lithium-drifted silicon.

8.10 Gamma spectrometry

(a) *Introduction*

Until 1964 the semiconductor counters which were available were of very limited value for gamma-ray detection. Essentially only silicon detectors with volumes up to about 3 cm² were in use. Owing to its low atomic number the absorption coefficient of silicon is quite low (see Fig. 1.7). Furthermore the Compton scattering process dominates the absorption between 50 keV and 15 MeV gamma-ray energy, and electrons of all energies up to $(E_\beta)_{\max}$ given by equation (1.17) are produced, so that the resulting Compton spectrum is of little value for spectrometry. A large total absorption peak, uniquely related to the gamma-ray energy, results only if the detector has a large volume and a high atomic number, Z. The photoelectric absorption coefficient increases as Z^5 and so germanium is about forty times more effective than silicon, though not as good as sodium iodide. At energies above about 1·5 MeV the pair-production process becomes significant and its contribution to the absorption varies at Z^2.

For these reasons, the development of high-resolution lithium-drifted germanium detectors, with volumes already up to 30 cm³, has opened a whole new field of possible applications for semiconductor counters. Although their full-energy peak efficiency is still about an order of magnitude less than that of typical sodium iodide crystals their energy resolution is superior by at least an order of magnitude. There is no reason why a number of germanium detectors could not be stacked together in order to achieve larger sensitive volumes. Hence, despite the necessity to cool germanium counters to below about 100° K in order to reduce intrinsic conduction, such detectors will probably replace sodium iodide to a large extent for gamma-ray studies in the field of nuclear physics. Already, by the end of 1965, the trickle of papers describing gamma-ray experiments with the new detectors is turning into a flood. Many groups are now actively preparing their own lithium-drifted germanium, by methods outlined in Chapter 6.

Following Ewan and Tavendale[60] in their comprehensive review of the application of germanium detectors to gamma-ray spectrometry, it is convenient to divide the range of energies studied into two parts, corresponding to the regions of photoelectric and pair-production absorption. Between about 30 keV and 1·5 MeV a useful full-energy peak efficiency is obtained through the photoelectric effect; above 1·5 MeV the pair-production process becomes increasingly important, as can be seen from Fig. 1.8.

(b) Photoelectric spectrometers

A method of mounting germanium detectors for gamma-ray experiments in the photoelectric region is shown in Fig. 8.23, due to Hansen and Jarrett.[61] The detector is cooled by

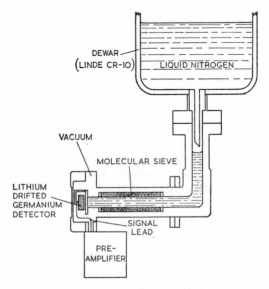

FIG. 8.23 A cryostat designed by HANSEN and JARRETT[61] for lithium-drifted germanium detectors

liquid nitrogen from a reservoir, such as the Linde CR-10.* The space around the detector is evacuated and a molecular sieve* maintains a low vapor pressure of condensible materials. The pre-amplifier is connected by as short a lead as possible to the detector.

In the energy region up to 1·5 MeV the energy resolution of good germanium detectors is at present limited by the performance of the best available pre-amplifiers. This can be seen from Table 8.1 which shows results obtained by H. M. Mann

* Obtainable from Linde Co., Division of Union Carbide, Speedway, Indiana, or, 8 Grafton Street, London W.1.

TABLE 8.1

Energy resolution and Fano factor in a 1 cm² × 4 mm Lithium-drifted Germanium detector.

Gamma-ray energy	Detector line-width	Pulser line-width	Fano factor
122 keV	2·14 keV	1·87 keV	0·20
1·33 MeV	3·0 keV	2·3 keV	0·19
6·6 MeV	5·8 keV	2·5 keV	0·20

Values obtained by H. M. Mann, private communication.

and his collaborators.[62] The Fano factor (see Chapter 1.4) is so low that statistical fluctuations in the production of electron-hole pairs are small. At about 77° K the detector leakage current is probably between 10^{-9} and 10^{-10} A so that little noise results from this source. Inhomogeneity of the charge collection efficiency over large-volume detectors is often appreciable, however, and it is advisable to use collecting fields of at least 1000 V/cm.

The improvement which this resolution offers over sodium iodide scintillation spectrometers is illustrated in Fig. 8.24 in which a Co⁶⁰ spectrum is compared in measurements with a 3·5 mm thick germanium detector and with a good 3 in. × 3 in. sodium iodide crystal.

By using a number of calibrated gamma-ray sources it is possible to study the absolute efficiency of a detector, for counts falling in the full-energy peak, as a function of gamma-ray energy. Figure 8.25 shows such a curve for two detectors, one of 2·5 cm² × 3·5 mm and the other 3 cm × 1·9 cm × 8 mm. The dashed curve is that calculated on the basis of photo-electric absorption alone for the smaller crystal; the observed efficiency is higher because multiple Compton processes can also contribute to the full-energy peak. The proportion of counts which fall in the full-energy peak can also be measured and is found to fall from 100 per cent at a few tens of keV to 1 per cent at about 1·5 MeV. In a very large crystal this ratio would be improved by the increased contribution of multiple Compton processes.

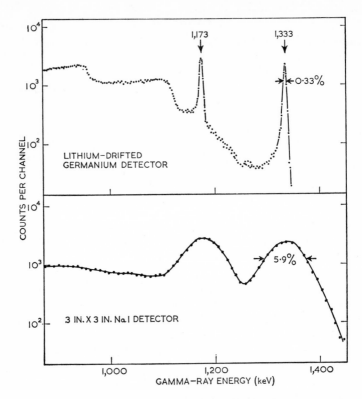

FIG. 8.24 Energy resolution of a lithium-drifted germanium detector for Co[60] gamma rays; from EWAN and TAVENDALE[60]

In some cases of complex spectra a large Compton background cannot be tolerated, but it can be largely removed by an anti-coincidence arrangement in which the detector is surrounded by a very large annular sodium iodide scintillator. If the efficiency of this for the detection of Compton-scattered gamma-rays escaping from the germanium crystal is high, most of the background can be eliminated. Figure 8.26 shows a typical arrangement of such a spectrometer, due to Holm and his colleagues.[63] The anticoincidence crystal, 12 in. long by 8 in. diameter, must be well shielded from the gamma-ray source and this necessitates heavy lead shielding. The lithium-drifted germanium detector is cooled by conduction along an

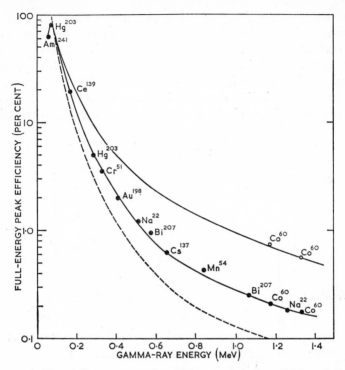

FIG. 8.25 The full-energy peak efficiency for two lithium-drifted germanium detectors as a function of gamma-ray energy; from EWAN and TAVENDALE[60]

aluminium tube. The reduction in Compton background achieved with this device is shown in Fig. 8.27.

The energy resolution of germanium detectors is matched only by that of the curved-crystal gamma-ray spectrometer. Above about 300 keV the germanium detector is superior, while for lower energies the curved-crystal spectrometer is still unsurpassed. However, its efficiency is lower by a factor of about 10^4 so that it can be used only with strong gamma sources. The resolution of lithium-drifted germanium detectors is ten to twenty times better than has been obtainable with sodium iodide scintillation crystals, and for the elucidation of complete gamma decay schemes this is invaluable. Their pulse rise-times are a few tens of nanoseconds, about ten times as fast as the sodium iodide scintillation (250 nsec), so that germanium detectors are more useful in coincidence experiments. However, the largest germanium detectors so far constructed[62] have a volume of only about 30 cm^3, giving a full-energy peak efficiency of about 4 per cent for 1 MeV gamma-rays, while the corresponding intrinsic efficiency of a 3 in. by 3 in. sodium iodide detector is about 20 per cent. In some measurements, such as gamma-gamma angular correlation

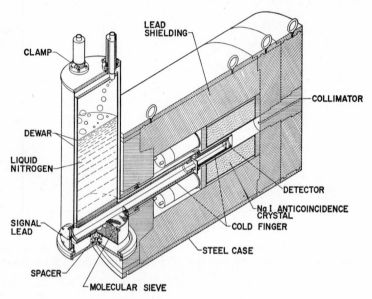

Fig. 8.26 A Compton anti-coincidence system, using a lithium-drifted germanium detector at the centre of a large annular sodium iodide scintillator, due to HOLM *et al.*[63]

studies, the overall efficiency must be high, and even larger germanium detectors, or stacks of detectors, will be required if they are to replace the scintillator entirely.

Most of the very extensive field of gamma-ray investigations in nuclear physics can be studied with advantage by means of the newly-developed lithium-drifted germanium detectors. As examples we shall outline a few experiments which have already proved successful. Shirley, Rosenblum, Frankel and Stone[64, 65] have investigated the complex gamma-ray spectra of several rare-earth isotopes with an energy

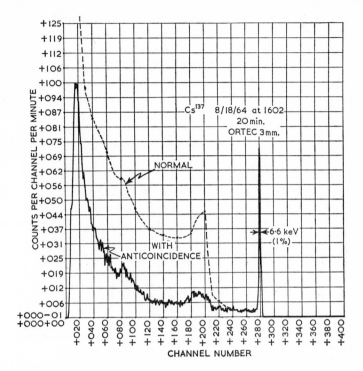

Fig. 8.27 Improvement on the Compton background in the case of Cs[137] gamma-rays achieved with the equipment shown in Fig. 8.26

resolution of about 5 keV. Doublet transitions to the ground state and 10 keV excited state of La[137] were clearly separated. Julian and Jha[66] have used lithium-drifted germanium detectors to study the gamma-decay of Ba[134] following beta-decay of the La[134]; it would be quite impossible to resolve the lines of this spectrum by means of a scintillation spectrometer. Ewan and Tavendale[60] have examined the gamma-ray spectra of Cs[134], Pm[151], Gd[153], Eu[156], Gd[159], Yb[177] and Ra[226], analyzing the energies and relative intensities of some scores of lines many of which are observed for the first time. Figure 8.28 shows as an example their measurements on the spectrum of Pm[151], made with a 2 mm thick germanium detector; lines only 5 keV apart are seen to be relatively well separated.

Gamma rays following thermal neutron capture in U[238] have

been studied by Motz, Jurney and Ford,[67] using a lithium-drifted germanium detector surrounded by an annular anti-coincidence crystal, as in Fig. 8.26. With an energy resolution of 8 keV many new transitions were observed. Day and Palms[68] have made use of a large-volume lithium-drifted germanium detector for the study of gamma rays following fast neutron

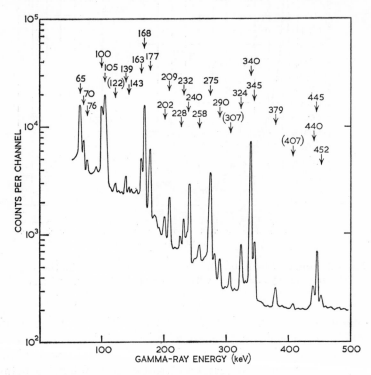

FIG. 8.28 Part of the spectrum of gamma-rays from Pm^{151} observed with a lithium-drifted germanium detector by EWAN and TAVENDALE[60]

inelastic scattering by a variety of elements which it would be impossible to investigate by a scintillation counter. Figure 8.29 shows the gamma-ray spectrum observed in the $Zr(n, n'\gamma)$ process, and it can be seen that two lines at 920 and 935 keV are very well resolved. The principal difficulty in this type of experiment is the background which results from the scattering of neutrons into the germanium crystal where they

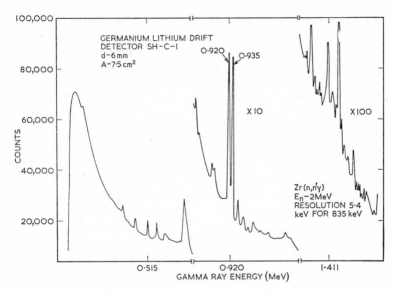

Fig. 8.29 Spectrum of gamma-rays following neutron inelastic scattering in zirconium observed with a lithium-drifted germanium detector by Day and Palms[68]

undergo inelastic scattering and excite a large number of transitions in the various isotopes of germanium. Day and Palms are attempting to eliminate most of this background by a fast timing technique. If the scattering sample is displaced about 30 cm from the detector it may prove possible to distinguish gamma-rays from the sample from those created within the detector by means of the time delay between the two types of event. Here the fast response as well as the good energy resolution of the detector is being employed to the full.

In the region of low gamma-ray energies Easley and his collaborators[69] have used lithium-drifted germanium detectors to study hyperfine structure of the 73 keV line from Ir[193], in a Mössbauer experiment. The extent of the splitting of the line in a known lattice field allowed a limit to be placed on the magnetic moment of the Ir[193] excited state. The work is being extended to even lower energy transitions. Another very different experiment involving low energy measurements with germanium detectors is the study of μ-mesic x-rays being made by Anderson, Hargrove, Hincks and Tavendale.[70]

(c) *Pair-production spectrometers*

In the absorption of high-energy gamma radiation by pair production an electron-positron pair is created, the total kinetic energy released being less than the gamma-ray energy by 1022 keV, the rest-energy of the pair. If there is a good probability of these particles coming to rest within the depletion layer of the detector, a line is observed in the spectrum, superimposed on the Compton continuum. For energies above 1·5 MeV the photo-electric efficiency is very small but the pair-production cross-section increases with energy, almost linearly. However, as can be seen in Fig. 1.8, the Compton cross-section in germanium exceeds the pair-production cross-section below about 8 MeV. Germanium is not greatly superior to silicon as regards the ratio of pair-production to Compton absorption, but it does allow useful

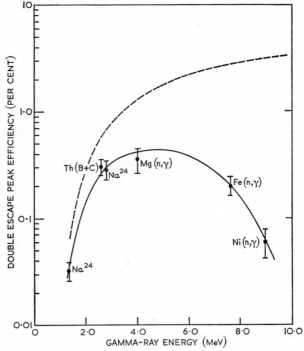

FIG. 8.30 The double-escape peak efficiency of a lithium drifted germanium detector as a function of gamma-ray energy, measured by EWAN and TAVENDALE[60]

detection efficiencies to be achieved. Figure 8.30 shows the pair-production peak efficiency measured by Ewan and Tavendale[60] for a 3·5 mm × 18 mm dia. lithium-drifted germanium detector, as a function of gamma-ray energy. The fall-off above 4 MeV is due partly to the escape of some electrons and positrons from the surface of the detection volume so that the measured pulse-height falls outside the peak, and partly to the escape of *bremsstrahlung* radiation emitted during the slowing-down of the pair. These losses are minimized by arranging that the gamma radiation passes through the crystal along its largest dimension as the pairs and *bremsstrahlung* are emitted largely in the forward direction. The thicker detectors now available are obviously more suitable for high-energy gamma-ray detection. The energy resolution attainable with large-volume germanium detectors is in the region of 8 keV for energies around 5 to 7 MeV, which is comparable with the performance of a high-resolution magnetic Compton spectrometer. The geometrical efficiency of the semiconductor detector is, however, vastly superior and it is much simpler to operate. The semiconductor detector allows the whole gamma-ray spectrum to be observed simultaneously, while with a magnetic spectrometer the spectrum must be slowly scanned. The latter is more suitable, however, for the observation of weak lines in the presence of intense radiation of higher energy.

In the case of a complex spectrum it may be impossible to tolerate a high background of pulses extending above and below the pair-production peak. At the expense of detection efficiency this background can be largely removed by a coincidence arrangement. The pair production process is characterised by the creation of a positron, which, on coming to rest undergoes annihilation with an electron to release a pair of 511 keV gamma rays (the so-called annihilation radiation). If these two quanta can be detected in coincidence by a pair of sodium iodine scintillation crystals flanking the germanium detector the resulting 'three-crystal spectrometer' will respond almost solely to pair-production events. It is obviously necessary to collimate the gamma rays so that they fall only on the centre crystal, parallel to its major dimension, and a typical arrangement used by Ewan and Tavendale[60] is shown in Fig. 8.31.

Figure 8.32 shows the improvement which results from this technique in the case of Na^{24} gamma rays of 2·75 MeV. The peak to background ratio is improved from 7:1 to 150:1. The overall detection efficiency is, however, greatly reduced.

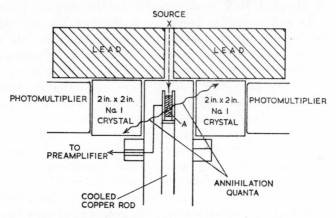

FIG. 8.31 Schematic diagram of a three-crystal spectrometer; after Ewan and Tavendale[60]

The arrangement shown in Fig. 8.26, in which a germanium detector is surrounded by a single annular sodium iodide scintillator can also be used in the coincidence mode as a pair-production spectrometer. In this way Motz, Jurney and Ford[67] have studied high-energy gamma-rays from thermal neutron capture in U^{235} and other targets. A number of new transitions, some of them rather weakly excited, were rendered observable. Similar studies in bismuth have been reported by Slaughter and Harvey[71] and the method will probably be very important in solving the energy level schemes of the heavier elements.

A certain degree of background reduction can be achieved in a much simpler way. Alexander, Pearson, Litherland and Broude[72] have shown that pulse-shape discrimination against detector pulses containing a slow component can give an improvement in the peak: background ratio by about a factor of two. This is because electrons which escape from the sensitive volume of the detector pass through a region of low collecting field and so give rise to a slow component to the pulse. Also, temporary trapping of carriers for a time comparable with the amplifier time-constants will remove pulses from the

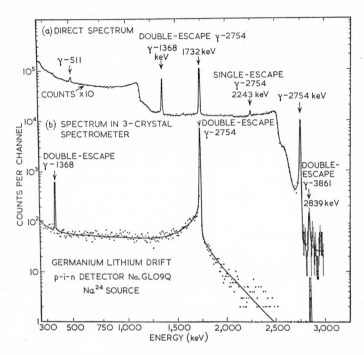

FIG. 8.32 The improvement in peak: background ratio achieved[60] with the instrument shown in FIG. 8.31

peak and contribute to the background. A circuit described by Alexander and Goulding[73] for pulse-shape discrimination in organic scintillators was found to be effective in removing these two types of background, and the method was applied to the study of gamma rays of between 5 and 12 MeV from the F^{19} $(d, n\gamma)$ Ne^{20} reaction.

(d) Silicon detectors for gamma spectrometry

In view of the great success of lithium-drifted germanium detectors in the field of gamma-ray spectrometry one may ask what rôle, if any, remains for the application of silicon detectors to this work. In the energy range of photoelectric spectro-meters silicon is virtually useless, as its photoelectric absorp-tion coefficient is only one-fortieth of that of germanium. At higher energies, above about 2 MeV, the pair-production process becomes important. The ratio of pair: Compton absorption coefficients depends linearly upon Z and so germanium is only about twice as good as silicon in respect to peak: background ratios. In some instances the fact that lithium-drifted silicon detectors may be operated at room temperature and are more easily handled may outweight this factor. The energy resolution which can be achieved with silicon detectors is almost as good as that obtainable with germanium, though only if a modicum of cooling, say to $0°$ C, can be provided. Room temperature leakage currents in silicon detectors of reasonable volume tend to exceed 10^{-6}A and so contribute to the observed linewidth.

8.11 Neutron detectors

Since the interaction between neutrons and electrons is very slight, taking place between their magnetic moments, it is insufficient to bring about ionization. Neutrons must therefore be detected by a two-stage process in which their energy is transferred to one or more charged particles, subsequently detected in the usual way.

The commonest method makes use of (n, p) or (n, a) reactions which lead to two charged products, the sum of the energies of which is equal to the incident neutron energy, E_n, together with the energy release of the reaction, Q. Light nuclei are favoured here since there is a smaller Coulomb barrier for separation of the charged products. Suitable positive Q reactions are: B^{10} (n, a) Li^7, $Q = 2·8$ MeV; Li^6 (n, a) H^3, $Q = 4·8$ MeV, and He^3 (n, p) H^3, $Q = 0·76$ MeV. The detector can be made by mounting a thin layer, or radiator, containing one of these isotopes between a pair of closely-spaced semiconductor counters. If the output pulses of the two counters are summed in coincidence a signal proportional to $(E_n + Q)$ is obtained. This is because the response of semiconductor detectors is linear and independent of particle type, and in this respect semiconductor counters are superior to scintillation crystals containing Li^6 or B^{10}. Semiconductor neutron detectors, utilizing the Li^6 (n, a) reaction were first described by Love and Murray.[74]

Neutron-induced fission results in high energy charged

fragments which can be used for neutron detection. Since Q is very large and the range of fragment energies is wide, it is not possible to distinguish between different incident neutron energies. The range of fission fragments is low so that the film thickness must be small. There also appear to be difficulties due to radiation damage produced by fragments depositing large amounts of energy in a shallow volume of the junction. Apart from the large output signal this method is therefore inferior to the preceding ones.

The simplest neutron detection process is by the elastic scattering of neutrons by hydrogen nuclei, resulting in a recoil proton which, depending on the angle of recoil ϕ with respect to the neutron direction, may have any energy E_p from zero to the full neutron energy, E_n.

$$E_p = E_n \cos^2 \phi \qquad (8.3)$$

The cross-section for this process is large, varies smoothly with energy and is accurately known over a wide range of neutron energies. The disadvantage for neutron spectroscopy is that unless ϕ is defined there is not an unambiguous relation between E_n and E_p. The method of adapting a junction detector for recoil proton detection is simply to mount in front of it a thin layer of hydrogenous material such as polyethylene.

For thermal neutron detection it is important to use a reaction with a high Q-value so that neutron-induced pulses are clearly separable from those due to gamma rays. The Li^6 (n, a), B^{10} (n, a) and fission processes can be applied, but not the proton-recoil method. The B^{10} reaction has a high thermal cross-section, 3800 barns, but gives two alpha groups to the ground and first-excited states of Li^7. The Li^6 reaction has a thermal cross-section of 900 barns but a larger and single valued Q-value, so that a thicker radiator can be used. De Cosnac, Noel, Bok and Schuttler[75] have studied detectors coated with Li^6F and with fissile materials, for thermal neutrons. Detection efficiencies of the order 10^{-3} can be obtained by such methods, and such devices are now commercially available. Murphy[76] has prepared diodes by diffusion of B^{10} into n-type silicon and Li^6 into p-type silicon; thermal neutron efficiencies of 4×10^{-3} and 1.3×10^{-2}, respectively, were measured.

For fast neutron detection the detector efficiency depends on the reaction cross-section, the thickness of radiator film which can be tolerated, and the geometry of the detector arrangement. Some relevant cross-sections are shown in Fig. 1.9, which enables a comparison to be made of the efficiency at different energies of a given detector with a fixed amount of radiator. The $1/v$ law leads to a change by three orders of magnitude in the efficiency of reaction-based detectors between thermal and fast neutron energies around 1 MeV. For different detection methods the thickness of radiator film which can be allowed depends upon the energy and type of particle produced in the reaction. The spread in energy of particles reaching the detectors determines the resolution of the system, and depends upon the stopping power of the radiator medium. Dearnaley, Ferguson and Morrison[77] considered the efficiencies of various types of fast-neutron detector on the basis of an equivalent spread in energy introduced by radiator thickness. The proton-recoil detector has the highest efficiency, an order of magnitude greater than the others. This method is therefore most suitable for the measurement of a fast neutron flux, but the broad spectrum of recoil protons does not easily allow measurement of a neutron energy spectrum. Collimation of the emergent protons, for the case of a directed neutron flux, reduces the efficiency below that obtainable by other means. The He³-filled counter has the highest efficiency of the remaining methods and furthermore the efficiency curve as a function of neutron energy is free from the resonances which cause strong fluctuations in the efficiency of the other detectors. The various types of fast neutron detector we have mentioned will now be described in greater detail.

In the proton recoil detector it is often necessary to distinguish recoil protons from charged particles produced by neutron-induced reactions with silicon nuclei within the depletion layer. This can be done by means of the double detector[78] shown in Fig. 8.33. This consists of two semicircular surface barrier detectors prepared on the same disc of silicon and of the same area. A thin foil of polyethylene is mounted in front of and close to one of the detectors, and the assembly is protected from dust and light in a small metal case lined with gold. The latter minimizes scattering and reactions at the walls of the case. It need not be evacuated since the protons are produced very close to the detector surface. By forming

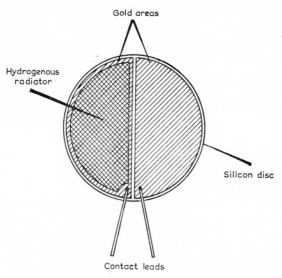

FIG. 8.33 Diagram of a semiconductor proton-recoil fast-neutron counter. Neutrons eject protons from the hydrogenous layer which covers one of the two semicircular surface barrier counters. This counter detects the protons plus background, while the uncoated counter measures the background only; from DEARNALEY and WHITEHEAD[9]

both counters on the same disc they are most likely to have the same resistivity and therefore the same depletion layer depth at the same bias. Background due to neutron-induced reactions in the depletion layer can therefore be eliminated by statistical comparison of the spectra from the two halves. Fig. 8.34 shows results obtained with monoenergetic neutrons of 4·2 MeV. The subtracted spectrum of recoil protons fits very well the theoretical shape[79] for the radiator thickness of 1·1 mgm/cm² which was used. Parker, White and Webster[80] have developed a Monte Carlo programme suitable for interpreting the subtracted spectrum from such a counter, taking into account the geometrical effect of a small spacing between the polyethylene and the detector surface.

By fitting the shape of the recoil spectrum for the appropriate radiator thickness and neutron energy and integrating the total counts from, say, 50 to 100 per cent of the maximum

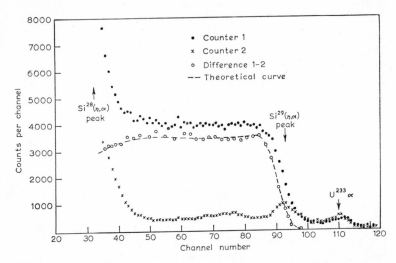

FIG. 8.34 Spectra obtained with the double proton-recoil fast-neutron monitor of Fig. 8.33, for monoenergetic neutrons of 4·2 MeV. The subtracted curve agrees well with the theoretical spectrum shape calculated for the radiator thickness, 1.1 mgm/cm², which was used; from DEARN-ALEY, FERGUSON and MORRISON[77]

pulse height it is possible to obtain an accurate value for the total yield of protons. With an accurate value for the scattering cross-section, the integrated neutron flux can be deduced. Besides its accuracy and stability the counter has the advantage of being very compact. It can therefore be mounted very close to the sample and the source of neutrons without introducing appreciable scattering.

A simpler application is in monitoring a neutron spectrum which does not change in shape during repeated measurements. A measurement of the neutron flux in each case is obtained simply from the number of proton-recoil counts above a fixed discriminator level. Here again stability and compactness are the main virtues of the counter, which, being very small and light gives little shadowing or scattering of the neutrons.

The upper limit of the range of operation of the counter is determined by the yield of reactions induced in the depletion layer of the silicon itself by fast neutrons. Charged particles from these reactions become prolific at about 7 MeV at which the Si^{28} (n, p) cross-section,[81] for instance, is 0·4 b. Greater radiator thicknesses can be tolerated at these energies, but the thickness of depletion layer to stop the recoil protons also increases. The depletion layer thickness must be kept only slightly greater than is necessary to stop the most energetic protons. The lower limit of operation is about 400 keV, set by the small thickness of radiator which can be tolerated at these energies. The pile-up of pulses due to gamma rays gives a background at low energies, minimized again by using small depletion layer widths. A radiator of gaseous hydrogen gives a lower stopping power than the equivalent amount of poly-ethylene and allows the amount of radiator to be varied conveniently.

There are two possible ways of extending the useful range of the proton recoil detection method, at the expense of detection efficiency. The first is to use a counter telescope consisting of a thin fully-depleted detector in coincidence with a junction counter or lithium-drifted counter with a relatively deep depletion layer. Most of the neutron-induced reactions will occur in the thick detector but will not be in coincidence with a count in the thin detector. Recoil protons from a polyethylene radiator may be collimated to pass through the two detectors and it may be arranged that the polyethylene can be rotated out of position for background measurements. White[82] has described such an arrangement, which gave a detection efficiency of about 2·5 × 10^{-5} and should be useful between neutron energies of 3·5 and 20 MeV.

A second method of avoiding background problems is to separate the detector from the hydrogenous radiator and shield it from the beam of neutrons. This can only be done when a directed flux of neutrons is to be studied. In order to retain the maximum counting efficiency the area of the radiator must be as large as possible. Potenza and Rubbino[83] have suggested an ingenious geometrical arrangement which also avoids too large an energy spread in the recoil protons reaching the detector. As shown in Figure 8.35, annular geometry is

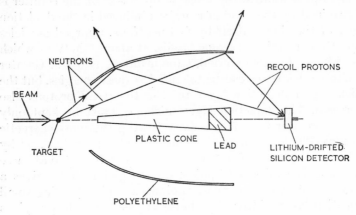

FIG. 8.35 The arrangement devised by POTENZA and RUBBINO[83] for neutron flux measurement at high energies

employed, a barrel-shaped film of polyethylene being supported between the neutron source and the detector, which is itself shielded from the direct neutron flux by a cone of plastic and lead. The whole system is mounted in an evacuated tank in order to avoid degradation of the recoil proton energy in air. Typically, the energy of neutrons emitted from a target bombarded by an accelerated beam will vary with the angle of emission. Potenza and Rubbino show how to calculate a radiator surface such that recoil protons arrive at the detector with only a small energy spread, for each group of neutrons emitted from the source reaction. The energy resolution is, of course, far below what can be achieved by the time-of-flight method, but the idea is of considerable value in fast neutron flux monitoring at the higher neutron energies, above about 5 MeV. Potenza and Rubbino claim an accuracy of determination of absolute neutron flux of about 5 per cent.

Other fast neutron detection systems make use of (n, p) or (n, γ) reactions in the radiator film.

Love and Murray[74] developed the Li^6-coated fast neutron detector shown in Figs. 8.36 and 8.37. A film of about 150 mgm/cm^2 of Li^6F is sandwiched between two surface barrier detectors.

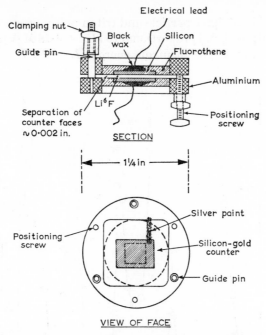

FIG. 8.36 Semiconductor fast neutron spectrometer, due to LOVE and MURRAY[74]. A layer
of Li^6F, of 150 $\mu gm/cm^2$ is evaporated on to the
face of one of the pair of silicon surface barrier
counters mounted parallel to each other

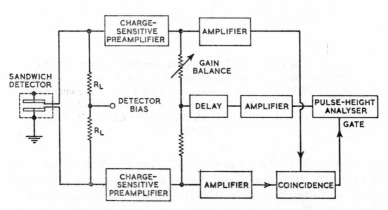

FIG. 8.37 A typical circuit arrangement for use with the sandwich-type
semiconductor fast-neutron spectrometer

The coincident alpha particle and triton pulses are summed to give an output signal proportional to $(E_n + 4.78\,\text{MeV})$; the linearity of output with neutron energy, E_n, was found to be

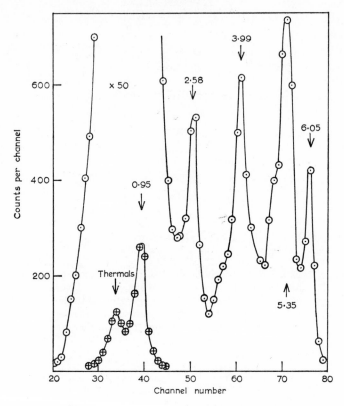

FIG. 8.38 Response of the sandwich counter of Figure 8.36 to neutrons from the Be^9 (d, n) reaction at a deuteron energy of 1·85 MeV. The numbers show the energies of the various neutron groups in MeV (After LOVE, T. A., MURRAY, R. B., MANNING, J. J. and TODD, H. A., *Nuclear Electronics* I, 415 (1962)

excellent. The efficiency is about 10^{-6} for 2 MeV neutrons, and the energy resolution about 300 keV. The response of such a detector to neutrons from the Be^9 (d, n) reaction is shown in Fig. 8.38. Because of the low efficiency such detectors are limited to reactions in which a high flux of neutrons is produced, and to cases in which time-of-flight methods with a pulsed neutron generator are inapplicable. The coincidence condition between the two counters reduces the effect of neutron-induced reactions within the silicon, but at energies above 8 MeV there is an appreciable coincident background due to particles which cross from one counter to the other.

Dearnaley, Ferguson and Morrison[77] modified this design of detector to make use of the He^3 (n, p) reaction. Two surface barrier detectors were mounted parallel to each other and enclosed in a small steel case which could be filled with He^3 gas at pressures up to 3 atm. Coincidences between a proton and triton were recorded, and the detector had an efficiency of about 10^{-5} for 2 MeV neutrons, with an energy resolution of 150 keV. Lee and Awcock[84] have reported efficiencies of about 3×10^{-6} and an energy resolution of 100 keV with a smaller gas volume. Figure 8.39 shows the response of their detectors

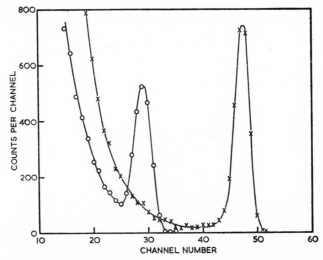

FIG. 8.39 Response of a He^3-filled semiconductor fast-neutron detector[84]

to 680 keV and 1·5 MeV neutron energies. In comparison with the Li^6 counter, the greater range of the reaction products, despite the lower Q-value, requires deeper depletion layer thicknesses and hence leads to a greater competition from neutron-induced reactions in silicon. The upper limit of usefulness of the He³ counter is therefore about 6 MeV. Pile-up pulses due to gamma-radiation can interfere with the spectrum at the lower energies and it is advantageous to use very short resolving times in the coincidence circuit. Lee and Awcock[84] conclude that although the He³ counter is simple in principle, it must be used with great care and the experimental conditions should be carefully assessed if reliable results are to be obtained.

There are two ways in which the background problem can be approached. Lee and Awcock suggest using two similar pairs of junction counters mounted so as to be subjected to the same neutron flux. The space between one pair of counters contains He³ gas while that between the second pair is evacuated. Subtraction of the two sum-coincidence spectra removes, to a reasonable approximation, the effect of neutron and gamma induced backgrounds within the silicon detectors. A second method is based on the kinematics of the reaction. Figure 8.40 shows a polar plot of the energies of the proton

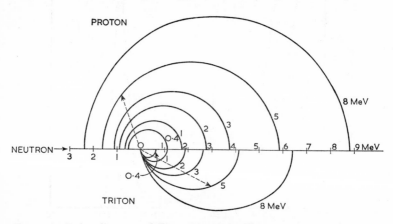

FIG. 8.40 Polar diagram of the proton and triton energies resulting from the He³ (n, p)H³ reaction[85]

and triton from the He³ (n, p)H³ reaction as a function of the laboratory angle of emission, for several incident neutron energies. Correlated angles of emission of the two particles are determined, as in the case of the two vectors shown, by the fact that the sum of their energies is equal to the incident neutron energy plus the reaction energy release, 776 keV. It is clear from this diagram that all the detectable tritons are emitted in the forward direction. Dearnaley[85] suggested that it may be possible to adapt the forward detector of the pair so that it responds only to tritons, and in this way unwanted coincidences due to protons and alpha-particles can be rejected. To achieve this a thin silicon dE/dx counter, about 25 microns in thickness, should be mounted close to and in front of the forward counter. By means of the electronics described in Section 7.3(b) the detector can be arranged to respond only when a triton is transmitted. The sum of the pulse heights from all three counters gives the neutron energy.

The He^3-filled semiconductor counter has the advantage over the He^3 proportional counter that He^3 recoils are eliminated by the coincidence condition. For the same reason the gas need not be so highly purified in order to eliminate beta pulses from the decay of the common contaminant, tritium. The disadvantage of the semiconductor counter is its low efficiency; that of a He^3 proportional counter can be several hundred times greater. The compact form of the detector does, however, allow it to be used in cases where scattering of neutrons by the detector must be minimized. It should be valuable for the measurement of neutron spectra within fast neutron critical assemblies and low-power reactors.

Problems of radiation damage by fast neutrons limit the life and applications of all these detectors. The subject will be discussed further in Chapter 10, but experimental measurements show that an integrated dose of 10^{12} to 10^{13} fast neutrons/cm^2 will cause an appreciable worsening in the energy resolution of a silicon junction counter. With a detection efficiency of 10^{-6} to 10^{-5} this means that the total neutron counts are limited to between 10^6 and 10^8.

8.12 Neutron-induced reaction studies

(a) *Introduction*

In this section we consider experiments which have as their aim the study of charged-particle reactions initiated by fast neutrons. The fission process often falls within this category but for convenience this large topic has been covered separately, in Section 8.6.

Some strikingly successful applications of semiconductor detectors have been made in this area, largely owing to the excellent performance of the detectors for measurements of charged-particle spectra. Activation methods are unable to distinguish transitions to different final excited states and information of such partial cross-section could only be obtained by the use of gridded ionization chambers; semiconductor counters are even more suitable for such studies.

The simplest and most widely investigated experiments for the study of neutron-induced reactions utilize as a target the medium of a radiation detector itself. The next two sections therefore are devoted to work on the silicon and germanium isotopes. Studies of other reactions are dealt with in the subsequent three sections.

(b) Neutron-induced reactions in silicon

The (n, p) and (n, α) reactions induced in the isotopes of silicon have been mentioned above as a serious source of background in fast neutron detectors which utilise silicon counters. The study of these reactions is important from this point of view, but also for their intrinsic interest: they are among the simplest types of nuclear rearrangement processes.

When a silicon junction counter is exposed to a flux of fast neutrons the charged particles produced cause ionization which, when it occurs within the depletion layer of the counter, gives pulses proportional to the total ionization. It must be remembered that two charged particles result from each of these nuclear reactions, the proton for instance being accompanied by a recoiling nucleus of aluminium. If these particles both ionize with equal efficiency the resulting pulse is proportional to their total kinetic energy, which is equal to the incident neutron energy together with the energy release of the reaction, Q. The work of Sattler[86] has shown that ions of mass close to that of silicon ionize effectively in silicon if their energy is above about 1 MeV (see Fig. 1.10). This has been so for most of the Si(n, α) reactions that have been studied; in the case of the (n, p) reactions only a little energy is carried by the heavy nucleus and the measurements have so far not been sufficiently precise to reveal the departure from full ionization. Transitions leading to excited states of the residual nucleus are followed by emission of a gamma ray, which has a negligible possibility of being absorbed within the detector. Hence the spectrum of pulse-heights recorded allows the yield to different final states to be measured separately. The energies of charged particles produced in these reactions are typically a few MeV and so it is easy to obtain detectors of sufficiently large sensitive volumes that the loss at the boundary is small and can be allowed for. The counting rate is a measure of the integrated cross-section, that is, summed over all angles of emission; a limitation of the method is that it is very difficult to obtain information regarding the angular distribution of the reaction products. Finally it should be mentioned that the very high purity of the silicon used in radiation detectors precludes any possibility of error due to contamination of the 'target'.

The simplicity of this type of experiment and the wealth of data that can be obtained have attracted a large number of investigators. So far most of the results relate to the commonest isotope of silicon Si^{28} (isotopic abundance 92 per cent). The Q values of (n, p) and (n, a) reactions in the three stable isotopes of silicon are listed in Table 8.2.

TABLE 8.2

Q-values of neutron-induced reactions in silicon.

Isotope	Abundance	$Q, (n, p)$	$Q, (n, a)$
	%	MeV	MeV
Si^{28}	92·21	−3·867	−2·663
Si^{29}	4·70	−3·185	−0·021
Si^{30}	3·09	−6.510	−4·192

Among the first to undertake such measurements, Bonner, Mainsbridge and Rabson[87] in 1961 reported cross-sections for the Si^{28} (n, p) and (n, a) processes in the neutron energy range 4·6 to 8·6 MeV. Deuchars and Lawrence[88] measured Si^{28} (n, a) cross-sections at 14 MeV for transitions to several states in Mg^{25}, using a shallow depletion layer so that essentially only the alpha spectrum was recorded. Lawrence[89] has studied in detail the corrections necessary for the escape of particles from the depletion layer. These higher energy measurements were considerably extended by Colli and her colleagues[90, 91] who have published (n, a) cross-sections covering the neutron energy range 12 to 19 MeV.

In the lower energy region Andersson-Lindström, Betz, Mausberg and Rössle[92] have published (n, p) and (n, a) cross-sections for Si^{28} and Si^{29} between the energies of 5·2 and 9 MeV. The absolute cross-section was obtained to an accuracy of about 20 per cent by measuring the neutron flux at the position of the silicon detectors by means of a Li^6 I scintillation crystal. Dearnaley, Ferguson and Morrison[77] (Fig. 8.41)

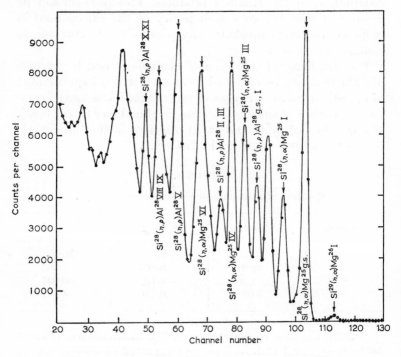

Fig. 8.41 Spectrum of neutron-induced reactions observed in a bare silicon surface-barrier detector, of 7000 ohm cm resistivity, bombarded with 11·2 MeV monoenergetic neutrons at a detector bias of 120 V. Roman numerals indicate the excited state formed in the residual nucleus; from DEARNALEY, FERGUSON and MORRISON[77]

suggested a more accurate method for obtaining absolute cross-sections in such experiments. A film of polyethylene of known thickness is placed in contact with the detector, which for this purpose should be fully-depleted so that the active volume is accurately defined. Then a comparison of the yield of recoil protons with that of the reaction products enables the cross-section to be calculated. Konijn and Lauber[93] have used this procedure to study the Si^{29} (n, a) cross-section between 2·4 and 3·8 MeV; this is a difficult experiment owing to the low abundance of Si^{29}. Mainsbridge, Bonner and Rabson[94] have published Si^{29} (n, a) cross-sections for neutron energies of 4·6 to 8·5 MeV and point out the potentialities of a fast-neutron spectrometer consisting of a junction detector prepared from separated Si^{29}. Neutrons of below 5 MeV excite only the ground-state transition in Si^{29}, so that the alpha particle spectrum bears a one-to-one relationship to the neutron spectrum. The reaction threshold is only 20 keV but the yield remains low up to 3 MeV. In many instances, however, detector efficiency may not be important when an energy resolution of 50 to 100 keV is possible. If such a spectrometer is ever realised the detail of the Si^{29} (n, a) cross-section curve will become very important.

The measurements referred to so far have been of integrated cross-sections; it is much more difficult to obtain differential cross-sections but a method has been described for accomplishing this. The arrangement, due to Aitken and Dixon,[96] is shown in Fig. 8.42. The high-resistivity surface-barrier detectors are mounted face-to-face with a gaseous proportional counter between them. A triple coincidence in this system indicates that a charged particle released in the silicon of one detector has crossed to the second. The particle energy is given by the sum of all three pulse heights and the magnitude of the pulse in the gaseous counter can be used to distinguish protons, deuterons and alpha particles. This arrangement clearly selects those particles emitted within a limited cone; by setting it at different angles to the neutron beam the angular distribution can be explored. Andersson-Lindström and his colleagues[92] have described similar measurements at lower neutron energies using a pair of spaced silicon detectors but with the proportional counter omitted.

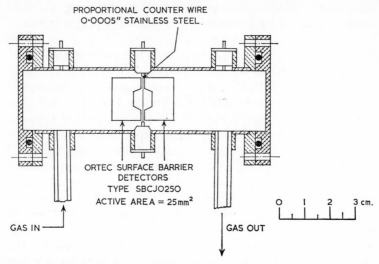

FIG. 8.42 Triple detector system used by AITKEN and DIXON[97] in the
study of neutron-induced reactions in silicon

The results of the experiments outlined in this section have
been important in supporting the picture of statistical fluctuation in reaction cross-section put forward by Ericson.[95] It is
desirable next to close the gap which remains in the published
data, between 9 and 12 MeV, and to study the observed
fluctuations in the greatest possible resolution in order to be
certain that the experimental energy resolution is sufficiently
small compared with the mean width of compound nucleus
states at the particular excitation produced.

(c) Neutron-induced reactions in germanium

The availability of lithium-drifted germanium detectors of
large sensitive volume has opened the way for the study of (n,
p) and (n, a) reactions in germanium on lines similar to that
described above in silicon. The Q-values of the reactions in the
five stable isotopes of germanium are listed in Table 8.3.

So far only one experiment on germanium has been reported[98] at neutron energies of 14·1 and 14·8 MeV. Aitken and
Dixon[97] deduced from their results the existence of two new
levels in Zn^{70}. By a calibration of the detector with gamma

TABLE 8.3

Q-values of neutron-induced reactions in germanium.

Isotope	Abundance	Q, (n, p)	Q, (n, a)
	%	MeV	MeV
Ge^{70}	20·52	−0·821	2·97
Ge^{72}	27·43	−3·219	1·07
Ge^{73}	7·76	−0·719	3·79
Ge^{74}	36·54	−4·870	−0·69
Ge^{76}	7·76	?	−8·37

rays of up to 5 MeV it was possible to compare the pulse-height due to charged reaction products with that of gamma rays of the same energy. The pulse-height of the recoil Zn nuclei produced with energies around 1 MeV by (n, a) reactions was found to be low by about 0·4 MeV. This observation is in agreement with the work of Sattler[98] who has shown that germanium ions of 1 MeV produce only about 50 per cent of the ionization of a 1 MeV electron, in germanium.

A rich variety of reactions can be studied in the germanium isotopes, but the energy resolution available will probably be limited by the spread in pulse height which results from the variation in the sharing of kinetic energy by the alpha-particle and zinc nucleus at different angles of break-up. The region of excitation and mass number of the target are such that the Ericson fluctuations[95] in cross-section will be very narrow and probably unobservable. It will probably be necessary to use neutron energies of 30 MeV or more in order to be able to compare the results with theory. However, cross-section measurements at lower energies remain useful from the point of view of establishing background levels to be expected in the use of germanium detectors in a fast-neutron flux.

(d) The B^{10} (n, a) reaction

The B^{10} (n, a) Li^7 reaction is probably the most widely utilized process for the purpose of neutron detection and has accordingly been the subject of many experiments. Perhaps the most thorough investigation has been made by Davis, Gabbard, Bonner and Bass[99] over the neutron energy range

0·2 to 8 MeV using a gridded ionization chamber filled with argon and $B^{10}F_3$. The total (n, α) cross-section had earlier been measured by Bichsel and Bonner[100] from 20 keV to 4·8 MeV with a $B^{10}F_3$ proportional counter.

An unusual feature of the reaction is the strength, at low neutron energies, of the transition to the first excited state of Li^7 at 478 keV. The ratio of the yield of this alpha particle group (α_1) to that of the ground state group (α_0) falls from about 16 for thermal neutrons to unity at 1·1 MeV. If the ratio of yields $(\alpha_1 : \alpha_0)$ were accurately known over this energy range the yield of 478 keV gamma rays from a boron sample would, in conjunction with the known total cross-section, enable the neutron flux to be measured very simply and with a high efficiency. The method would then be useful in time-of-flight experiments with pulsed neutron generators.

Dearnaley[85] has shown it to be possible to use semiconductor counters for measurement of the $\alpha_1 : \alpha_0$ ratio, taking advantage of the good energy resolution of these detectors. In work begun in collaboration with P. D. Miller, a thin self-supporting foil of B^{10} was mounted between a pair of silicon surface-barrier detectors, the alpha-particle and recoiling lithium ion being counted in coincidence. Figure 8.43 shows the summed pulse-height spectrum obtained when the sandwich was irradiated with neutrons of about 80 keV. The α_0 and α_1 groups are almost resolved; a thinner boron film would give better resolution. The lower energy peaks are due to reactions in which one of the products escapes detection; a closer setting of the detectors will reduce this loss to an acceptable level. In order to exclude thermal neutrons the array was shielded with 0·03 inches of cadmium, but it is advisable to minimise the background flux of thermal neutrons owing to the large thermal cross-section of the reaction. The neutron energy can be determined very accurately by a time-of-flight method. This work is being continued at A.E.R.E. by N. H. Gale and A. Siddiq.

(e) Other neutron-induced reactions

All the neutron-induced reactions in silicon have negative Q-values (Table 8.2) and hence contribute no background in the study of positive Q charged-particle reactions. A target is

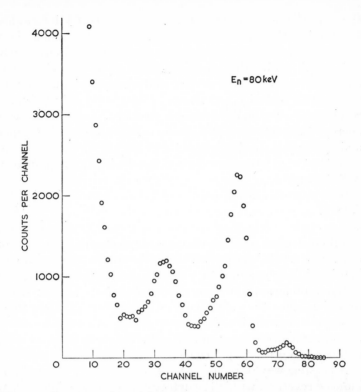

Fig. 8.43 Spectrum of particles observed from the $B^{10}(n, a)$ reaction in a sandwich detector[85]

merely placed close to a silicon detector in a monoenergetic neutron flux and the spectrum is recorded. The target must, however, be sufficiently thin for the charged particle to escape without excessive degradation of energy and this severely limits the yield. The neutron flux may not be too great or pile-up of pulses from reactions induced within the counter may obscure the spectrum. The number of experiments that have been carried out in this way is therefore rather small.

Marcazzan, Tonolini and Zetta[101] have studied (n, a) reactions in several heavy elements at a neutron energy of 14·7 MeV. The targets, of weight about 20 mgm/cm², were mounted 4 mm from the face of a silicon junction counter, 1 cm² in area. By reversing the arrangement alpha particles emitted in the forward and backward hemispheres could be studied separately. The Ta^{181} (n, α) and Au^{197} (n, α) reactions both show a strong forward asymmetry, taken to indicate the dominance of direct reaction processes. Alpha-particle spectra from Ho^{165} and Lu^{175} were also studied. By a similar method Cuzzocrea, Notarrigo and Rubbino[102] have investigated (n, α) reactions in the molybdenum isotopes at 15 MeV neutron energy. Enriched targets were used of six different isotopes, and by varying the distance between the target and the silicon detector the angular distribution was deduced and compared with theory.

At lower energies Konijn and Lauber[93] have studied the Ni^{58} (n, p) cross-section for neutrons between 2·2 and 3·8 MeV. The neutron flux in this experiment was measured by a proton recoil counter using a silicon detector as described in Section 8.11. The results agreed with flux determinations by a conventional 'long counter' to an accuracy of 7 per cent, but the authors preferred the semiconductor recoil counter determination since the small bulk of the device allows it to be placed closer to the irradiated sample and causes less modification of the neutron flux in its vicinity. The method is now being extended to other target elements.

A possible way of reducing the background due to neutron-induced reactions within the detector in such experiments is to adapt the idea of Aitken and Dixon.[96] A shallow gaseous proportional counter can be constructed between the target and the silicon detector, with its anode wire parallel to the detector surface. Coincidences between the two detectors eliminate most of the background pulses, and the product of the pulse-heights, as in a dE/dx and E telescope, allows protons and alpha-particles to be distinguished. In the case of (n, p) reactions at the higher neutron energies a thin silicon dE/dx detector may replace the gaseous counter, with the advantage of a shorter detector resolving time.

(f) Neutron cross-section measurements with nuclear explosion sources

A recent and novel application of semiconductor counters to the study of neutron-induced reactions has been made by a large group at Los Alamos Scientific Laboratory. A nuclear detonation, in an underground test facility, is utilized as a high intensity source of neutrons of short time duration. The neutron flight time determines the neutron energy. An evacuated vertical shaft, carefully designed as a neutron beam collimator produces a flux of the order 10^{18} neutrons/cm²/sec over

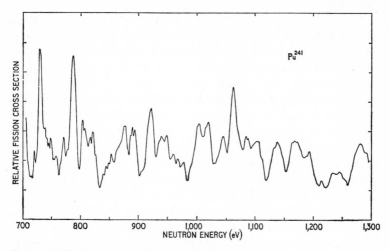

FIG. 8.44 Fission cross-section of Pu²⁴¹ measured by using a nuclear explosion as a neutron source from DIVEN *et al.*[35]

an area of about 1 cm², and since the flight path is some hundreds of metres the resolution, typically 0·5 *n*sec/metre, is comparable with that obtainable in laboratory time-of-flight experiments with accelerators. It has been estimated, however, that to obtain a comparable integrated flux would take 1000 years with present-day accelerators.

The neutron beam is arranged to fall on a series of foil targets. Charged particles emitted from these are detected by silicon junction counters, which are themselves shielded from the neutrons. The method has so far been mainly applied to the study of fission cross-sections but is of general applicability to any neutron-induced charged-particle or gamma cross-section.

The mode of operation of the detectors is of particular interest. The rate of arrival of particles at the detectors is so large that individual particle detection is impossible. Instead the detectors are operated in the current mode, that is the current flow due to the release of carriers by ionization is used as a measure of the energy release in the detector. In order to limit statistical fluctuations to about 1 per cent, some 10^4 events are required within the time resolution of about 10^{-7} sec.

This method of operation of detectors was thoroughly tested before the experiment, by Hemmendinger, Silbert and Moat,[29] who simulated the experimental conditions by means of bursts of low energy protons from a pulsed accelerator. It was observed that certain surface-barrier detectors exhibit pulse amplification when the total output charge exceeds 2 × 10^{-7} Coulomb. The effect is attributed to injection tunnelling of electrons through the oxide layer at the detector surface, as was observed by Walter[27] in the detection of fission fragments. Diffused junction counters do not show this effect, though a non-linearity of response was observed at a limiting input current of about 10 μA.

The current output of the detectors is amplified by an array of logarithmic current amplifiers the output of which is displayed on a bank of oscilloscopes and recorded by high-speed streak cameras. The data must be read from the film by optical scanning but a single run can yield cross-section values over a range from a few keV to 14 MeV neutron energy. The neutron spectrum which is required for the analysis of the data is obtained by the use of samples such as Li^6 and U^{235}, of known cross-sections.

As mentioned in Section 8.6 the method is of especial value in the study of fission cross-sections in materials with a high rate of spontaneous fission or with a high alpha activity. In such cases a shutter, interposed between the target and the detectors, may be opened for the duration of the neutron burst, which is only a few milliseconds.

The same group has also measured capture gamma-ray cross-sections by means of Moxon-Rae detectors modified to make use of semiconductor counters. The original detector devised by Moxon and Rae[103] consisted of a graphite converter and a thin scintillator. Gamma rays produce Compton electrons in the graphite and these are detected in the scintillation counter. The system has a relatively low sensitivity to scattered neutrons but too high a sensitivity for the type of experiment described above. Hemmendinger, Silbert and Moat[29] used a fully-depleted silicon junction detector, 200μ thick, in place of the scintillation counter. A modified converter, 2·4 cm thick and containing about 9 atom-per cent of bismuth, gave a detection probability proportional to the gamma-ray energy, between 1 and 12 MeV. This is required in order that the response should be independent of the detailed gamma decay scheme; the output depends only upon the total gamma-ray energy in a cascade.

REFERENCES

For this chapter

1. Benoit, R. G., Bertolini, G. and Restelli, G. B., *Nucl. Instr. & Methods*, **29**, 149 (1964).
2. Chetham-Strode, A., Tarrant, J. R. and Silva, R. J., *I.R.E. Trans. Nucl. Sci.*, NS-8, No. 1, 59 (1961).
3. Ghiorso, A., Sikkeland, T., Larsh, A. E. and Latimer, R. M., *Phys. Rev. Letters*, **6**, 473 (1961).
4. Walter, F. J., Dabbs, J. W. T., Roberts, L. D. and Wright, H. W., *Oak Ridge National Laboratory Report CF 58-11-99* (1958).
5. Halbert, M. L. and Blankenship, J. L., *Nucl. Instr. & Methods*, **8**, 106 (1960).
6. Williams, C. W., Kiker, W. E. and Schmitt, H. W., *Rev. Sci. Instr.*, **35**, 1116 (1964).
7. Ewing, R. I., *I.R.E. Trans. Nucl. Sci.*, NS-9, No. 3, 207 (1962).
8. Parkinson, W. C. and Bilaniuk, O. M., *Rev. Sci. Instr.*, **32**, 1136 (1961).
9. Dearnaley, G. and Whitehead, A. B., *Nucl. Instr. & Methods*, **12**, 205 (1961).
10. Cedarlund, R., Horn, A., and Scolnick, M., *Nucl. Instr. & Methods*, **13**, 305 (1961).
11. McKenzie, J. M. and Bromley, D. A., *Phys. Rev. Letters*, **2**, 303 (1959).
12. Almqvist, E., Kuehner, J. A. and Bromley, D. A., reported by Bromley, D. A., in *NAS-NRC Publication*, **871**, 61 (1961). Ed. Dabbs, J. W. T. and Walter, F. J.
13. Huth, G. C., Bergeson, H. E. and Trice, J. B., *Rev. Sci. Instr.*, **34**, 1283 (1963).
14. Huth, G. C., Trice, J. B., Shannon, J. A. and McKinney, R. A., *I.E.E.E. Trans. Nucl. Sci.*, NS-12, No. 1 (1965).

15. Bromley, D. A., *NAS-NRC Publication* **871**, 61 (1961). Ed. Dabbs, J. W. T. and Walter, F. J.
16. Wegner, H. E., *Nuclear Electronics*, I, 427, I.A.E.A. (Vienna, 1962).
17. Wegner, H. E., *I.E.E.E. Trans. Nucl. Sci.*, NS-12, No. 1 (1965).
18. Chasman, C. and Bromley, D. A., *Bull. Amer. Phys. Soc.*, Ser. II, **7**, 36 (1962).
19. Halbert, M. L., *Nuclear Electronics*, I, 403, I.A.E.A. (Vienna, 1962).
20. Anderson, C. E., Bromley, D. A. and Sachs, M., *Nucl. Instr. & Methods*, **13**, 238 (1962).
21. Mollenauer, J. F., Wagner, S., and Miller, G. L., *Brookhaven National Laboratory Report*, BNL 737 (T-266) (1962).
22. Gemmell, D. S., *I.E.E.E. Trans. Nucl. Sci.*, NS-11, No. 3, 409 (1964).
23. Evans, J. E., Kuehner, J. A. and Almqvist, E. (*to be published*).
24. See discussion in *NAS-NRC Publication* **871**, 27 (1961). Ed. Dabbs, J. W. T. and Walter, F. J.
25. Wegner, H. E., Britt, H. C and Shlaer, W. J., *Bull. Amer. Phys. Soc.*, Ser. II, **7**, 36 (1962).
26. Schmitt, H. W., Neiler, J. H., Walter, F. J. and Silva, R. J., *Oak Ridge National Laboratory Report ORNL-3268*, p. 94 (1962).
27. Walter, F. J., *I.E.E.E. Trans. Nucl. Sci.*, NS-11, No. 3, 232 (1964).
28. Gibson, W. M., and Miller, G. L., *private communication* to F. J. Walter.
29. Hemmendinger, A., Silbert, M. G. and Moat, A., *I.E.E.E. Trans. Nucl. Sci.*, NS-12, No. 1 (1965).
30. Walter, F. J., Neiler, J. H., Silva, R. J. and Schmitt, H. W., *Oak Ridge National Laboratory Report ORNL-3268*, p. 54 (1962).
31. Schmitt, H. W., Kiker, W. E. and Williams, C. W., *Phys. Rev.*, 1965 (*to be published*).
32. Stein, W. E. (*to be published*).
33. Williams, C. W., Schmitt, H. W., Walter, F. J. and Neiler, J. H., *Nucl. Instr. & Methods*, **29**, 205 (1964).
34. Huizenga, J. R., Vandenbosch, R. and Warhanek, H., *Phys. Rev.*, **124**, 1964 (1961).
35. Diven, B. C., Moat, A., Silbert, M. G. *et al.*, *private communication*.
36. Schultz, H. L., reported by Bromley, D. A., *I.R.E. Trans. Nucl. Sci.*, NS-9, No. 3, 135 (1962).

37. Bizzeti, P. G. and Bizzeti-Sona, A. M., *Il Nuovo Cimento*, **26**, 1412 (1962).
38. Lokan, K. H., Hogg, G. R., Cannington, P. H. and Stewart, R. J. J., *Physics Letters*, **11**, 73 (1964).
39. Ullrich, H., *Physics Letters*, **12**, 114 (1964).
40. Scheer, Schlüpmann, and Triantafyllidis, *Physics Letters*, **7**, 269, (1963).
41. Scheer, Schlüpmann, and Triantafyllidis, *Nucl. Phys.*, **56**, 113 (1964).
42. Miller, G. L., Foreman, B. M. and Yuan, L. C. L., *I.R.E. Trans. Nucl. Sci.*, **NS-8**, No. 1, 73 (1961).
43. Van Putten, J. D. and Vander Velde, J. C., *I.R.E. Trans. Nucl. Sci.*, **NS-8**, No. 1, 124 (1961).
44. Koch, L., Messier, J. and Valin, J., *Nuclear Electronics*, I, 465, I.A.E.A. (Vienna, 1962).
45. Rossi, B., *High-Energy Particles*, p. 32, Prentice-Hall, Inc. (New York, 1952).
46. Sternheimer, R. M., *Phys. Rev.*, **115**, 137 (1959).
47. Sun, C. R., *I.R.E. Trans. Nucl. Sci.*, **NS-9**, No. 3, 211 (1962).
48. Blumenfeld, H. and Pandolfi, F. P., *I.E.E.E. Trans. Nucl. Sci.*, **NS-12**, No. 1 (1965).
49. Tepper, L., Miller, G. L. and Kycia, T., *I.E.E.E. Trans. Nucl. Sci.*, **NS-11**, No. 3, 431 (1964).
50. Berényi, D. and Fényes, T., *Nucl. Instr. & Methods*, **27**, 122 (1964).
51. Goulding, F. S., *I.E.E.E. Trans. Nucl. Sci.*, **NS-11**, No. 3, 177 (1964).
52. Bertolini, G., Capellani, F., Fantechi, R. and Restelli, G. B., *Mem. Soc. Roy. Sci. de Liège*, X, No. 2, 255 (1964).
53. Casper, K. J. and Thompson, R. H., *Bull. Amer. Phys. Soc.*, **9**, 17 (1964).
54. McKenzie, J. M. and Ewan, G. T., *I.R.E. Trans. Nucl. Sci.*, **NS-8**, No. 1, 50 (1961).
55. Fox, R. J. and Borkowski, C. J., *I.R.E. Trans. Nucl. Sci.*, **NS-9**, No. 3, 213 (1962).
56. Blankenship, J. L. and Borkowski, C. J., *I.R.E. Trans. Nucl. Sci.*, **NS-9**, No. 3, 181 (1962).
57. Mann, H. M., Haslett, J. W. and Janarek, F. J., *Proc. Third Annual Nuc. Eng. Education Conf.*, Argonne National Laboratory (1962).
58. Rae, E. R. and Bowey, E. M. (*to be published*).
59. Tove, P. A. and Jonasson, L. G., *Nucl. Instr. & Methods*, **27**, 45 (1964).

60. Ewan, G. T. and Tavendale, A. J., *Can. J. Phys.*, **42**, 2286 (1964).
61. Hansen, W. L. and Jarrett, B. V., *Lawrence Radiation Laboratory*, Report No. **UCRL-11589**.
62. Tavendale, A. J. (*to be published*).
63. Holm, D., *et al.* (*to be published*).
64. Shirley, D. A. and Rosenblum, S. S., *Bull. Amer. Phys. Soc.*, **9**, 498 (1964).
65. Stone, N. J., Frankel, R. B., and Shirley, D. A., *Bull. Amer. Phys. Soc.*, **9**, 486 (1964).
66. Julian, G. M. and Jha, S. *Bull. Amer. Phys. Soc.*, **9**, 663 (1964).
67. Motz, H. T., Jurney, E. T. and Ford, W. T., *Bull. Amer. Phys. Soc.*, **9**, 664 (1964).
68. Day, R. B. and Palms, J. M., *private communication*.
69. Easley, W., Huntzicker, J., Matthias, E., Rosenblum, S. S. and Shirley, D. A., *Bull. Amer. Phys. Soc.*, **9**, 435 (1964).
70. Anderson, H. L., Hargrove, C. K., Hincks, E. P. and Tavendale A. J., (*to be published*).
71. Slaughter, G. G. and Harvey, J. A., *Bull. Amer. Phys. Soc.*, **9**, 664 (1964).
72. Alexander, T. K., Pearson, J. D., Litherland, A. E. and Broude, C., *Phys. Rev. Letters*, **13**, 86 (1964).
73. Alexander, T. K. and Goulding, F. S., *Nucl. Instr. & Methods*, **13**, 244 (1961).
74. Love, T. A. and Murray, R. B., *I.R.E. Trans. Nucl. Sci.*, **NS-8**, No. 1, 91 (1961).
75. De Cosnac, B., Noel, J.-P., Bok, J. and Schuttler, R., *Nuclear Electronics*, I, 451, I.A.E.A. (Vienna, 1962).
76. Murphy, J. F., University of California, *Lawrence Radiation Laboratory Report UCRL-6505* (1961).
77. Dearnaley, G., Ferguson, A. T. G. and Morrison, G. C., *I.R.E. Trans. Nucl. Sci.*, **NS-9**, No. 3, 174 (1962).
78. Dearnaley, G. and Ferguson, A. T. G., *Nucleonics*, **20**, 84 (1962).
79. Rossi, B. B. and Staub, H. H., *Ionization Chambers and Counters*, Chap. 7 (McGraw-Hill, 1949).
80. Parker, J. B., White, P. H. and Webster, R. J., *Nucl. Instr. & Methods*, **23**, 61 (1963).
81. Howerton, R. J., University of California, *Lawrence Radiation Laboratory Report UCRL-5226* (1959).
82. White, P. H., *Mem. Soc. Roy. Sci. de Liège*, **X**, No. 2, 341 (1964).
83. Potenza, R. and Rubbino, A., *Nucl. Instr. & Methods*, **26**, 93 (1964).

84. Lee, M. E. and Awcock, M. L., A.E.R.E., *Harwell Report* No. SM-36/55 (1962).
85. Dearnaley, G., *Prog. in Fast Neutron Physics*, p. 173, ed. Phillips, G. C., Marion, J. B. and Risser, J. R. (Univ. of Chicago Press, 1963).
86. Sattler, A. R., *Bull. Amer. Phys. Soc.*, 9, 655 (1964).
87. Bonner, T. W., Mainsbridge, B. and Rabson, T. A., *Bull. Amer. Phys. Soc.*, Ser. II, 6, No. 5, 440 (1961).
88. Deuchars, W. M. and Lawrence, G. P., *Nature*, 191, 995 (1961).
89. Lawrence, G. P., Ph.D. Thesis, Australian National University, Canberra, Australia (1964).
90. Colli, L., Iori, I., Marcazzan, M. G., Milazzo, M. and Tonolini, F., *Physics Letters*, 1, 120 (1962).
91. Colli, L., Iori, I., Marcazzan, M. G., and Milazzo, M., *Nucl. Phys.*, 43, 529 (1963).
92. Anderson-Lindström, G., Betz, G., Mausberg, W. and Rössle, E., *Mem. Soc. Roy. Sci. de Liège*, 10, No. 2, 265 (1964).
93. Konijn, J. and Lauber, A., *Nucl. Phys.* 48, 191 (1963).
94. Mainsbridge, B., Bonner, T. W. and Rabson, T. A., *Nucl. Phys.*, 48, 83 (1963).
95. Ericson, T., *Advances in Physics*, 9, 425 (1960).
96. Aitken, J. H. and Dixon, W. R., *Physics Letters*, 2, 152 (1962).
97. Aitken, J. H. and Dixon, W. R., *to be published*.
98. Sattler, A. R., *private communication*.
99. Davis, E. A., Gabbard, F., Bonner, T. W. and Bass, R., *Nucl. Phys.*, 27, 448 (1961).
100. Bichsel, H. and Bonner, T. W., *Phys. Rev.*, 108, 1025 (1957).
101. Marcazzan, G. M., Tonolini, F., and Zetta, L., *Nucl. Phys.*, 46, 51 (1963).
102. Cuzzocrea, P., Notarrigo, S. and Rubbino, A., *Nucl. Phys.*, 55, 364 (1964).
103. Moxon, M. C. and Rae, E. R., *Nucl. Instr. and Methods*, 24, 445 (1963).

CHAPTER 9

OTHER APPLICATIONS OF
SEMICONDUCTOR COUNTERS

9.1 Introduction

The energy resolution of semiconductor counters is the best available for very many experimental situations in nuclear physics. It is this single fact which has been the impetus behind the large amount of work on semiconductor counters during the last few years, and which accounts for the present position. Nevertheless, semiconductor counters have other properties which should eventually prove attractive in a number of other fields, although it must be admitted that the attention they have received so far is slight by comparison.

First, let us list these characteristics, and the ways in which they might be used to advantage.

(*i*) Semiconductor counters are small and light in weight, and can be presented in a rugged form.

(*ii*) They can be made in a wide variety of shapes and their effective volume may (in the case of junctions) be varied by changing the bias voltage.

(*iii*) They have very modest power requirements and can conveniently be supplied from dry batteries.

(*iv*) They can detect many types of nuclear radiation, particularly if coatings of fissile or other materials are used.

These properties immediately suggest a wide spectrum of applications in medicine, in space physics, in reactor instrumentation, in military and civil defence fields and in personnel and plant monitoring. Work in many of these areas has begun, but it is still in its infancy, so that accounts are necessarily brief and incomplete. It is possible that in some cases unsatisfactory performance results because the only available devices, developed for nuclear physics experiments, are not optimised for other applications. This should be a temporary state of affairs however, because the demand for counters for these activities could far exceed those needed for nuclear physics, clearly justifying separate device development should this prove necessary.

9.2 Radiation monitoring

The smallness and sensitivity of semiconductor counters combined with great flexibility in use make them immediately attractive for portable monitoring instruments intended either to measure the radiation flux at any point, or to search for localized radioactive contamination. Only occasionally is it important to discriminate between closely spaced energy peaks, but it is usually necessary to measure alpha, beta and gamma radiation separately because of their different relative biological effectiveness (R.B.E.). For any type of radiation it is also important to have a response which measures the health hazard without precise knowledge of the radiation spectrum, and monitoring instruments are usually required to have a response calibrated in Rads/hour, independent of the energy spectrum of the radiation. Although the response of an instrument as a function of particle energy can be adjusted by surrounding the detector with suitable metallic absorbers this inevitably reduces the overall sensitivity, and may add appreciably to the size and weight of the equipment. It is therefore important that the natural response of the instrument should be independent of particle energy.

Two kinds of instrument are important for measuring dose rate. One is the homogeneous counter consisting of suitably doped cadmium sulphide crystals, which may be used either in the 'photoconducting' mode, (in which a mean current, a function of dose rate, is measured) or as a pulse counter. The second kind of instrument uses junction counters of silicon, always in the pulse counter mode. These will be described in turn.

(a) Cadmium sulphide radiation monitors

Cadmium sulphide crystals equipped with soldered indium electrodes have been known to respond to gamma radiation for some years. In fact this is probably the oldest semiconductor counter to be regarded as a serious commercial proposition. Crystals prepared by sublimation under certain conditions were found to exhibit 'gain' by the process described as Case IV in Section 3.4 due to minority carrier trapping. Sensitivities as high as 1 μA per Rad per hour have been recorded, so that a simple instrument consisting of a cadmium sulphide cell, a 100 volt dry cell and a current meter can have sufficient sensitivity for most gamma ray monitoring applications. There are severe practical difficulties with such monitors, all of which are associated with the preparation of the material. The fact that cadmium sulphide sublimes at temperatures below its melting point means that it is not amenable to purification and crystallization processes developed for germanium and silicon. There is still insufficient control of purity and crystal perfection for cadmium sulphide crystals to be reproducible, and great variations in sensitivity are commonplace. The crystals usually have shallow traps as well as the deep ones taking part in the current gain process, and the former reduce carrier mobilities, increasing the response time by much more than the gain factor. The most sensitive crystals commonly have response times of tens of seconds, or even longer.

Methods of combating this last problem have been put into practice by the A.E.I. Research Laboratories.[1] They have shown that the response time is reduced at high signal levels, and so they introduce a small 'priming signal' from a radioactive source encapsulated with the crystal to bring the operating point onto a faster part of the response time characteristic. In an elaboration of the basic instrument they use the bias voltage derived by passing the counter current through a load resistor to control the frequency of a pulse generator feeding a loudspeaker. This is a very neat way of obtaining an audible output the urgency of which increases with radiation dose rate, and it could prove both cheaper and more robust than a meter reading instrument.

The same laboratory has also made crystals which show some current gain, but retain sufficient speed to give discrete output pulses. 5 MeV alpha particles have been shown to give sufficient output to drive a small loudspeaker directly, giving a very cheap and portable alpha particle meter.

There have apparently been no measurements of the relative sensitivity of cadmium sulphide over a range of gamma ray energies, but the atomic weights of the constituent atoms are sufficiently different from those of body tissue that some correction of the response is likely to be necessary. The sensitivity has usually been measured for ^{60}Co gamma radiation.

(b) Silicon p-n junction counters

Silicon junction counters can also be used for radiation monitoring, but because they are pulse counters, registering individual particles, they require more complicated circuits to produce a suitable audible or metered output. However, they offer a number of compensating advantages.

(i) Sensitivity to alpha, beta and gamma radiation with discrimination in mixed fluxes.

(ii) Mechanical robustness.

(iii) No high voltages, high value resistors or electrometer valves are needed.

An instrument has been described by Moncaster, Northrop and Raines[2] in which the sensitive element is an encapsulated diffused junction made from high resistivity p-type silicon. Using 10,000 Ω cm crystals, and applying a bias of 50 volts to the junction gives a depletion layer thickness of about 0·3 mm, which is adequate for the detection of several per cent of an incident flux of gamma rays. The r.m.s. noise level in the counters is between 15 and 20 keV equivalent particle energy, so that in principle gamma rays down to this energy can be detected. Over almost the whole of the gamma energy range from 20 keV to 2 MeV the Compton process dominates the absorption, so that mono-energetic gamma rays give rise to a complete spectrum of secondary electron energies from zero to a maximum just less than the gamma energy. With a depletion layer thickness of 0·3 mm many of the more energetic secondaries will escape before losing all their energy, so that the pulse height spectrum produced by the counter will be almost triangular in shape. Two such spectra for different gamma-ray energies are shown in Fig. 9.1, which illustrates

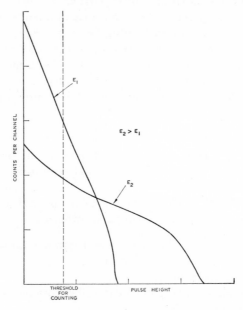

Fig. 9.1 Schematic diagram showing pulse height spectra for two different gamma ray energies (After MONCASTER, NORTHROP and RAINES[2])

schematically how the count rate above a certain threshold will depend both on the number of incident quanta and on their quantum energy, so that the count rate could well be proportional to the dose rate in rads per hour over the whole range of gamma energies. This is borne out by an experimental determination of the count rate at a fixed dose rate for gamma-ray energies shown in Fig. 9.2. Clearly, then, a straightforward silicon p-n junction has considerable possibilities for measuring gamma-ray dose rate, and has the advantage over cadmium sulphide in working at lower dose rates and in having a much faster response time. Typically a counter of 3 cm² area gives

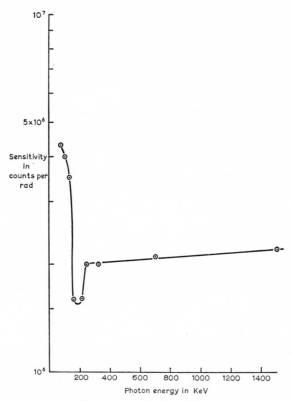

FIG. 9.2 Sensitivity of a silicon *p-n* junction to
photons of various energies (After Jones[3])

several counts per second for a dose rate of 1 mR per hour,
with a response time of a few μsec.

The performance of a portable instrument is likely to depend
more on the associated circuitry than on the counter because
the need for lightness and low battery drain dictates the use
of transistors, which have an inherently more noisy performance than vacuum tubes. There is a further difficulty in that
the low-noise charge sensitive transistor amplifiers described
in the literature have rather poor temperature stability and
are therefore unsuitable for use outside the laboratory. Moncaster, Northrop and Raines have chosen to use a straightforward voltage amplifier with double emitter follower input

to the amplifier, and use two blocking oscillators in cascade to provide power for the loudspeaker and logarithmic ratemeter. With the circuit diagram shown in Fig. 9.3 the counting threshold has to be set at about 60 keV to exclude amplifier noise, and the count rate is correspondingly reduced to about 2 counts per second per mR/hr.

By using a complete metal encapsulation it is possible to exclude low energy charged particles, and therefore to count only gamma rays, even in mixed fluxes of radiation. Alternatively an open window encapsulation gives sensitivity to all types of radiation, but it is possible to achieve a degree of discrimination against gamma rays by reducing the thickness of the depletion layer so that each charged particle loses just enough energy in it to give a signal above the counting threshold. For alpha particles this is best achieved by using no external bias, when the discrimination is complete, but for beta particles a higher bias is required and the discrimination is not so good. Clearly any of these detector types can be used with the same circuit and indicating system, giving a very versatile instrument.

There are many possible applications of semiconductor detectors in industrial processing, such as the monitoring of thickness of metal sheet or foil, the thickness of paper or plastic sheets, the thickness and profile of wires. In all cases the detectors would have sufficient sensitivity and speed of response to achieve automatic control without requiring a dangerously powerful radioactive source.

9.3 Military and civil defence applications

Much of the discussion in the previous two sections is of direct relevance to military and civil defence requirements and instrumentation for general personnel monitoring and for the care of the wounded, but there are three more specific military applications of semiconductor devices which deserve special mention here. Firstly, there is the measurement of fast high intensity bursts of gamma radiation such as those characteristic of a nuclear explosion. Lindsay[4] has used simple junction counters and even commercial rectifier diodes to integrate the signals due to such essentially coincident gamma rays, and

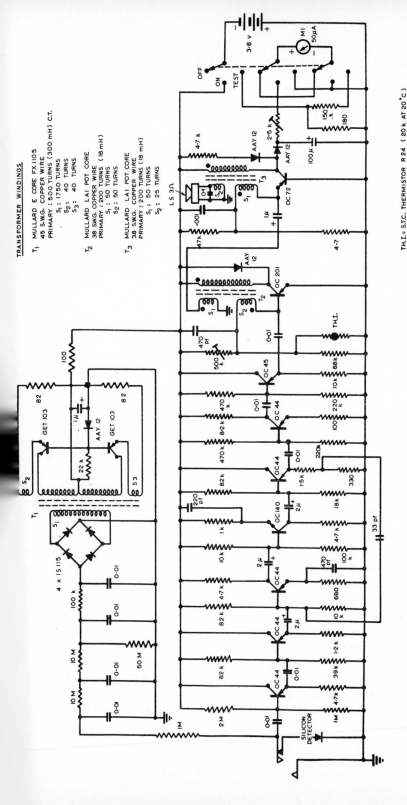

TRANSFORMER WINDINGS

T_1 MULLARD E CORE FX 1105
45 S.WG. COPPER WIRE
PRIMARY : 500 TURNS (300 mH) C.T.
    S_1 : 1750 TURNS
    S_2 : 40 TURNS
    S_3 : 40 TURNS

T_2 MULLARD LA1 POT CORE
38 S.W.G. COPPER WIRE
PRIMARY : 200 TURNS (18 mH)
    S_1 : 50 TURNS
    S_2 : 50 TURNS

T_3 MULLARD LA1 POT CORE
38 S.W.G. COPPER WIRE
PRIMARY : 200 TURNS (18 mH)
    S_1 : 50 TURNS
    S_2 : 25 TURNS

T.H.I.= S.T.C. THERMISTOR R 24 (20 k AT 20°C)

M_1 = WESTON M.C. METER MODEL S 32

L.S. = W.B. STENTORIAN MODEL S 1·75

FIG. 9.3 Circuit diagram of a transistorized radiation monitor (After MONCASTER, NORTHROP and RAINES[2])

estimates that in a counter of 1 cm² area the sensitivity is about 5×10^{-13} μA per micron of depletion layer depth for each 1 MeV cm^{-2} sec^{-1} of gamma-ray energy incident. This holds roughly for the gamma photon energy range 1–3 MeV.

Secondly, the need to measure beta particles in contaminated drinking water and foodstuffs may be best satisfied by the use of silicon junction counters because of the degree of discrimination which they offer against gamma rays. These measurements might, in an emergency, have to be made in a relatively intense gamma-ray field, where the use of scintillation counters or Geiger-Muller counters would require extensive shielding, either in the form of a lead castle, or a deep hole in the ground. Semiconductor counters could be used to measure beta contamination and to give information about the energy spectrum of the radiation with far less interference from gamma rays than any other method available.

Finally, it is worth anticipating a little of what is to be said about radiation damage in the final chapter by mentioning the use of commercial rectifying junctions as integrating dose meters for neutrons. Any neutron of more than 200 eV energy can create a lattice defect in silicon which then acts as a recombination centre and lowers the carrier lifetime. A measurement of reverse current, or of any other parameter dependent on the lifetime can be made to yield a value of the total neutron dose received.

9.4 Applications in nuclear engineering

Semiconductor detectors have been applied successfully to a number of applications in nuclear engineering, including the measurement of neutron spectra inside reactors, and the analysis of spent fuel rods. It seems likely that they will achieve other uses in a wide range of industrial plant handling radioactive materials or using radioactive tracers.

The measurement of neutron spectra in reactors is of primary importance, because of the role of neutrons in maintaining the reaction. Such measurements are difficult because of the very high radiation flux in the core of a reactor, and they require a counter with a very fast recovery time to avoid complete saturation. Pioneer work on measurement of neutron fluxes and spectra has been reported by Ajdačić, Barucija, Lalović and Petrović[5, 6].

To measure neutron fluxes they used an evacuated aluminium tube 6 metres long, 41 mm diameter and 0·5 mm wall thickness inserted into the core of the reactor. At one end of the tube, in the reactor core, is placed a target of a light element, Li^6 or B^{10}, or a fissile material U^{235} or Pu^{239}. At the other end of the tube outside the core, a semiconductor counter detects the fission fragments or charged particles coming from the target due to neutron induced reactions.

There are several problems in relating the count rate at the detector to the neutron flux absolutely, but they are largely overcome in this design of equipment. The use of aluminium causes a very small reduction in the neutron flux; the use of a thin foil target of known weight and isotopic composition allow accurate estimation of the number of atoms in the target and their cross-section for neutrons and reduces absorption and scattering of the reaction products to small proportions. The only other large error in initial experiments was associated with the scattering of reaction products from the walls of the tube, which produced changes in flux and energy spectrum which were hard to calculate accurately. This situation was improved by placing a 1 cm diameter collimator about 2 metres from the target, and so restoring the fission fragment spectrum to that obtained with target and detector 5 cm apart.

The geometrical efficiency with a counter area $12·57 \pm 0·25$ mm^2 was $2·644 \times 10^{-8}$, and the measured flux in the Vinca reactor at 6·5 MW was $(3·47 \pm 0·13) \times 10^{13}$ neutrons cm^{-2} sec^{-1}, the accuracy being ± 4 per cent. This accuracy enables detailed calculations to be made of reactor performance, and enables the results of fine adjustments of the reactor to be observed.

At higher fluxes another very elegant method of measurement becomes possible, which eliminates many of the inaccuracies of that described above. The counting rate becomes a function of time because of the 'burn-up' of target material, and the count rate decays according to the formula

$$n = GN_0\sigma \exp(-\sigma\varphi t) \qquad (9.1)$$

where N_0 is the initial number of reacting atoms in the target,

σ is their neutron cross section, φ is the neutron flux and G the geometrical efficiency. The slope of the decay curve log n vs t gives $\sigma\varphi$, so that the flux is measured as accurately as the slope and σ can be determined.

The same workers have also measured fast neutron spectra in the reactor core, using a sandwich counter of Li^6F between two semiconductor detectors and adding the signals obtained in coincidence from the two counters from the products of the $Li^6(n, \alpha) H^3$ reaction. The two main difficulties with this kind of measurement are

(i) the energy resolution of the system worsens as the reactor power is increased, an effect attributed to the gamma ray flux,

(ii) the high flux of thermal neutrons, with an efficiency 4×10^3 times that of fast neutrons in the above reaction seriously affects the lower part of the energy spectrum due to pulse pile up.

In this particular experiment the resolution of the counter rose from 220 keV at zero reactor power to 530 keV at 5 watts, so that no neutron spectra could be measured at reactor powers greater than 6 watts. Their results for the total reaction product energy spectrum are shown in Fig. 9.4; they have to be multiplied by the neutron transmission through the shield and the cross section of the reaction, and the energy scale should be reduced by the Q value for the reaction, 4·77 MeV. A disadvantage of semiconductors for this application is that their useful life in a neutron flux is 10^{12} neutrons cm^{-2}. Furr and Runyon[7] have used a fast neutron spectrometer similar to one described in Chapter 8 for reactor flux measurements.

Beets, Colle, Deckers, Gierts and de Leeuw[8] have pointed out that a measurement of the neutron spectrum at intermediate energies can be made by studying the angles of emission of the alpha particle and triton in the reaction $Li^6 (n, \alpha)H^3$. At low neutron energies the particles are emitted in almost opposite directions, but the precise angle between them is a measure of the neutron energy. Beets *et al.* tabulate the theoretical form of the dependence between angle and neutron energy and have developed a detection system based up on it.

Shown schematically in Fig. 9.5, it consists of a thin layer of Li[6] supported on a thin foil with semiconductor detectors on either side of it. One is fixed in position relative to the foil, and it is a surface barrier detector subtending an angle of 0·5° at the foil. The second is also a surface barrier, but with an annular sensitive area. It is placed on the opposite side of the

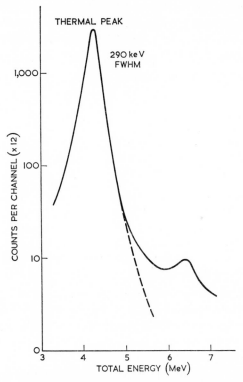

FIG. 9.4 Pulse height spectrum for neutrons inside a nuclear reactor (After ADJACIC *et al.*)

foil and can be moved along the axis of symmetry of the system. A count of coincident pulses in the two counters is a measure of that part of the neutron spectrum which is appropriate to the angle defined by the two detectors. This method is of great potential value for diagnostic studies of fast reactor critical assemblies.

Holm[9] and his associates have developed two interesting

pieces of equipment for measurements on plutonium loaded
fuel elements for fast reactors. The first of these is an accelerated life test of the encapsulation carried out by heating a
single fuel element electrically to 1100° C and using surface
barrier detectors to find escaping plutonium by detecting
alpha particles from the natural radioactive decay of plutonium. To avoid overheating the detector a series of five polished
nickel foils are used as radiation shields. They reduce the alpha
particle energy by only 1 MeV. The alpha activity has to be
detected against an intense gamma ray background, but by

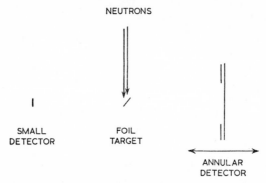

FIG. 9.5 Annular Detector Arrangement for
Measurement of Neutron Spectra (After
BEETS *et al.*)

using a fast electronic system to minimise pulse pile up, and
shallow depletion layer devices to cut down gamma ray
sensitivity Holm can detect 1 μgm of Plutonium on the outside of the fuel element.

The second piece of equipment is more elaborate. The idea
is to examine gamma ray spectra collimated from different
parts of a fuel element to study the segregation of fission products, the degree of fuel burn-up and the level of the contents
within the tube. Precise mechanical controls enable the element to be moved by remote handling techniques by a few
thousandths of an inch, and to be rotated about its axis, to
expose different parts of the element to the fine lead collimator. The detection system, described in Chapter 8 and
illustrated in Fig. 8.26 has to resolve complex and closely
spaced lines in the gamma ray spectrum. This is achieved by

using a lithium drifted germanium detector cooled to liquid nitrogen temperature and surrounded by a large annular sodium iodide crystal coupled to a photomultiplier. The sodium iodide is not directly exposed to the radiation from the fuel element, but only detects gamma rays which have undergone Compton scattering in the germanium detector. Using only those signals from the germanium detector in anti-coincidence with those from the sodium iodide reduces the Compton spectra by a factor of about 10. Fig. 9.6 shows spectra taken with and without anticoincidence, illustrating the improved signal: background ratio of the lower energy photoelectric peaks.

A development which could be of great importance in reactor instrumentation is forshadowed in recent work at Westinghouse Research Laboratories by Canepa, Malinaric, Campbell and Ostroski.[10] They have fabricated p-n junctions in silicon carbide, growing n-type crystals by sublimation in nitrogen and diffusing aluminium to form the p-type layer. The best devices, which were made from the highest purity crystals, could operate up to 700° C, and had a resistance to radiation damage 100 times greater than that of silicon devices.

In addition to the examples cited there would appear to be other possible uses of semiconductor detectors in nuclear engineering of a more straightforward kind, such as reactor shielding measurements and the monitoring of plant in which radioactive materials are processed. The neutron spectrometers decribed in Section 8.11 are readily adaptable as neutron dose rate meters, for they can give all the information needed to estimate the health hazard associated with a given neutron flux over a wide range of energies. Instruments similar to those mentioned in Section 9.2 might also find uses in monitoring engineering plant, where their small physical size and portability would give them advantages over gaseous counters and scintillator systems.

9.5 Measurements in space

Semiconductor counters possess a number of features which make them well suited for the measurement of nuclear radia-

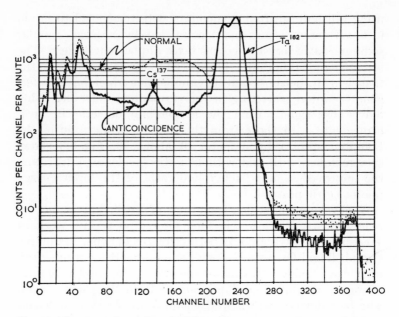

Fig. 9.6 Spectra taken with and without anticoincidence counting in an arrangement consisting of a germanium lithium drift counter inside an annular sodium iodide crystal (After HOLM et al.[8])

tion in space. They are light, compact and can be made very robust. The associated circuitry can be small, and though an amplifier is required, no high-voltage supply and associated corona discharge problems are involved. By comparison with scintillation detectors, the bulky and delicate photomultiplier tube can be eliminated. Semiconductor detectors, as we have seen, are very versatile and can easily be arranged in different telescope systems and arrays. Finally, they will operate under conditions of high counting rate. They are, however, very susceptible to radiation damage; some of the problems which can arise from this effect are discussed in the next chapter.

Measurements on low energy protons and heavier ions can be made with conventional junction counters or lithium-drifted junctions, with or without absorbers. Pieper[11] and his associates successfully operated four diffused junction counters in the 'Injun' satellite of July 1961, while the TRAAC satellite carried six guard-ring diffused junction counters for proton and alpha measurements, together with 20 neutron detectors incorporating boron-loaded radiator foils.

For higher energy measurements combinations of detectors in various telescope arrangements have been devised. Friedland, Ziemba, Olson and Delyser[12] have described a twin-detector proton spectrometer which utilizes a diffused junction, with a 0·15 mm depletion layer thickness, followed by a lithium drifted detector with a 1 mm deep intrinsic layer. Between the two detectors is an absorber of 0·2 mm of silicon, formed by the undepleted silicon of the first counter together with the window thickness of the second. Fig. 9.7 shows the response of these two counters to protons of energies between 1 and 200 MeV; the approximate energy range is distinguished according to whether a signal above the discriminator level is observed in one or both of the counters. According to the energy range, the output of one or other detector is recorded in a pulse height analyser and from a calibration in the laboratory the particle energy can be obtained.

An even more elaborate arrangement of ten detectors has been constructed to cover the proton energy range 24 to 210 MeV with a small angle of acceptance. Absorbers are placed between the detectors so that in a similar way roughly equal logarithmic increments of energy are covered in each of its stages. Despite this complexity the detector housing is only 2·9 by 2·6 by 2·2 inches and weighs 3 lb, while the 16 amplifiers and the logic circuitry should weigh 1 lb, with a power consumption of about 1 watt.

Another method of using semiconductor detectors for measurements on high-energy particles in space has been devised by Tuzzolino, Hubbard, Perkins and Fan.[13] In this work a photomultiplier tube was avoided by making use of the high photosensitivity of surface barrier detectors to detect the scintillation signal from a CsI (Tl) scintillator. Despite the difficulties of coupling the detector optically to the crystal without destroying the surface junction, an energy resolution of 22 per cent was obtained for 74 MeV protons. The detection efficiency is much better than can be obtained with a thin photocathode, and it should be possible to improve this resolution. A fuller description of the photoelectric properties of junctions is given in Section 9.7.

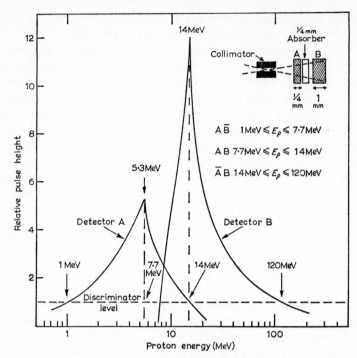

FIG. 9.7 Twin detector proton spectrometer for measurements
in space. Detector A is a silicon diffused junction, B a lithium-
drifted silicon detector. A pulse height analyser is gated to analyse
the response of detector A between 1 MeV and 7.7 MeV, and
detector B for proton energies between 7.7 MeV and 120 MeV;
(After FRIEDLAND et al.[12])

Friedland, Ziemba, Olson and Delyser[12] have also described
a magnetic beta-ray spectrometer for space flight, utilizing a
linear array of ten silicon junction counters along its focal
plane, each with a separate preamplifier. The detectors operate
within the spectrometer magnetic field, which is about 800
oersteds. This type of spectrometer was flown on Discoverers
XXIX and XXXI and the results have been reported by
West, Mann and Bloom.[14]

A series of measurements of the energies and densities of
electrons and protons in the van Allen radiation belts has been
made with silicon junction detectors flown in the Telstar sat-
ellites. The design of these experiments and an analysis of the

results have been reported by Brown and his co-workers[15,16]. The construction and properties of the counters have been described by Buck, Wheatley and Rodgers.[17] Of primary importance in this case was the reliability of the detectors over long periods, both at ground level and in outer space.

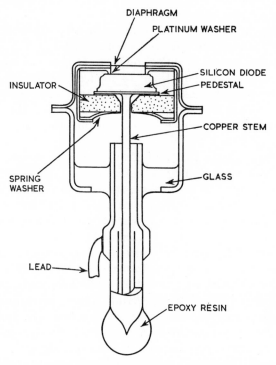

FIG. 9.8 Encapsulated silicon *p-n* junction (After
BUCK, WHEATLEY and RODGERS[17])

Of less importance was the energy resolution obtained in the experiment, and these features indicated a fully encapsulated *p-n* junction structure, hermetically sealed by a thin Kovar diaphragm. The design is shown in detail in Fig. 9.8.

The diodes were made from 10,000–20,000 ohm cm *p*-type silicon by diffusing an *n*-type impurity to a depth of about 3 microns. Only small devices were required because of the high particle fluxes in the radiation belts, and the size of the device can be judged by the fact that the 8 micron thick Kovar window is 2 mm in diameter. Equivalent noise line widths of 10 to 15 keV were found, and the minority carrier lifetime in the finished devices was about 30 μsec. The encapsulation stood up well under severe vibration and humidity tests and temperature and bias cycling.

The results obtained with these counters, which were used in arrays with various thicknesses of absorber in front of them have greatly increased our knowledge of the radiation belts, and of the effects upon them of nuclear explosions, but of equal interest and significance for the designer of semiconductor counters are the encapsulation method, and the detailed measurements of surface effects in p-n junction detectors discussed in Section 6.4.

Patterson, Turkevitch and Franzgrote[18] at the University of Chicago are developing an equipment to be landed on the moon for analyses of its surface. Its operation is based on the fact that the recoil energy of an alpha particle backscattered from a solid surface is a function of the atomic weight A of the scatterer. The equipment consists of a small box containing an alpha particle source and three semiconductor detectors arranged around it to measure the energy spectrum of the alpha particles scattered at $170°$ to the incident beam. The expected form of the spectrum is that shown in Fig. 9.9, where the series of energy thresholds are the maximum energies for atoms of different atomic weight. The method is best for the lighter elements, since these introduce the greatest dispersion in the recoil energies, and it is hoped to achieve an accuracy of 1 per cent in the mass analysis of the elements up to iron in the periodic table. The equipment has been tested on various chemical mixtures with a variety of textures and surfaces and has achieved this performance.

In the final design it is intended to incorporate an arrangement for tamping down the surface to be measured, and to allow the box to be moved from point to point on the moon's surface to obtain a picture of local variations in composition. About 24 hours are needed to accumulate sufficient data at any one point. The experiment is to form part of the Surveyor series.

9.6 Medical and biological applications

The uses of radiation in the diagnosis and therapy of cancer, and the uses of radio isotopes in investigating the uptake of various materials at particular sites in the body are of very great importance. All these measurements are best performed using small probes placed at the position of interest, for the calculation of scattering and absorption in such an inhomo-

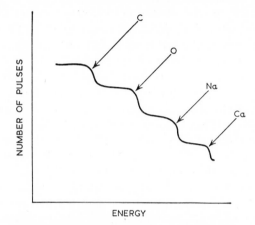

Fig. 9.9 Spectrum of alpha particles back-scattered from a solid target (schematic)

geneous entity as the human body is practically impossible. Probes have to be as small as possible, but with high density to obtain the maximum sensitivity per unit volume. They have to operate for long periods at body temperatures in conditions of high humidity, so that high voltages and high impedance circuitry are to be avoided. All these considerations point to the use of solid state devices.

The measurements to be made are of two kinds. In measurements during radiotherapy the dose rates will generally be very high, and it will be necessary to measure dose rate and integrated dose. On the other hand there is a need for high sensitivity devices working at small dose rates in dynamic experiments concerned with the rate of uptake of P^{32} in tumour tissue, or with the circulation of the blood.

Devices for measuring integrated dose are commonly solids

exhibiting colouration or permanent changes in other physical properties as a result of irradiation, or they use thermoluminescence or infra red stimulated emission in which the system is activated by radiation. They operate over the wide range of 10^{-1} to 10^9 rads, and all suffer from the disadvantage that they have to be removed for examination before the dose is known. They do not give a continuous indication whilst under irradiation. The functioning of these integrating devices is outside the scope of this book, but it is likely that radiation damage in semiconductor detectors, discussed in Chapter 10, could compete in sensitivity and have the advantage of a continuous indication of accumulated dose.

For measurements of dose rate semiconductor counters have an advantage in sensitivity per unit volume and in compatibility with environment over all other systems. It should prove possible to use them even in relatively inaccessible sites such as the heart, the thorax and the bladder by insertion at the end of a catheter. They would normally be used as pulse counters, operating in the familiar mode fully described already, but Jones[19] has pointed out that at very high dose rates the direct current properties can be used, relating average current to dose rate. For photoconductive detection the rate of charge generation in the depletion layer must exceed the dark current noise. Jones plots the signal current in a *p-n* junction irradiated with about 60 R/min Co^{60} gamma rays as a function of bias, and compares it with the theoretical and measured leakage currents. His graphs, reproduced in Fig. 9.10, show the inherently low sensitivity and the way in which the ratio of signal current to leakage current deteriorates with increasing bias. A better method in most situations would be that of using the *p-n* junction as a photovoltaic detector with no externally applied bias, so avoiding the worst of the junction noise. There is however some noise remaining because of the dynamic nature of the charge balance across the junction, for the electron and hole currents across the junction interface which are associated with the formation of the potential barrier only cancel when averaged over a long period, and lack of detailed correlation between electron and hole motion constitutes a source of current noise, even at zero bias.

When a junction is irradiated with a load resistor *R* connected between its terminals a current I flows and a potential V is established across the load resistor, these quantities being related by the equation

$$I = A\left[\exp\frac{eV}{kT} - 1\right] + \frac{V}{R} \tag{9.2}$$

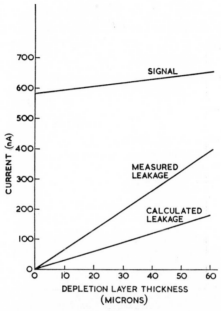

FIG. 9.10 Signal and Leakage Current as a function of depletion layer thickness (bias) in a silicon p-n junction (after JONES[19])

where A is a constant characteristic of the diode. The first term on the right hand side is simply the current through a shallow depletion layer device biased by a potential difference V. It is interesting to consider special cases which reduce equation (9.2) to a simpler analytical form. In the open circuit case ($R = \infty$)

$$V_0 = \frac{kT}{e}\left\{\ln\left(\frac{I}{A}\right) + 1\right\} \tag{9.3}$$

so that if the radiation induced current is simply the charge generation rate of the incident radiation the output voltage is found to increase as the logarithm of the dose rate with a slope of about 60 mV per decade. Fig. 9.11 shows experimental results confirming this prediction.

For small values of V ($<< 25$ mV)

$$V = \frac{I}{\dfrac{Ae}{kT} + 1/R} \qquad (9.4)$$

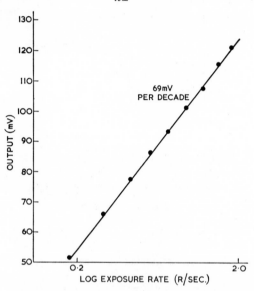

FIG. 9.11 Output as a function of exposure rate for a silicon *p-n* junction used in the photovoltaic mode (After JONES[19])

i.e. the open circuit voltage approximates to a linear function of radiation dose rate.

As R is reduced the current approaches its short circuit value as the second term on the right hand side of equation (9.2) becomes the dominant one. The current then approaches the charge generation rate in the depletion layer. Figure 9.12 shows a typical variation of current and voltage developed as the load resistor is varied.

To complete this short description of a comparatively large topic we now mention some specific applications of semiconductor detectors in nuclear medicine and biology, but the reader requiring more detailed background is referred to the recent review article by Fowler.[20]

Measurements in the stomach are possible using a stomach probe such as that developed by ORTEC. and shown in Plate II(*a*). It consists of a small junction detector encapsulated in silicone rubber and mounted at the end of a long flexible tube containing the leads and a means of mechanically deflecting the probe, to position it correctly. The use of such a probe in

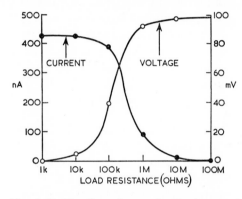

FIG. 9.12 The dependence of output current and voltage of a silicon *p-n* junction on load resistance (After JONES[19])

diagnosing malignant conditions of the stomach has been described by Otto, Horwitz, Kurtzman and Lofstrom.[21] Correct positioning of the detector near the suspected malignancy was achieved by fluoroscopy, and the uptake of P[32] in that area compared with normal regions nearby. Increased uptake proved to be an accurate indication of malignancy and the indications are that this could be a powerful diagnostic method.

The same corporation have also designed an *in-vivo* probe and an eye probe shown in Plate II(*b*) and (*c*). The former is intended for insertion into tissue by means of a hypodermic syringe, in the same way as a needle Geiger tube. The latter, and a miniature eye probe which will slip behind the eye are intended for detection of tumours and detached retinas using the P[32] uptake method.

All these devices are encapsulated in polyesters and epoxy resins and can be sterilised in alcohol and possibly autoclaved. They are comparable in counting efficiency to Geiger tubes now in use, i.e. about 0·01 counts per disintegration per cc of solution for P^{32}, but they have lower working voltages (10 volts) and much lower background counting rates, at about 1 per minute.

A silicon probe produced by 20th Century Electronics has been tested by Parker.[22] It consists of two surface barrier detectors made by cutting a narrow cylinder of silicon along its axis, evaporating gold on the curved faces and aluminium on the flats, and then cementing the flat surfaces to a phosphor bronze strip. The finished device is 2·8 mm in diameter and 10 mm long giving a sensitive surface area of 60 mm². It is encapsulated in a stainless steel tube 3 mm in diameter and 60 mg cm⁻² thick, but it is hoped to replace this by a thinner plastic casing.

In another important review article Hine[23] lists a series of devices being developed by Solid State Radiations Inc. for specific medical applications. A brain probe consists of a silicon lithium drifted detector mounted inside a stainless steel tube 1 mm in diameter and ·005 cm. wall thickness which can be inserted into the brain through a small burr hole and may be used to locate brain tumours through the uptake of P^{32} in the form of sodium phosphate. This instrument has already been used with success in surgical procedures. Another instrument under development for use in the treatment of brain tumours is an alpha particle probe. The suggested method of treatment is to load the brain tumour with B^{10} through the differential take-up of the borate ion from circulation at malignancies. Irradiation of the patient with slow neutrons initiates the $B^{10}(n, a)Li^7$ reaction with consequent localised irradiation of the tumour with densely ionizing a-particles. To obtain an effective measure of the radiation dose an alpha particle probe must be placed in the tumour, where it must operate in a very high gamma ray background and a resulting noise level of about 0·5 MeV. There are grounds for believing that this can be done.

Gastro-intestinal probes are also being developed consisting of a semiconductor detector 2·5 mm in diameter and 12 mm

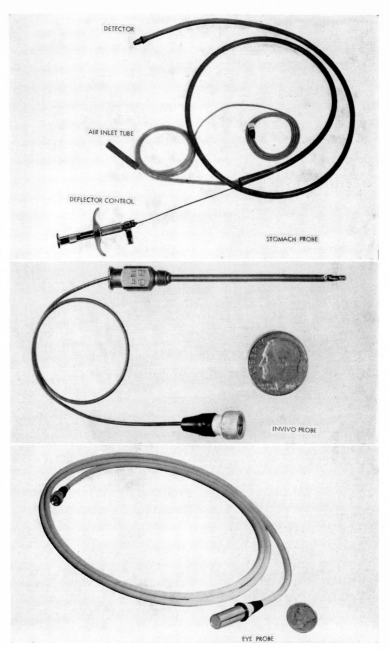

DETECTOR

AIR INLET TUBE

DEFLECTOR CONTROL

STOMACH PROBE

INVIVO PROBE

EYE PROBE

PLATE II   (a) Stomach probe, (b) *Invivo* probe, (c) Eye probe.
Reproduced by courtesy of Oak Ridge Technical Enterprises Corporation, Oak Ridge,
Tennessee, U.S.A.

in length mounted with a miniaturized preamplifier into an assembly feeding into perhaps 25 feet of cable. It is suggested that using P[32] injected into the blood stream as a tracer this instrument would rapidly locate intestinal bleeding, which is a fairly common kind of emergency. It could equally well be used to detect regions of inadequate blood supply by seeking points of minimum activity in the gastro-intestinal tract. Once again this instrument has passed feasibility examination and awaits clinical tests.

Fowler[20] also mentions the potentialities of cadmium sulphide and cadmium selenide counters for gamma ray dosimetry, but although they have been used in peripheral equipment, such as a radiochemical separation plant at the Medical Research Council's cyclotron unit they appear not to have been used yet for *in vivo* measurements of any kind.

It is obviously possible to perform a whole range of experiments on plant physiology using radioactive tracers and suitable semiconductor counters, and at least one such experiment has been reported. Rechenmann and de Swart[24] have used a pair of silicon surface barrier detectors separately encapsulated with a thin plastic window mounted face to face on either side of the stem of oat seedlings. By this means they have attempted to study the take up of phosphorus, calcium, and caesium as a function of climatic conditions. Their results show that the method is perfectly feasible, using microcurie quantities of radiotracers.

9.7 Silicon *p-n* junction photocells

Two recent applications of junction photocells call for devices so similar in design to junction radiation detectors that it may be worth making a brief digression to describe the applications and the properties of the junctions. The first application, mentioned briefly in Section 9.5, is the use of junction photocells to replace photomultipliers in scintillation counter assemblies to be flown in outer space. It is their small physical size, robustness and small power requirements which make them attractive. The second application is in communication links and ranging systems using gallium arsenide lamps and lasers. Very high speed of modulation with response times in the region of a nanosecond is an important characteristic of these light sources, and it is necessary to match them in the detector. Although the photomultiplier has an adequate pulse rise time the electron transit time through the tube, normally about a microsecond, is often a drawback in range determinations. Other advantages of the silicon junction photocell are again physical size and power requirements and the fact that it does not saturate at low ambient light levels, as the photomultiplier does.

Either a diffused junction or a surface barrier could be used to detect optical radiation, with a preference for the gold surface barrier for the blue end of the visible spectrum and the ultra violet, but with the diffused junction preferred at the red end of the visible and the near infra red. The reasons are associated with absorption and reflection by the window. The gold film, though thin, can absorb and reflect radiation, and in the infra-red a gold film of resistance 350 ohms per square has an absorption of 50 per cent and a reflectivity of 25 per cent. At shorter wavelengths the absorption reduces, and gold has quite a good transmission window in the ultra violet. In contrast, the absorption in the diffused layer of a p-n junction falls towards long wavelengths, as the absorption constant falls. The reflectivity of a silicon-air interface is about 30 per cent throughout the visible and near infra-red spectrum.

Figure 9.13 shows computed curves for the sensitivity of silicon p-n junctions as a function of wavelength for different values of diffusion depth and depletion layer thickness. It illustrates clearly the fall-off in sensitivity at short wavelengths due to thick windows, and at long wavelengths due to incomplete absorption in the depletion layer. Radiation absorbed beyond the depletion layer may diffuse to the junction, increasing the current through an increase of minority carrier concentration in the base material, but the response time for this contribution is comparatively slow, about 10^{-6} seconds. It is not included in the above curves, which also make no allowance for reflection losses at the silicon surface or in any glass window of an encapsulated device. These losses amount to nearly 40 per cent when no precautions are taken, but anti-reflection coatings may reduce them considerably.

In practice photodiodes have been made approaching closely

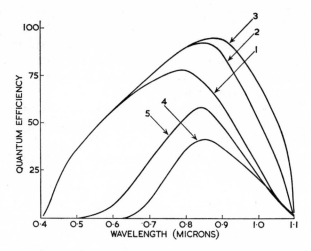

FIG. 9.13 Predicted Spectral Response Curves for Silicon *p-n* Junctions

Curve	Window	Depletion Layers
1	1μ	20μ
2	1μ	50μ
3	1μ	100μ
4	10μ	20μ
5	5μ	20μ

this theoretical prediction, with overall quantum efficiency of about 50 per cent throughout the visible. Rather higher than average sensitivity is obtained at the emission wavelengths of gallium arsenide, to which silicon is particularly well matched.

The speed of response and signal : noise ratio obtainable are those given in the discussion of these characteristics of particle counters, with some additional noise due to ambient light, in many applications. In more familiar terms photodiodes and pulse amplifiers can be made with an equivalent noise input of 10^{-14} watts in a 1 c.p.s. bandwidth and with a response time of 10^{-9} seconds. But at the moment amplifier design does not allow these limits to be obtained simultaneously.

Recently a number of laboratories working on semiconductor lamp and laser systems have begun to use *p-n* junctions of the type described by Huth, Trice and McKinney[25] (cf Chapter 5) in which amplification by impact ionization is available without loss of speed. It is likely that there will be rapid developments in this area in view of the great interest in laser systems, although the technology is likely to centre on comparatively low resistivity silicon (∼ 100 ohm. cm.) where the depletion layer thickness is quite adequate for the absorption of optical radiation and where the operating voltage will not be inconviently high (∼ 1000 volts).

Blamires[26] has reported measurements made with surface barrier detectors, using two thicknesses of gold, and also a latticed electrode structure. The relative responses of these three devices as functions of wavelength are shown in Fig. 9.14. The latticed electrode gave greatest sensitivity over the

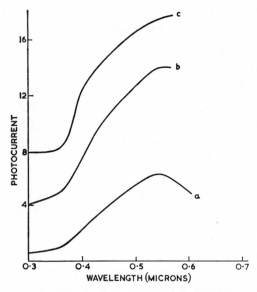

FIG. 9.14 Spectral Response of Gold-Silicon
Surface Barriers (After BLAMIRES[26])

(a) 100 μgm/cm² gold on 2·5 cm²
(b) 20 μgm/cm² gold on 2·5 cm²
(c) Lattice of ·010 inch gold strips separated by
    ·020 inch gaps, joined by an outer gold ring.
    Total area inside ring 2·5 cm²

whole spectrum of measurements but when coupled optically to a scintillator it suffered serious deterioration of reverse leakage current. Used in conjunction with a zinc sulphide screen it showed an efficiency of one electron-hole pair for 70 electron volts deposited by an alpha particle. However the noise was equivalent to 14,000 electron hole pairs, making the overall signal: noise ratio worse than that achieved with a photomultiplier, even though the signal conversion is better in the photodiode. It should be possible to improve on this efficiency, but even without an improvement the system may have uses in space measurements.

REFERENCES

For this chapter

1. A.E.I. Research Laboratories, *private communication*.
2. Moncaster, M. E., Northrop, D. C. and Raines, J. A., *Nucl. Instr. and Methods*, **22**, 157 (1963).
3. Jones, A. R., *Health Physics*, **8**, 1 (1962).
4. Lindsay, W. F., University of California, *Lawrence Radiation Laboratory, Report* **UCRL-7198** (1961).
5. Ajdačić, V. S., Lalović, B. I. and Petrović, B. P., *Proceedings of Paris Symposium on Nuclear Electronics*, Nov. 1963.
6. Ajdačić, V. S., Lalović, B. I., Barucija, M. and Petrović, B. P., *Proceedings of 3rd Geneva Conference of the International Atomic Energy Agency*, Aug. 1964.
7. Furr, A. K. and Runyon, R. S., *Nucl. Instr. and Methods*, **27**, 292 (1964).
8. Beets, C., Colle, P., Deckers, H., Gierts, G. and de Leeuw, S., *Mem. Soc. Roy. Sci. de Liège*, X, No. 2, 317, (1964).
9. Holm, D., Los Alamos Scientific Laboratory, *private communication*.
10. Canepa, P. C., Malinarik, P., Campbell, R. B., and Ostroski, J., Westinghouse Research Laboratory, Pittsburg 35, Pa., *private communication*.
11. Pieper, G. F., Zmuda A. J., Bostrom, C. O. and O'Brien, B. J. *J. Geophys. Res.*, **67**, 4959, (1962).
12. Friedland, S. S., Ziemba, F. P., Olson, R. M. and Delyser, H., *I.R.E. Trans. Nucl. Sci.*, **NS-9**, No. 3, 391 (1962).
13. Tuzzolino, A. J., Hubbard, E. L., Perkins, M. A. and Fan, C. Y., *J. Appl. Phys.*, **33**, 148 (1962).
14. West, H. L., Mann, L. G. and Bloom, S. D., *Bull. Amer. Phys. Soc.*, Ser. **11**, 7, 62 (1962).
15. Brown, W. L., Buck, T. M., Medford, L. V., Thomas, E. W., Gummel, H. K., Miller, G. L. and Smits, F. M., *B.S.T.J.*, **42**, 899 (1963).

16. Brown, W. L., Gabbe, J. D. and Rosenzweig, W., *B.S.T.J.*, **42**, 1505 (1963).
17. Buck, T. M., Wheatley, G. H. and Rodgers, J. W., *I.E.E.E. Trans. on Nucl. Sci.*, **NS-11**, 3 (1964).
18. Patterson, J. H., Turkevitch, A. L. and Franzgrote, E., *J. Geophys. Res.*, *(to be published)*.
19. Jones, A. R., *Phys. Med. Biol.*, **8**, 451 (1963).
20. Fowler, J. F., *Phys. Med. Biol.*, **8**, 1, 1963).
21. Otto, D. L., Horwitz, N. H., Kirtzman, R. S. and Lofstrom, J. F., *Amer. J. Roentgenology*, **91**, 784 (1964).
22. Parker, R. P., *Brit. J. Radiology*, **36**, 781 (1963).
23. Hine, G. (private communication).
24. Rechenmann, R. V. and de Swart, J. G., *Mem. Soc. Roy. Sci. de Liège*, X, No. 2, 357 (1964).
25. Huth, G. E., Trice, J. B. & McKinney, *Rev. Sci. Instrum.* **35**, 1220, (1964).
26. Blamires, N. G., *A.E.R.E. Report*, No. **M 1185**.

CHAPTER 10

RADIATION DAMAGE IN
SEMICONDUCTOR DETECTORS

10.1 Introduction

In this chapter we shall consider some long-term effects of the passage of nuclear radiation through semiconductor detectors. We have so far been concerned with the effects of ionization, that is the displacement of *electrons* from their initial energy states in the lattice. Ionization effects disappear very rapidly in recombination of carriers either at the boundary electrodes or at centres within the crystal. It is possible, however, during interaction between the nuclear radiation and the nuclei of the semiconductor, for *atoms* to be displaced from their equilibrium sites, leaving vacancies and interstitial atoms in the lattice. In some semiconductors transmutation of one of the constituent isotopes through nuclear reactions may lead to observable effects. Such processes bring about long-lasting changes in the properties of the semiconductor which it is difficult or impossible to remove. Hence radiation damage may limit the useful life of semiconductor detectors in certain applications, and it is important to be able to assess the rates of damage by various radiations and to take precautions to minimize the effects of damage. In some applications, for instance in measurements in space, changes may occur in detectors which cannot be recovered for recalibration. Then it is important to know how the detector properties may change under irradiation, since the signals may otherwise lead to erroneous results. Finally, since almost any effect induced by nuclear radiation can be used to make some sort of counter, the damaging effects of radiation on semiconductor properties can be used in flux measurement, and such a device must be classed as a semiconductor detector.

Although a greater study has been made of radiation damage in germanium this chapter will deal almost entirely with the effects in silicon, because of its relatively greater importance in present-day semiconductor counters, though it is to be expected that other materials, such as SiC, will increase in importance for purposes of flux measurement by radiation damage.

10.2 Processes of radiation damage

(a) Defect formation

An atom which is displaced by a nuclear particle will generally come to rest as an interstitial a short distance from its vacated site. In many cases this 'primary' recoiling atom may have sufficient energy to create several secondary displacements before coming to rest. Each pair of interstitial and vacancy sites is called a Frenkel[1] defect or Frenkel pair (illustrated in Fig. 10.1). Although such a defect can be created by a reversible process with an expenditure of only about 5 eV energy, in collision processes there is no time for the neighbouring atoms to adjust their positions, and the threshold energy, E_d, for displacement is between 15 and 30 eV. The value appears

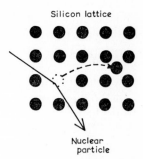

Silicon lattice

Nuclear particle

FIG. 10.1 Formation of a vacancy-interstitial pair, or Frenkel defect

to vary with the energy and probably with the type of radiation. It has also been found[2] to vary with the direction of the radiation with respect to the crystal axes.

The number and energy distribution of recoiling atoms depends upon the magnitude and energy dependence of the interaction, and thus different types of radiation produce quite different distributions of damage sites. For this reason it is convenient to consider separately three types of radiation: neutrons, charged particles, and electrons. With the last are included gamma rays which cause damage mainly through the Compton electrons or photo-electrons they produce. In bombardment with heavy particles of high energy, such as fission fragments, almost all the atoms along the path of the particle may be displaced. The drastically disordered volume left in the wake of such a particle has been called[3] a displacement 'spike'. It is almost impossible to make useful calculations of the density of defects created under such circumstances.

Nuclear transmutation, particularly under intense thermal neutron irradiation, can in certain semiconductors introduce products with donor or acceptor properties, and in sufficient numbers to affect the electrical behaviour. This is not, however, a significant process of damage in silicon.

Most of the effects of radiation damage can be related to the density of Frenkel defects created. In the next sections we shall summarize the formulae relevant to calculating the rate of defect formation for different radiations. Several authors[4,5,6] have treated the general case, but here a particular study will be made of the processes in silicon.

(b) Damage by neutrons

Equation (1.1) shows that the maximum energy, $\hat{E}_{Si}$, transferable in an elastic collision between a neutron of energy E_n and a silicon nucleus is given by

$$\hat{E}_{Si} = 0\cdot133E_n \qquad (10.1)$$

The recoil energies, E_{Si}, are distributed up to this maximum value according to a function W_d (E_n, E_{Si}) which gives the probability that, given a collision, the primary recoil energy will be E_{Si}. For fast neutrons the collisions are mainly of the hard-sphere type, that is with a cross-section which is essentially independent of neutron energy, and with a value of about 2-3 barns.[7] Under these conditions W_d is constant for all recoil energies up to $\hat{E}_{Si}$, and

$$W_d(E_n, E_{Si}) = 1/\hat{E}_{Si} \qquad (10.2)$$

Since the displacement energy, E_d, is only about 25 eV, $\hat{E}_{Si} \gg E_d$ for fast neutrons, so that most of the collisions lead to displacement and therefore the displacement cross-section, σ_d, is equal to the scattering cross-section. The mean free path between collisions is, from the value above, equal to about 1 cm, so that the primary displaced atoms are produced relatively far apart. The average recoil energy, $\bar{E}_{Si}$, is, because of the uniform energy distribution, simply $\hat{E}_{Si}/2$. The energy spectrum of neutrons in a graphite-moderated reactor shows a distribution roughly proportional to $1/E_n$, and Billington and Crawford[5] show that the average recoil energy is then given by

$$\bar{E}_{Si} \simeq \tfrac{1}{2}\hat{E}_{Si}/\log_e(\hat{E}_{Si}/E_d) \qquad (10.3)$$

The primary recoil particles so produced may themselves create secondary displacements, and a total of $\nu(E_{Si})$ defects result from a single primary event. The simplest treatment of secondary displacements has been made by Kinchin and Pease,[8] who showed that if $E_{Si} \gg E_d$,

$$\nu(E_{Si}) \simeq E_{Si}/2E_d \qquad (10.4)$$

A more elaborate derivation by Harrison and Seitz[9] gave

$$\nu(E_{Si}) \simeq 0 \cdot 56(E_{Si} + E_d)/E_d \qquad (10.5)$$

The *average* number of displacements, $\bar{\nu}$, is given approximately by

$$\bar{\nu} \simeq \bar{E}_{Si}/2E_d \qquad (10.6)$$

Thus for a 1 MeV neutron this equation would lead to a value of $\bar{\nu}$ around 1000. However, some of the more energetic recoiling atoms may lose energy by ionization rather than by creating secondary displacements. Equation (1.26) shows that the ionization threshold, E_{th}, for silicon ions in silicon is about 7 keV. If displacements are neglected above this threshold,

$$\bar{\nu} \simeq E_{th}/2E_d \qquad (10.7)$$

leading to a constant value of $\bar{\nu}$ about 150. This, however, is a lower limit since some displacements will occur above the ionization threshold.

Equation (10.1) shows that neutrons of energy below about 200 eV cannot produce displacements in silicon, since $\hat{E}_{Si} < E_d$. The only damaging effect of such neutrons is that of transmutation. Slow neutrons absorbed in Si^{28} and Si^{29} induce a pure (n, γ) process and hence do not lead to transmutation. In Si^{30} (isotopic abundance 4 per cent), however, the neutron absorption is followed by β-emission by which the Si^{31} is converted to stable P^{31} which can act as a donor. However, electrons emitted in the decay of Si^{31} have energies ranging up to 1·5 MeV and these may cause displacements in the lattice. Tanenbaum and Mills[10] have studied the introduction of donors into silicon by thermal neutron irradiation, followed by annealing at 600° C for 16 hours to remove Frenkel defects. Considerable changes in resistivity were observed as a result of irradiation with 10^{20} thermal neutrons per cm^2, and the minority carrier lifetime was reduced. The reaction rate is very low, since the thermal neutron capture cross-section of Si^{30} is only 0·11 barn. Since detectors cannot be annealed at such high temperatures it is likely that the principal effect of thermal neutron irradiation is to cause defects, but at a rate very much lower than in the case of fast neutron damage.

(c) Damage by charged particles

The interaction between a charged particle and the nuclei of a semiconductor takes place almost entirely by Rutherford scattering. A useful parameter in this process is the classical distance of closest approach, b, given by

$$b = 2zZe^2/\mu v^2 \tag{10.8}$$

where z, Z are the atomic numbers of projectile and target, v is the relative velocity, and μ the reduced mass

$$\mu = mM/(m + M) \tag{10.9}$$

In terms of this parameter the displacement cross-section, σ_d, in silicon is given by

$$\sigma_d \simeq \tfrac{1}{4}\pi b^2 \hat{E}_{Si}/E_d \tag{10.10}$$

For protons of energy E_p, equation (1.1) shows that

$$\hat{E}_{Si} = 0\cdot133 E_p \tag{10.11}$$

and therefore, assuming $E_d = 30$ eV, and measuring E_p in MeV,

$$\sigma_d(E_p) = 1\cdot5.\ 10^{-20}/E_p\ cm^2 \tag{10.12}$$

The mean energy per primary recoil is

$$\bar{E}_{Si} \simeq E_d \log_e (\hat{E}_{Si}/E_d) \tag{10.13}$$

$$\simeq 30 \log_e (E_p/2\cdot25 \times 10^{-4}) eV \tag{10.14}$$

The mean number of displacements per primary is

$$\bar{\nu} \simeq 0.12 + 0.56 \log_e (E_p/2.25 \times 10^{-4}) \qquad (10.15)$$

The corresponding formulae for alpha particles of energy E_a MeV in silicon are:

$$\hat{E}_{Si} = 0.437 E_a \qquad (10.16)$$

$$\sigma_d \simeq 2.36 \; 10^{-19}/E_a \; cm^2 \qquad (10.17)$$

$$\bar{E}_{Si} \simeq 30 \log_e (E_a/6.9 \times 10^{-5}) eV \qquad (10.18)$$

and $$\qquad \bar{\nu} \simeq 0.12 + 0.56 \log_e (E_a/6.9 \times 10^{-5}) \qquad (10.19)$$

Thus $\bar{\nu}$ varies only slowly with energy and for protons and alpha-particles it lies between 4 and 6 over most of the range of energies that are of interest for semiconductor counters. These small values show that each primary recoil produces only a very small volume of secondary damage. The primary recoils produce very little ionization since their energy distribution function, $W_d(E, E_{Si})$ is of the form

$$W_d = E_d/E^2_{Si} \qquad (10.20)$$

and few recoil atoms are produced with energies above the ionization threshold, E_{th}.

The total number, N_F, of Frenkel defects produced by a particle in traversing a distance dx of material with N_o nuclei/cm³ is

$$N_F = N_o \sigma_d \bar{\nu} \, dx \qquad (10.21)$$

so that the number of defects produced during an energy loss dE by the incident particle is

$$N_F = N_o \sigma_d \bar{\nu} \, dE/(dE/dx) \qquad (10.22)$$

If the stopping power, dE/dx, is known as a function of particle energy this equation may be integrated to give the total number of Frenkel defects produced along the track. However, the major contribution comes from the low energy region in which dE/dx fails to obey equation (1.2), so that experimental values must be used. For protons in silicon dE/dx can be deduced from the values[11] for aluminium, which have been measured down to a proton energy of 40 keV, near which the value is fairly constant. At lower energies the value tends to fall owing to charge exchange processes which reduce the rate of energy loss by ionization. The assumption of a constant value for dE/dx of 100 MeV/cm for protons of below 60 keV in silicon leads to a lower limit for the total number of defects. The resulting values of N_F are given approximately by

$$N_F = 130 + 6E_p \qquad (10.23)$$

It is interesting to consider also the number of defects created in each unit interval of the particle track; this is simply $dN_F/dx = N_0\sigma_d\bar{\nu}$, and the values of this function for protons and alphas in silicon are shown in Fig. 10.2. So that

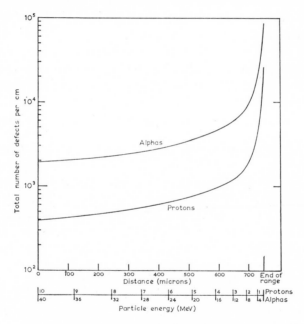

FIG. 10.2 The number of Frenkel defects produced per unit distance in silicon during the slowing-down of protons and alpha-particles as a function of the distance; from DEARNALEY[28]

both types of particle have the same range, the initial alpha particle energy is taken as 40 MeV while that of the proton is 10 MeV. The sharp concentration of damage at the end of the track is clearly shown and is characteristic of damage by heavy charged particles.

(d) Damage by electrons and gamma rays

Because of relativistic effects equations (10.9) to (10.23) do not apply for electrons. Instead the maximum recoil energy is given by

$$\hat{E}_{Si} = 2(E_e + 2m_ec^2)E_e/Mc^2 \qquad (10.24)$$

where E_e, m_e are the electron kinetic energy and rest mass and M is the mass of the silicon nucleus. Seitz and Koehler[4] have solved the relativistic equations for σ_d and shown that it approaches a nearly constant value for high electron energies, given by

$$\sigma_d \rightarrow \pi b^2(1 - \beta^2)\hat{E}_{Si}/4E_d \qquad (10.25)$$

in which β is the electron velocity relative to that of light. Cahn[12] has calculated the total number of defects introduced during the slowing down of electrons of initial energies up to 7 MeV, in silicon. The results are shown in Fig. 10.3, in which the two curves are for displacement thresholds of 15 and 30 eV. In silicon the energy below which an electron cannot transfer sufficient energy to cause displacements is about 250 keV; in germanium the threshold is nearly 600 keV. The energy transferred to recoiling ions is low even for electron energies up to 10 MeV, and so very few secondary displacements are created. The complex localized regions of damage which result from a cascade of displacements are avoided and, in contrast with the case of fast neutron damage, electrons produce a relatively uniform distribution of defects.

In the case of gamma irradiation, the most important absorption process in silicon for gamma rays of between 60 keV and 15 MeV is due to Compton scattering. The recoil electrons produced in this process are responsible for most of the radiation damage caused by gamma rays. In order to calculate the displacement cross-section, σ_d, for gamma rays it is necessary to make three integrations, one over the distribution of recoil energies for an electron of given energy, the second over the electron range to find the energy distribution of electrons with this initial energy, and the third over the Compton

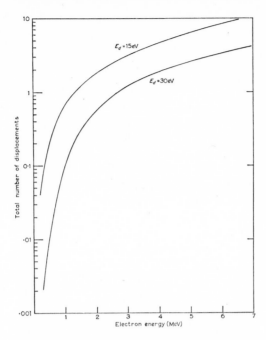

FIG. 10.3 The total number of displacements
produced in silicon in the slowing-down of
electrons as a function of the initial energy, for
two assumed values of the displacement
energy, E_d; from CAHN[12]

spectrum to include the effect of different Compton recoil
energies resulting from a given gamma-ray energy. Cahn[12] has
calculated the displacement cross-section in silicon for gamma
rays of energies 1 to 7 MeV and the results are shown in
Fig. 10.4, in which the two curves are again for displacement
thresholds of 15 and 30 eV. These cross-sections are very
low; for instance, the probability that a gamma ray of 1 MeV
energy will produce a single defect in traversing 1 mm of
silicon is only about 0·001. The rate of introduction of damage
by reactor gamma rays has been estimated in silicon to be
approximately $9·10^{-3}$ vacancy – interstitial pairs/cm^3 for
each photon/cm^2. This rate is so much less than the one for
neutron-induced defects that it can in most cases be neglected.

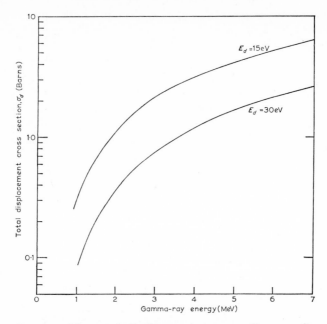

FIG. 10.4 The total displacement cross section, σ_d, for gamma rays in silicon as a function of gamma-ray energy, for two assumed values of the displacement energy, E_d; from CAHN[12]

10.3 The effect of radiation damage on detector performance

(a) The influence of defects on semiconductor properties

The electrical properties of a near-intrinsic semiconductor crystal suitable for use as a radiation detector are governed by a very small concentration of impurity atoms and crystalline defects. For this reason semiconductor detectors are very susceptible to radiation damage, and for the same reason the effects of damage in semiconductors are useful in the measurement of an intense flux of radiation.

In some of the earliest discussions of the electrical effect of a Frenkel defect it was thought that the interstitial, with excess valence electrons, should show donor, and the vacancy, lacking electrons, acceptor properties. A simple model treating each on the basis of a hydrogen-like atom was proposed by James and Lark-Horovitz[13] and did account for some of the observed effects. It is now known, however, that the situation is much more complex than was at first anticipated. The vacancies are mobile at all but the lowest temperatures and can migrate through the crystal to associate with impurity centres, such as oxygen, phosphorus, lithium, etc. The electron energy levels introduced into the band gap of silicon therefore depend on the impurity content of the crystal. Nevertheless, certain reasonably well-defined levels have been located and assigned to particular defect pairs, mainly by electron spin resonance

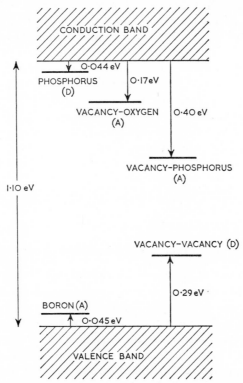

FIG. 10.5 Energy levels in the band gap of irradiated silicon

and infra-red absorption techniques. Figure 10.5 shows the most important energy levels introduced in irradiated silicon. The proximity of defects to one another can of course spread these levels into bands.

The level of 0·17 eV below the conduction band appears only in silicon which contains oxygen, such as occurs in pulled crystals. The level is attributed to oxygen-vacancy pairs. In the vacuum float-zone silicon most commonly used for detector preparation there is little or no oxygen. The level most strongly introduced is then at 0·40 eV below the conduction band, and is thought to be due to vacancy-phosphorus pairs. At very low temperatures (20° K) these levels do not appear, but are observable when the crystal temperature is raised to about 100° K, supporting the idea that the vacancies must migrate in order to produce them. The third most important level, at about 0·29 eV above the valence band is thought to be due to vacancy-vacancy pairs. The interstitial has never been found to play any important rôle electrically; possibly its migration rate is so high that it is able to move to some dislocation site even at very low temperatures. Studies of thermal conductivity show that the levels introduced at room temperature are stable. Early work of Fan and Lark-Horovitz[14] later confirmed by Bemski and Augustyniak[15] has shown this, although a certain amount of migration and reordering of the defects can take place over a period of a few days after irradiation. Annealing at an elevated temperature will remove a large proportion of the defects in silicon; temperatures around 200°C are required in order to accelerate the process appreciably, however.

The positions of the energy levels created in silicon seem to be independent of the mode of irradiation; thus protons and electrons introduce the same levels[16] and neutrons give rise to at least the same upper two levels.

It is probably a fortuitous result of the complex circumstances of defect formation that in silicon, whatever the initial resistivity and type, irradiation is found to increase the resistivity eventually to the intrinsic region. The reduction in conductivity arises from the simultaneous production of donor and acceptor levels which shift the Fermi level towards the centre of the band-gap, in much the same way as gold-doping acts in silicon. These deep levels trap carriers and are very effective in promoting carrier recombination, by alternate trapping of electrons and holes. Figure 10.6 shows results obtained by Cleland and his associates[17] during fast-neutron irradiation of silicon crystals. The carrier lifetime is also reduced, by the greater probability of trapping and recombination, and it is found that the reciprocal of the carrier lifetime varies linearly with the dose of radiation, as shown in

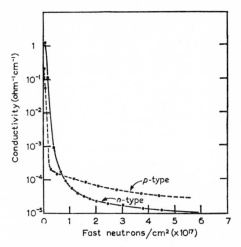

FIG. 10.6 The conductivity of silicon as a function of fast neutron dose; from BILLINGTON and CRAWFORD[6]. The n-type sample was irradiated at 48°C, the p-type sample at 63°C.

Fig. 10.7, which is taken from a paper by Schuttler and his colleagues.[18] The mobility of carriers may also be reduced by irradiation. This is because defect centres act like impurity sites and enhance the scattering of carriers, particularly at the lower temperatures where scattering by thermal lattice vibrations is less dominant. Irradiation thus may alter the dependence of carrier mobility on temperature.

So far we have been considering what takes place in bulk semiconductor as opposed to the depletion region of a reverse-biased diode. In the latter case there are very few equilibrium carriers and hence carrier recombination ceases to be a very likely process. Instead, excess carriers tend to become trapped at defect centres, and may or may not be subsequently released. If the trapping is largely of a temporary nature the effect corresponds to an effective reduction of carrier mobility.

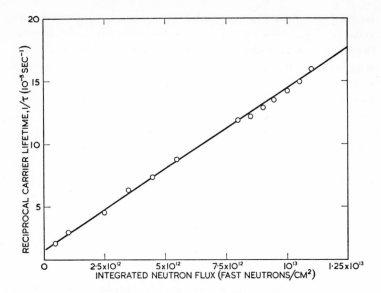

F IG. 10.7 The dependence of carrier lifetime on neutron dose in irradiated silicon; from S CHUTTLER[18]

Trapped carriers may, particularly in high-resistivity material, modify the space-charge due to ionized impurities if the defect centres introduced have a greater tendency to trap one type of carrier rather than the other. As we shall see later, there is a greater probability for electrons to be trapped rather than holes, so that the trapped carriers constitute a net negative space charge, which can modify the depletion layer thickness. Defect centres also act as generation centres for carrier production, as discussed in Chapter 6. The leakage current in the depletion layer is therefore enhanced, although changes also brought about in the surface leakage current may be even more significant. This is particularly so if the irradiation takes place in air, since ionized radicals are then produced which may induce new surface states on the semiconductor.

We are now in a position to consider the likely effects of irradiation of a semiconductor junction detector. In a junction counter the most important characteristics are the depletion layer depth and the energy resolution. The depletion layer depth, d, is inversely proportional to the square root of the

mean density of space charge in the layer, N. If the accumulation of trapped charge tends to alter N, d will also change.
The energy resolution of junction detectors is governed by
two factors. One is the electrical noise due to fluctuations
in detector current, and the second, and frequently the more
important factor, is the effect of non-uniform charge collection
due to variation in carrier lifetime, τ, over the depletion
layer. Both these effects are linked to the magnitude of τ,
in the way that was discussed in Chapter 6. The space-charge
generated current is, for mid-band recombination centres,
inversely proportional to τ, while the fraction of carriers lost
by trapping is governed by the transit time divided by τ, the
latter being a function of the carrier density. It is thus to be
expected that changes in leakage current and changes in
energy resolution should appear together during the course of
irradiation, corresponding to a significant reduction in carrier
lifetime. After very heavy exposure to radiation the charge
collection efficiency will be appreciably reduced and the output signal from the detector will consequently decrease.

In the case of neutron irradiation yet another effect may
occur. We have seen in Section 10.2(b) that neutrons produce
small, intensely disordered regions, each containing 150-1000
Frenkel pairs. These regions possess an intrinsic resistivity
and are surrounded by material retaining essentially its initial
resistivity; since the disordered regions have no mobile charge
carriers they have been termed 'voids'. The carrier lifetime
within these disordered regions will be very low, and hence
the collection efficiency for carriers produced by the subsequent passage of an ionizing particle through a 'void' will be
small. George and Gunnersen[19] have considered the consequences of such an effect, which it seems may account for the
decrease in pulse height for alpha particles in a detector
previously exposed to a heavy flux of neutrons. The density
of disordered regions is proportional to the neutron dose.

The effect of a change in the space charge of the depletion
layer brought about by radiation damage is naturally greater
if the initial space charge is low, that is in high resistivity
material. Curtis[20] pointed out that under such circumstances
irradiation may cause a significant change in depletion layer
thickness before any drastic change in carrier lifetime occurs.

In low resistivity silicon the change in carrier lifetime is expected to be the predominant effect of nuclear irradiation. Experimental confirmation of these predictions has now been obtained and the results are described in the next section.

(b) The observed effects of radiation damage in junction counters

A number of investigations have been made of the effects of fast neutron irradiation on the performance of silicon junction detectors. Klingensmith[21] exposed seven silicon surface-barrier detectors to a U^{235} fission neutron spectrum, and observed the damage effects by noting changes in the response to Pu^{239} alpha particles. After an exposure of about $3 \cdot 10^{11}$ fast neutrons/cm^2 the low-energy side of the alpha peak showed a definite but broad secondary peak. With increasing dose the original peak broadened but retained its pulse height and the secondary peak decreased in pulse height and became very broad. The total counting rate remained constant, being shared between the two peaks. After about $2 \cdot 10^{12}$ neutrons/cm^2 the original single peak response was no longer evident. Figure 10.8 shows the increase in reverse current observed in one detector as a function of the integrated dose; the deterioration in energy resolution took place over the same range, 10^{12}-10^{13} neutrons/cm^2, as that over which the leakage current increased rapidly. In this experiment the initial resistivities were around 3000 Ω cm (n-type), and a low reverse bias of $6 \cdot 4$ V was applied; the collecting field was therefore very low and so the effects of carrier lifetime reduction may be expected to be particularly noticeable. Gunnersen[19] has also studied the multiple peaking observed in an alpha particle spectrum when a detector has been damaged by fast neutrons. It was found that the secondary peak appeared with a pulse height about 20 per cent lower than the primary peak. The secondary peak can perhaps be attributed to the most probable value of charge efficiency, while the upper peak, decreasing in intensity during irradiation, corresponds to full charge collection. One would expect the *mean* pulse height to fall linearly with neutron dose, but this has not yet been verified.

Kramer[22] studied the effects of fast neutron irradiation in seven diffused junction counters of 6000 Ω cm p-type silicon,

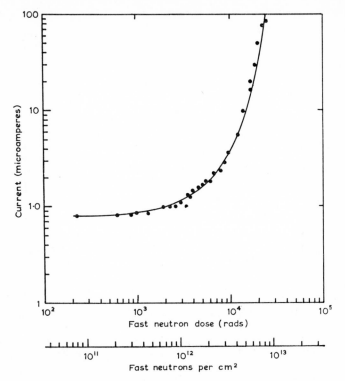

FIG. 10.8 Increase in current in a 1/4 cm² silicon surface barrier counter as a function of fast neutron dose. The detector bias voltage was 6.4 V; from KLINGENSMITH[21]

using a potential difference of 100 V. The output pulse height was found to decrease with irradiation as shown in Fig. 10.9. A convenient measure of the change in carrier lifetime is obtained by studying the collected charge as a function of the applied voltage; the charge which is lost is proportional to the ratio of transit time to carrier lifetime so that if trapping is appreciable the collected charge will vary with bias voltage. Figure 10.10 shows the reciprocal pulse height as a function of the reciprocal bias voltage in a detector before and after irradiation with $5 \cdot 3 \times 10^{13}$ fast neutrons/cm², and it is obvious that serious trapping of carriers is introduced. A charge-sensitive amplifier with a long differentiation time constant was used in order to minimize effects due to a change in

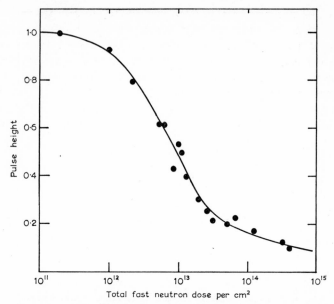

FIG. 10.9 Pulse height due to 5 MeV alpha particles in seven different silicon detectors as a function of fast neutron dose. The dose rates in individual cases grouped here varied from 1.65×10^9 to 3.1×10^{15} neutrons/cm²/sec; from KRAMER[22]

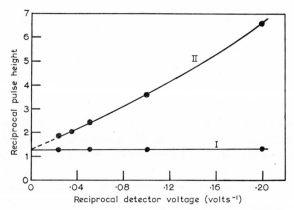

FIG. 10.10 The reciprocal pulse height, due to 5 MeV alpha particles, as a function of reciprocal detector voltage I before irradiation, and II after irradiation of a silicon junction counter with 5.3×10^{13} fast neutrons/cm²; from KRAMER[22]

detector rise-time. Irradiation was found to increase the rise-time from the order of 10^{-9} sec to 6×10^{-6} sec following a dose of $3{\cdot}4 \times 10^{14}$ fast neutrons/cm². This increased rise-time was correlated with a change in resistivity of the undepleted base region of the detector, which showed an increase by three orders of magnitude after only 5×10^{13} neutrons/cm². George and Gunnersen,[19] using surface-barrier detectors, observed a decrease in junction capacitance during irradiation,

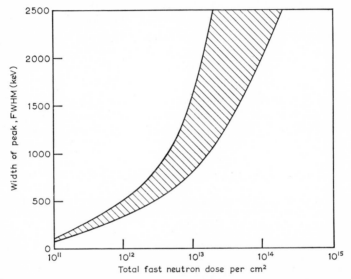

FIG. 10.11 Deterioration of energy resolution for 5 MeV alpha particles as a function of fast neutron dose. The shaded area represents the spread in values obtained for 14 diffused junction counters; from KRAMER[22]

corresponding to an increase in depletion layer thickness. Kramer[22] and Babcock, using diffused-junction counters of p-type silicon, reported an increase of capacitance as a result of neutron irradiation. These effects are explained by supposing that electrons are trapped more readily than holes and so build up a net negative space charge, which acts like an increase in the acceptor concentration. Kramer found that the energy resolution, determined by the full width at half maximum of the response to $8{\cdot}78$ MeV alpha particles, deteriorated as shown in Fig. 10·11 under neutron bombardment. The band between the two curves represents the spread in values measured in 14 diffused junction detectors. Gorton and his associates[24] measured the change in carrier lifetime in silicon diffused junction diodes under fast neutron irradiation. They found the reciprocal carrier lifetime to increase linearly with the integrated fast neutron flux, with a mean slope of 65 rad^{-1} sec^{-1}, or approximately $1\cdot9 \times 10^{-7}$ sec^{-1} per neutron/cm^2. No significant change in this rate of damage resulted from different rates of bombardment ranging from 6 to 25 000 rad/sec.

Some of these observations can be explained in terms of a simple model. We have seen that neutrons create small volumes of intense disorder containing about $10^2 - 10^3$ displaced atoms, these volumes being distributed uniformly through the crystal. If we suppose that the neutron flux creates N of these damaged volumes per cm^3 per second, each of volume a cm^3, in a depletion layer of total volume V it is easily shown that the undamaged volume, V_0, remaining after time t is given by

$$V_0 = V\mathrm{e}^{-Nat} \qquad (10.26)$$

The volume, V_1, subjected once to damage is

$$V_1 = VNat.\mathrm{e}^{-Nat} \qquad (10.27)$$

while that damaged n times over is

$$V_n = V(Nat)^n.\mathrm{e}^{-Nat}/n \qquad (10.28)$$

If the efficiency of charge collection from the once-damaged volume is η and that from n-times damaged material is η^n, the pulse height P will be related to the initial pulse height P_0 by

$$P = P_0\mathrm{e}^{-Nat}(1 - \eta^n) \qquad (10.29)$$

Alternatively, if we suppose that the charge collection efficiency is η for all the damaged volume,

$$P = P_0\mathrm{e}^{-Nat} + \eta P_0(1 - \mathrm{e}^{-Nat}) \qquad (10.30)$$

The latter expression fits the data of Kramer[22] rather better than does (10.29). From the fitted curve we can derive the volume, a, of the regions from which charge collection is small. The radius of these regions is deduced in this way to be about 5000 Å, which seems reasonable. This volume extends beyond that of the initial atomic displacements because vacancies can migrate to some extent through the lattice, and the collection field is modified over an even larger volume. The two distinct components of pulse-rise time which have been observed[19] are attributed to collection from the damaged and undamaged parts of the crystal. The secondary peak which is seen in the alpha-particle spectrum with a detector damaged by fast neutrons corresponds to the most probable value of charge collection over an alpha-particle track. The full-energy peak, which decreases in intensity as irradiation proceeds, corresponds to the finite probability of an alpha-particle missing all the damaged volumes, a situation which marks a well-defined cut-off to the pulse-height distribution.

Instead of results such as Kramer's[22] in which the peak of the pulse-height distribution was recorded, it would be preferable to have data for the mean pulse height for alpha particles, averaged over the whole spectrum. The distribution rapidly becomes skew, so that there is an appreciable difference between the most probable pulse height and the mean.

At the Asheville Conference[25] on Semiconductor Detectors (September, 1960) a number of reports were made on the effects on detector performance of irradiations with charged particles. Most of these were carried out accidentally and therefore not under very well-controlled conditions. With monoenergetic charged particles most of the damage is produced in a shallow volume corresponding to the end of the particle range. The greatest density of carriers is also produced in this region and hence the effects of recombination centres are most pronounced just here. The influence of different electric fields at this depth in the counter must be considered; damage will be more serious if the depletion layer depth is comparable with the particle range. Dearnaley[26] studied the effects of irradiation with 5·48 MeV Am[241] alpha particles, using a strong source for damage production and substituting a weak source of good energy definition for measurements of detector energy resolution. The range of 5 MeV alpha particles in silicon is only about 25 μ so that a low detector bias had to be used in order to obtain a depletion layer depth comparable to the depth of damage. Several surface barrier detectors of around 1000 Ω cm silicon were exposed to irradiations up to 10^{11} alphas/cm^2 in measurements extending over several days. Significant variations in the effects of damage were observed and were attributed to different lifetime distributions in the initial material. In all cases the leakage current rose after an irradiation of 10^8 to 10^9 alphas/cm^2, while the energy resolution began to deteriorate at the same time. Figure 10.12 shows the leakage current and

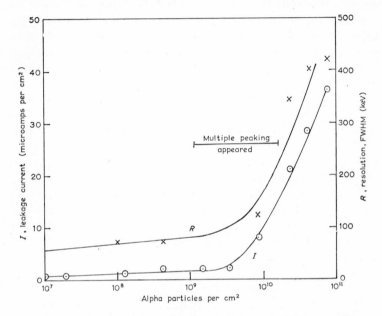

FIG. 10.12 Energy resolution and current in a 1000 ohm cm silicon surface barrier detector as a function of the dose of 5·5 MeV alpha particles. The detector bias voltage was 2 V; from DEARNALEY[28]

energy resolution of one detector operated at 2 volts bias, during the course of irradiation; 10^{11} alphas/cm^2 produced a serious deterioration. Often, during the intermediate stages, two and, occasionally, three, peaks were observed in the spectrum, the satellite peaks growing in intensity and eventually merging into one broad peak. This behaviour is very similar to that observed by Klingensmith[21] during fast neutron irradiation. At the higher bias of 20 volts there is a much smaller influence of irradiation on energy resolution; this is to be expected since the collecting field over the alpha track is increased by $\sqrt{10}$. The ratio of the change in energy resolution observed at 20 V bias compared with 2 V bias is in fact about 3. The heating of one detector to 120° C for 24 hours produced no appreciable improvement in energy resolution, but there was evidence of a slow improvement at room temperature over a period of several days. Very similar experiments and conclusions have been published by Baranov.[27]

In another experiment[28] the effect of a more uniform distribution of damage by charged particles was observed in exposure to a flux of protons, deuterons and alpha-particles

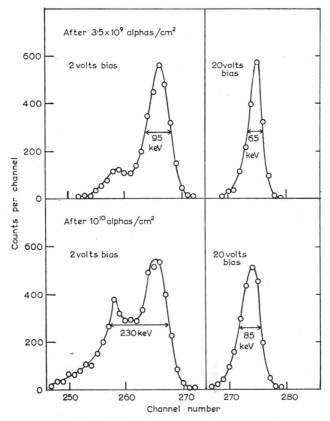

FIG. 10.13 Pulse-height spectrum for monoenergetic 5·5 MeV alpha particles in a 1000 ohm cm silicon surface barrier detector at two stages of alpha-particle irradiation, and for two different detector voltages; from DEARNALEY[28]

extending over all energies from zero to over 20 MeV, and produced by lithium ion bombardment of a boron target. Scattered lithium ions were excluded by a thin absorber foil in front of the detector, which was initially of 3000 Ω cm n-type silicon. A mean counting rate of 10^2 to 10^3 counts per second was observed over a period of 10 days almost continuous irradiation, during which time a number of nuclear physics experiments were carried out (Morrison, G. C., Miller, P. D., Gale, N. H. and Dearnaley, G., to be published), so that a total of about 10^9 particles/cm^2 entered the counter. From time to time measurements were made of the depletion layer depth, d, by noting the maximum proton pulse height corresponding to protons of range equal to the depletion layer depth. The resistivity deduced from these measurements rose progressively to 5200, 8000, and finally over 12 000 Ω cm, yet the energy resolution remained good. Figure 8.6 shows the response of the detector, towards the end of the experiment, to a proton and deuteron spectrum observed through a 0·01 cm. aluminium absorber. The cut-off in the proton spectrum is at about 6·5 MeV with a detector bias of only 30 V. Calculation of the mean density of Frenkel defects introduced in this irradiation leads to values comparable with the initial donor density of $7·10^{11}$/cm^3.

The results bear out the prediction of Curtis[20] that a significant change in the depletion layer depth may, in high-resistivity material, precede any drastic change in carrier lifetime.

This suggests that under more controlled conditions, using electrons to give a more uniform damage through the crystal, compensation of n-type silicon to give detectors of larger sensitive volumes can be usefully carried out. It is paradoxical that radiation damage may actually improve a detector.

One measurement remains in disagreement with these ideas. Scott[29] found that after the proton irradiation of p-type diffused junction counters the capacitance increased. This discrepancy has not yet been resolved and deserves some further investigation.

A number of measurements have been made of the effect of electron irradiation on silicon junction counters. George and Gunnersen[19] found an increase in the depletion layer thickness and a corresponding decrease in capacitance in surface-barrier detectors following 10^{13} electrons per cm², of 2 MeV energy. On the other hand Scott[29] observed a decrease in the capacitance of several diffused junction detectors, of p-type silicon, after electron irradiation. Dearnaley, Hooton, Nath and Wingfield[30] have studied the effect of 4 MeV electrons on surface-barrier detectors of various types. In this work a detector was mounted in an evacuated cell provided with a thin entrance window (Fig. 10.14). An alpha-particle source

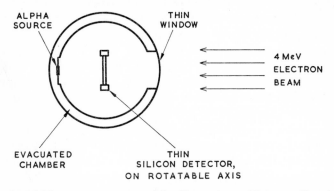

FIG. 10.14 The arrangement used by DEARNALEY, HOOTON, NATH and WINGFIELD for the study of electron radiation damage in silicon detectors

was used to test the response of the detector, which could be rotated to face the source or the electron beam as required. Alpha spectra were recorded at a number of bias voltages between each stage of the irradiation. By using fully-depleted detectors of thickness several times the alpha-particle range it is possible to study the charge-collection efficiency for electrons and holes separately. When the alphas enter through the negative (gold) electrode the electrons cross the major part of the depletion layer and thus contribute most of the observed pulse height, when alphas enter through the positive (aluminium) electrode, the holes contribute most of the pulse. It was found that the pulse height and energy resolution deteriorated more rapidly in the former case, showing that electrons have a greater tendency to be trapped than do holes. In this work a significant difference was found between the behaviour of partially depleted and fully depleted detectors. Thus 1 mm thick partially depleted detectors would withstand only $10^{13} - 10^{14}$ electrons per cm² before showing greatly increased leakage current, poor energy resolution and low breakdown voltages. On the other hand, after irradiations of $10^{15} - 10^{16}$ electrons per cm², several 0·005 inch thick fully-depleted detectors were little impaired. The cause of this striking difference is not understood. After irradiation the voltage necessary to give full charge collection for alpha-particles incident on the positive electrode of one detector decreased from 36 to 12 volts, showing the degree of compensation brought about by the trapped electrons.

Finally, we turn to some results on the effects of radiation damage by fission fragments in silicon detectors. Britt and Benson[31] studied the response of surface-barrier and diffused junction detectors to fission fragments following damage by the same particles. Integrated doses of the order of 10^8 fragments per cm² produced a significant decrease in the output pulse height and an increase in leakage current. It was also found that the pulse height defect, δ, (see Section 8.6) increased on irradiation at a linear rate of the order of 5×10^{-8} MeV/fragment/cm². The rate of increase of δ was appreciably greater for the high energy (lower mass) fragment group than for the low energy group. Possibly this is because the region of greatest ionization density for fission fragments is near the beginning of the range, while the greatest damage is produced towards the end of the range. The shorter range fragments can thus cause damage in a region where the longer range fragments are still producing a high density of carriers. The loss of carriers which is the origin of the pulse height defect can thus be more severe for the higher-energy fragments. Britt and Benson[31] found that surface barrier detectors (of n-type silicon) were more susceptible to damage than diffused junction detectors (or p-type material). Since in the former case electrons are making a longer traverse of the depletion layer than holes, and since we have seen that electrons tend to be trapped more readily than holes at radiation-induced defect sites, this result is not surprising. The rate of increase of the pulse height defect was greatly reduced by operating the detectors with a higher collecting field.

(c) Effects of radiation damage on lithium-drifted detectors

In these detectors a high degree of impurity compensation has been achieved so that the net space charge of ionized impurities is very low. Irradiation can upset this balance by introducing a space charge due to trapped electrons and the electric field may then cease to be uniform. The field gradient may alter so much that the field no longer extends through the crystal and a region of low or zero collecting field may appear. The collecting fields in lithium-drifted detectors are initially much lower than those in conventional junction detectors and this is likely to make them more susceptible to damage effects. This is found in practice.

Mann and Yntema[32] have observed the effect of proton and alpha-particle bombardment of lithium-drifted silicon detectors. Loss of energy resolution and an increase of leakage current were apparent after only 10^8 to 10^9 particles/cm², while after 10^{10} alpha-particles/cm² of 40 MeV energy the detectors showed severe multiple peaking. This must be due to the formation of regions in which the collecting field is low. It was found possible to restore detectors by a period of further drifting of the lithium, suggesting that the initial degree of compensation can be recovered and that the lithium-defect centres so formed have small trapping cross-sections for carriers. The same authors[32] studied the effect of fast neutron irradiation and found that the reverse current increased linearly with neutron dose at a rate of the order of a few microamps for 10^{11} neutrons/cm². This increase of current showed no signs of disappearing during a period of 3 months at room temperature.

Coleman and Rodgers[33] found significant changes in charge collection efficiency and pulse rise-time in lithium-drifted silicon detectors after exposure to as little as 10^5R of Co^{60} gamma-rays. Such a dose would give negligible damage in conventional junction counters. 5 MeV alpha-particles were used to test the detector performance and some results are shown in Fig. 10.15. Most of the observed effects could be explained in terms of a reduced electron lifetime and a reduced electron mobility. The latter is brought about by multiple temporary trapping of electrons at shallow traps near the

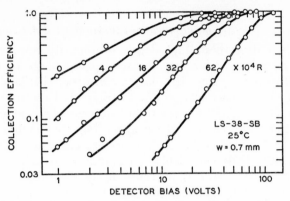

Fig. 10.15 The change in charge collection efficiency in a lithium-drifted silicon detector as a result of irradiation by Co^{60} gamma-rays; from COLEMAN and RODGERS[33]

conduction band. A field-dependent mobility and other complications occurred at low bias voltages, for which the detectors were only partially depleted. As in the case of damage by charged particles, the detectors could be restored by a period of drifting at 1000 V for 48 hours at 80–100° C.

(d) Limitations on experiments

Table 10.1 shows doses at which appreciable damage has been observed to occur to various types of semiconductor

TABLE 10.1

Typical Allowable Detector Exposures

Radiation	Surface-barrier or diffused junctions	Lithium-drifted detectors
5–50 MeV alphas	10^{10}/cm^2	10^8/cm^2 (32)
5–10 MeV protons	10^{11}/cm^2	10^8–10^9/cm^2 (32)
2–5 MeV electrons	10^{13}–10^{14}/cm^2 (19) (29)	?
Fast Neutrons	10^{12}–10^{13}/cm^2 (19) (22)	10^{11}/cm^2 (32)
Gamma Rays	$> 10^8$ R (22)	10^5 R (33)
Fission fragments	10^8–10^9/cm^2 (31)	?

This table shows doses at which significant damage has been observed in typical cases. However, the effects of damage can often be reduced by a high collecting field, so this table should be regarded as only a general guide. References are given in parentheses.

detector in fairly typical cases. Of course, as we have already seen, the degree of damage depends upon such factors as the magnitude and extent of the collecting field in the detector so that it is impossible to state a definite dose for the onset of damage. Some experiments do not require very high energy resolution in the detector and are less sensitive to radiation damage. Table 10.1 should therefore be used only as a general guide and not be taken too literally.

It is obvious, however, that lithium-drifted detectors are very much more susceptible to radiation damage than any of the conventional junction counters. This may often affect the choice of detector for some applications. Absorbers, to exclude large fluxes of short-range background particles, can extend the useful life of a detector. If redrifting of lithium-compensated detectors can be carried out the problem of expense becomes less serious.

The sensitivity of all forms of silicon detectors to fast-neutron damage is such that they can only rarely be useful in a reactor environment. The life of fast-neutron spectrometers which make use of silicon detectors (Chapter 8.11) is severely limited by radiation damage.

Sometimes surface effects are encountered which may be even more serious than the bulk effects of radiation damage we have considered above. Careful design of detector encapsulation may be essential in order to minimise these changes, due to the build-up of surface charge configurations. As an example of the careful planning of an experiment in space using semiconductor detectors, in which all these factors were considered, the work of Buck, Wheatley and Rodgers[34] is of great interest. A series of tests was carried out on detectors of various designs in the planning of the Telstar Satellite, and as a result the detector performance under severe conditions in the Van Allen radiation belt achieved a high reliability.

10.4 The use of radiation damage effects in fast neutron flux measurement

Since fast neutrons can produce observable effects by radiation damage throughout the depletion layer of a semiconductor diode it is an attractive possibility to apply the changes in diode characteristics to the measurement of a fast neutron flux. Such an instrument could be very compact and relatively insensitive to gamma rays. It is important that the sensitivity of different devices should be uniform, and that the response should be independent of the dose rate.

Gorton and his colleagues[24] have made an intensive study of the application of diffused silicon junctions as fast neutron dosimeters. Two parameters of the diodes change under neutron irradiation; these are the current drawn at a fixed reverse voltage, and the minority carrier lifetime. As we have seen, the latter property is relatively sensitive to neutron irradiation, though unambiguous measurements of carrier lifetime in a shallow diode are not easy to make. The reciprocal of the carrier lifetime, τ, was found to vary linearly with neutron dose, with a slope which was called the 'damage constant' of the device. In measurements with 50 diodes the mean damage constant was found to be about 65 rad^{-1} sec^{-1}, but wide variations from one unit to another were observed and attributed to variations in the silicon from which the diodes were prepared, and to variations in the method of preparation. The other parameter, the current at a given reverse bias voltage, is a simpler quantity to measure, but again wide variations were observed between one detector and another. No significant change in the sensitivity was produced by varying the dose rate from 6 to 25 000 rad/sec. Attempts at annealing the damage effects produced no significant changes after 5 minutes at 100° C but a 50 per cent recovery after 1 hour at 250° C. Schuttler[35] has confirmed that the rate of annealing of radiation-induced defects is low below 200-250° C in silicon.

Amelincx and his associates[36] have studied the value of silicon carbide p-n junctions as neutron dosimeters. The junctions are grown by a method described by Lely. It was found that the reverse current increases with neutron irradiation following a dose of the order of 10^{15} fast neutrons/cm^2. The impurity concentration in the best available silicon carbide crystals is at present about 10^{18} atoms/cm^3, and hence a larger dose is required to produce a noticeable change in the characteristic. The bulk resistivity was found to show a rapid rise after some 10^{16} fast neutrons/cm^2. The advantage of devices of silicon carbide is that they can be operated at temperatures up to 500° C and therefore could be useful for flux measurements within relatively high-temperature reactors.

REFERENCES

For this chapter

1 Frenkel, J., *Z. Physik*, **35**, 652 (1926).

2. George, G. G. and Gunnersen, E. M., *Proc. Int. Conf. on the Physics of Semiconductors*, Paris (July 1964), *(to be published)*.

3. Brinkman, J. A., *J. Appl. Phys.*, **25**, 961 (1954).

4. Seitz, F. and Koehler, J. S., *Solid State Physics*, **2**, 307 (1956).

5. Dienes, G. J. and Vineyard, G. H., *Radiation Effects in Solids*, Interscience Publishers (New York, 1957).

6. Billington, D. S. and Crawford, J. H., Jr., *Radiation Damage in Solids*, Princeton University Press (Princeton, 1961).

7. Howerton, R. J., University of California, *Lawrence Radiation Laboratory Report UCRL 5226* (1958).

8. Kinchin, G. H. and Pease, R. S., *Reports on Progress in Physics*, **18**, 1 (1955).

9. Harrison, W. A. and Seitz, F., *Phys. Rev.*, **98**, 1530 (1955).

10. Tanenbaum, M. and Mills, A. D., *J. Electrochem. Soc.*, **108**, 171 (1961).

11. Whaling, W., *Handbuch der Physik*, **34**, 193, Julius Springer (Berlin, 1985).

12. Cahn, J., *J. Appl. Phys.*, **30**, 1310 (1959).

13. James, H. M. and Lark-Horovitz, K., *Z. Physik. Chem.*, **198**, 107 (1951).

14. Fan, H. Y. and Lark-Horovitz, K., *Halbleiter und Phosphore*, ed. Schon, M. and Welker, H., Vieweg und Sohn (1958).

15. Bemski, G. and Augustyniak, W., *Phys. Rev.*, **108**, 645 (1957).

16. Carter, J. R. Jr., *I.E.E.E. Trans. Nucl. Sci.*, **NS-11**, No. 1, 290 (1964).

17. Cleland, J. W. and Crawford, J. H., Jr., reported in ref. 5 above.

18. Schuttler, R., *Mem. Soc. Roy. Sci. de Liège*, X, No. 2, 127 (1964).

19. George, G. and Gunnersen, E. M., *Conf. on Nuclear Chemistry*, Oxford (Sept., 1962).

20. Curtis, O. L., discussion in ref. 27 below, p. 133.

21. Klingensmith, R. W., *I.R.E. Trans. Nucl. Sci.*, **NS-8**, No. 1, 112 (1961).

22. Kramer, G. L., reported by Mayer, J. W., *I.R.E. Trans. Nucl. Sci.*, **NS-9**, No. 3, 124 (1961).

23. Babcock, R. V., *I.R.E. Trans. Nucl. Sci.*, NS-8, No. 1, 98 (1961).
24. Gorton, H. C., Mengali, O. J., Zacaroli, A. R., Crooks, R. K., Swartz, J. M. and Peet, C. J., *Quarterly Progress Reports on Experimental & Research Work in Solid State Neutron Dosimetry*, Battelle Memorial Institute, Columbus, Ohio (1959–).
25. *Proc. Asheville Conf. on Semiconductor Detectors*, Sept., 1960, *NAS-NRC Publication* 871, ed. Dabbs, J. W. T. and Walter, F. J. (1961).
26. Dearnaley, G. and Whitehead, A. B., *Nucl. Instr. & Methods*, 12, 205 (1961).
27. Baranov, I. A., *Instr. & Exper. Tech.*, Nov. 1964, p. 377.
28. Dearnaley, G., *I.E.E.E. Trans. Nucl. Sci.* NS-10, No. 1, 106 (1963).
29. Scott, R. E., *I.E.E.E. Trans. Nucl. Sci.*, NS-11, No. 3, 206 (1964).
30. Dearnaley, G., Hooton, B. W., Nath, N. and Wingfield, J., (*to be published*).
31. Britt, H. C. and Benson, G. C., *Rev. Sci. Instr.*, 35, 842 (1946).
32. Mann, H. M. and Yntema, J. L., *I.E.E.E. Trans. Nucl. Sci.*, NS-11, No. 3, 201 (1964).
33. Coleman, J. A. and Rodgers, J. W., *I.E.E.E. Trans. Nucl. Sci.*, NS-11, No. 3 213 (1964).
34. Buck, T. M., Wheatley, G. H. and Rodgers, J. W., *I.E.E.E. Trans. Nucl. Sci.*, NS-11, No. 3, 294 (1964).
35. Schuttler, R., private communication.
36. Amelincx, S., Heerschap, M., Nagels, P., De Coninck, R. and Denayer, M., *Solid State Detector for Neutrons* (*Quarterly Progress Reports*) *Centre d'Etude de l'Energie Nucleaire* (1960–).

For general reading

References 4, 5 and 6 above, and the *Proceedings of the Conference on Radiation Effects in Semiconductors*, Gatlinburg, Tennessee (May, 1959), *J. Appl. Phys.*, 30, 1116 (1959).

THE PHYSICAL PROPERTIES OF NEAR-INTRINSIC SILICON AND GERMANIUM

Property	Silicon	Germanium
Periodic table	Group IV b	Group IV b
Atomic number	14	32
Atomic weight	28·09	72·60
Stable isotope mass numbers	28, 29, 30	70, 72, 73, 74, 76
Crystal structure	diamond type	diamond type
Lattice constant	5·42 Å	5·657 Å
Number of atoms per cm³	$4·96 \times 10^{22}$	$4·41 \times 10^{22}$
Density	2·33 gm/cm³	5·33 gm/cm³
Melting point	1420° C	936° C
Boiling point	2600° C	2825° C
Cofficient of thermal expansion (linear)	$4·2 \times 10^{-6}/°$ C	$6·1 \times 10^{-6}/°$ C
Thermal conductivity	0·20 cal/cm/sec/° C	0·14 cal/cm/sec/° C
Specific heat (0°-100° C)	0·181 cal/gm/° C	0·074 cal/gm/° C
Dielectric constant	12	16
Refractive index	3·5 (12 000 Å)	4·14 (18 000 Å)
	3·4 (26 000 Å)	4·07 (26 000 Å)
Energy gap	1·106 eV	0·75 eV
Intrinsic resistivity (300° K)	230 000 Ω cm	47 Ω cm
Intrinsic carrier concentration (300° K)	$1·5 \times 10^{10}$/cm³	$2·35 \times 10^{13}$/cm³
Electron drift mobility (300° K)	1450 cm²/volt sec	3800 cm²/volt sec
Hole drift mobility (300° K)	480 cm²/volt sec	1800 cm²/volt sec
Electron diffusion constant (300° K)	35 cm²/sec	92 cm²/sec
Hole diffusion constant (300° K)	12·4 cm²/sec	44 cm²/sec
Electron drift mobility (77° K)	21 000 cm²/volt sec	36 000 cm²/volt sec
Hole drift mobility (77° K)	11 000 cm²/volt sec	42 000 cm²/volt sec
Work function	5·0 eV	4·8 eV
Debye temperature	640° C	370° C
Energy loss of minimum ionizing particles	400 keV/mm	830 keV/mm

CLASSIFIED BIBLIOGRAPHY

Semiconductors – bulk properties

Backenstoss, G., Evaluation of the surface concentration of diffused layers in silicon. *Bell System Tech. J.*, **37**, 699 (1958).

Batdorf, R. L., Chynoweth, A. G., Dacey, G. C. and Foy, P. W., Uniform silicon *p-n* junctions; I, Broad-area breakdown. *J. Appl. Phys.*, **31**, 1153 (1960).

Beyen, W. J., Remarks on photoconductivity and gold-doped silicon. *National Academy of Science National Research Council Publication* **871**, p. 121 (1961).

Bridgers, Scaff and Shive (eds.), I. Biondi (ed.) II and III. *Transistor Technology.* D. van Nostrand Co. (New York, 1957).

Brooks, H., Theory of the electrical properties of germanium and silicon, *Advances in Electronics and Electron Physics.* **1**, 117 (1955).

Chynoweth, A. G., Internal field emission in silicon *p-n* junctions. *Phys. Rev.*, **106**, 418 (1957).

Chynoweth, A. G. and Pearson, G. L., Effect of dislocations on breakdown in silicon *p-n* junctions. *J. Appl. Phys.*, **29**, 1103 (1958).

Chynoweth, A. G., Multiplication processes in *p-n* junctions. *National Academy of Science National Research Council Publication* **871**, p. 171 (1961).

Collins, C. B., Carlson, R. O. and Gallagher, C. J., Properties of gold-doped silicon. *Phys. Rev.*, **105**, 1168 (1957).

Davis, W. D., Lifetimes and capture cross-sections in gold-doped silicon. *Phys. Rev.*, **114**, 1006 (1959).

Dunlap, Jr. W. C., Electrical properties of gold-germanium alloys. *Phys. Rev.*, **91**, 1282 (1953).

Dunlap, Jr., W. C., Acceptor states of gold in germanium. *Phys. Rev.*, **91**, 208 (1953).

Dunlap, Jr., W. C., Gold as an acceptor in germanium. *Phys. Rev.*, **97**, 614 (1955).

Fuller, C. S. and Severiens, J. C., Mobility of impurity ions in germanium and silicon. *Phys. Rev.*, **96**, 21 (1954).

Fuller, C. S. and Ditzenberger, J. A., Diffusion of donor and acceptor elements in silicon. *J. Appl. Phys.*, **27**, 544 (1956).

Hall, R. N. and Racette, J. H., Diffusion and solubility of copper in extrinsic and intrinsic germanium, silicon and gallium arsenide. *J. Appl. Phys.*, **35**, 379 (1964).

Haynes, J. R. and Hornbeck, J. A., Temporary traps in Si and Ge. *Phys. Rev.*, **90**, 152 (1953).

Herlet, A., Die Abhangigkeit der Stromdichte eines *p-i-n* Gleich-richters von der Breite seiner Mittelzone. *Z. Physik*, **141**, 335 (1955).

Herlet, A. and Spenke, E., Gleichrichter mit *p-i-n* bezw. mit *p-s-n* struktur unter Gleichstrombelastung. *Z. Angew. Physik*, **7**, 99 (1955).

Jansen, B., A Rapid and accurate method for measuring the thickness of diffused layers in silicon and germanium. *Solid-state Electronics*, **2**, 14 (1961).

Jenny, D. A. and Wysocki, J. J., Temperature dependence and lifetime in semiconductor junctions. *J. Appl. Phys.*, **30**, 1692 (1959).

Kaiser, W. and Wheatley, G. H., Hot electrons and carrier multi-plication in silicon at low temperature. *Phys. Rev. Letters*, **3**, 335 (1959).

Koenig, S. H. and Gunther-Mohr, G. R., The low temperature electrical conductivity of *n*-type germanium. *Phys. Chem. Solids*, **2**, 268 (1957).

Larrabee, R. D., High field effect in boron-doped silicon. *Phys. Rev.*, **116**, 300 (1959).

Lawrence, H. and Warner, R. M., Diffused junction depletion layer calculations. *Bell System Tech. J.*, **39**, 389 (1960).

Lederhandler, S. R. and Giacoletto, L. J., Measurement of minority carrier lifetime and surface effects in junction devices. *Proc. I.R.E.*, **43**, 477 (1955).

Lothrop, R. P., Diffusion of phosphorus in Si from the azeotrope of phosphorus pentoxide and water. *J. Appl. Phys.*, **33**, 2656 (1962).

Ludwig, G. W. and Watters, R. L., Drift and conductivity mobility in silicon. *Phys. Rev.*, **101**, 1699 (1956).

McKay, K. G., Avalanche breakdown in silicon. *Phys. Rev.*, **94**, 877 (1954).

Mackintosh, I. M., The diffusion of phosphorus in silicon. *J. Electrochem. Soc.*, **109**, 392 (1962).

Messier, J., Changes in resistivity produced in high resistivity P-type silicon by thermal neutrons. *Comptes Rendus*, **255**, 2083 (1962).

Messier, J., Obtention de silicium de haute résistivité obtenu par compensation nucléaire. *Mem. Soc. Roy. Sci. de Liège*, X, No. 2, 115 (1964).

Morin, F. J. and Maita, J. P., Electrical properties of silicon containing arsenic and boron. *Phys. Rev.*, **96**, 28 (1954).

Pell, E. M. and Roe, G. M., Reverse current and carrier lifetime as a function of temperature in silicon junction diodes. *J. Appl. Phys.*, **27**, 768 (1956).

Prior, A. C., The field-dependence of carrier mobility in silicon and germanium. *J. Phys. Chem. Solids*, **12**, 175 (1959).

Robbins, H. and Schwartz, B., Chemical etching of silicon, I: the system HF, HNO_3 and H_2O. *J. Electrochem. Soc.*, **106**, 505 (1959).

Sah, C. T., Noyce, R. N. and Shockley, W., Carrier generation and recombination in junctions and *p-n* junction characteristics. *Proc. I.R.E.*, **45**, 1228 (1957).

Sclar, N. and Burstein, E., Impact ionization of impurities in germanium. *Phys. Chem. Solids*, **2**, 1 (1957).

Smits, F. M., Measurement of sheet resistivities with the four-point probe. *Bell System Tech. J.*, **37**, 711 (1958).

Stevenson, S. and Keyes, R. J., Measurement of carrier lifetimes in germanium and silicon. *J. Appl. Phys.*, **26**, 190 (1955).

Taft, E. A. and Horn, F. H., Gold as a donor in silicon. *Phys. Rev.*, **93**, 64 (1954).

Tanenbaum, M. and Mills, A. D., Preparation of uniform resistivity *n*-type silicon by nuclear transmutation. *J. Electrochem. Soc.*, **108**, 171 (1961).

Tannenbaum, L., Detailed analysis of thin phosphorus-diffused layers in *p*-type silicon. *Solid-state Electronics*, **2**, 123 (1961).

Trumbore, F. A., Solid solubilities of impurity elements in germanium and silicon. *Bell System Tech. J.*, **39**, 205 (1960).

Van Roosbroeck, W., Theory of current-carrier transport and photoconductivity in semiconductors with trapping. *Bell System Tech. J.*, **39**, 515 (1960).

Vogl, T. P. and Hansen, J. R., Photoconductive time constants and related characteristics of *p*-type gold-doped germanium. *J.O.S.A.*, **51**, 70 (1961).

Williams, E. L., Boron diffusion in silicon. *J. Electrochem. Soc.*, **108**, 795 (1961).

Semiconductors – Surface properties

Andreyeva, V. V. and Shishakov, N.A. The structure of the surface layers of germanium and silicon from optical and electron diffraction data. *Zh. Fis. Khimii*, **35**, 1351 (1961).

Archer, R. J., Optical measurement of film growth on silicon and germanium surfaces in room air. *J. Electrochem. Soc.*, **104**, 619 (1957).

Bardeen, J., Surface states and rectification at a metal semiconductor contact. *Phys. Rev.*, **71**, 717 (1947).

Buck, T. M. and McKim, F. S., Effects of certain chemical treatments and ambient atmospheres on surface properties of silicon. *J. Electrochem. Soc.*, **105**, 709 (1958).

Buck, T. M., Surface effects on silicon particle detectors, *National Academy of Science National Research Council Publication* **871**, p. 111 (1961).

Carlson, R. O., Gold on silicon surface. *J. Appl. Phys.*, **29**, 1001 (1958).

Damany, H., The electrical conductivity of thin films of gold on a silicon base. *Comptes Rendus*, **250**, 1615 (1960).

deMars, G. A., Statz, H. and Davis, L., Jr., Measurement and interpretation of conductance of *p*-type inversion layers on germanium. *Phys. Rev.*, **98**, 539 (1955).

Eriksen, W., Statz, H. and deMars, G. A., Excess surface currents on Ge and Si diodes. *J. Appl. Phys.*, **28**, 133 (1957).

Garrett, C. G. B. and Brattain, W. H., Some experiments on, and a theory of, surface breakdown. *J. Appl. Phys.*, **27**, 299 (1956).

Green, M. and Kafalas, J., Oxidation of clean surfaces of Ge below 25° C. *Phys. Rev.*, **98**, 1566 (1955).

Green, M. and Maxwell, K. H., The adsorption of oxygen on clean silicon surfaces. *J. Phys. Chem. Solids*, **13**, 145 (1960).

Hagstrum, H. D., Oxygen adsorption on Si and Ge. *J. Appl. Phys.*, **32**, 1020 (1961).

Henisch, H. K., *Rectifying Semiconductor Contacts*. The Clarendon Press (Oxford, 1957).

Kingston, R. H., *Semiconductor Surface Physics*. University of Pennsylvania Press (1957).

Komatsubara, K., On the change of surface states of germanium by irradiation. *J. Phys. Soc., Japan*, **17**, 62 (1962).

Larrabee, G. B., The contamination of semiconductor surfaces. *J. Electrochem. Soc.*, **108**, 1130 (1961).

Mann, H. M. and Janarek, F. J., Adherent gold plating on silicon. *Rev. Sci. Instr.*, **33**, 557 (1962).

Many, A., The electrical structure of semiconductor surfaces. Brooks, H. (ed.), *Advances in Semiconductors*. Pergamon Press (New York, 1959).

Robertson, H. M., McNamara, J. E. and Warner, R. M., A note on silicon oxide film thickness measurement. *J. Appl. Phys.*, **33**, 2909 (1962).

Statz, H., deMars, G. A., Davis, L., Jr. and Adams A., Jr., Surface states on silicon and germanium surfaces. *Phys. Rev.*, **101**, 1272 (1956).

Statz, H., deMars, G., Davis, L., Jr. and Adams A., Jr., Surface states on silicon and germanium surfaces. *Phys. Rev.*, **106**, 455 (1957).

Statz, H., Semiconductor surface effects, *National Academy of Science National Research Council Publication* **871**, 99 (1961).

Strikha, V. I. and Kilchinskaya, S. S., Measurement of thin oxide films on the surface of germanium and silicon. *Prib. Tekhn. Eksper.*, May–June 1964, No. 3, 177.

Sullivan, M. H. and Eigler, J. H., Electroless nickel plating for making contacts to silicon. *J. Electrochem. Soc.*, **104**, 226 (1957).

Terman, L. M., An investigation of surface states at a silicon/silicon oxide interface employing metal-oxide-silicon diodes. *Solid-state Electronics*, **5**, 285 (1962).

Turner, D. R., Electroplating metal contacts on Ge and Si. *J. Electrochem. Soc.*, **106**, 786 (1959).
See also Proceedings of the 2nd Conference on Semicondutor Surfaces, *J. Phys. Chem. Solids*, 14 (1960).

Ionization in semiconductors

Baldinger, E. and Czaja, W., On the energy expended per electron-hole pair produced in *p-n* junction detectors. *Nucl. Instr. & Methods*, **10**, 237 (1961).

Baldinger, E. and Czaja, W., An exact determination of the energy per electron-hole pair in silicon counter diodes. *Helv. Phys. Acta*, **35**, 559 (1962).

Bichsel, H. and Liu, H-C., Relation between pulse height and particle energy in silicon detectors. *Bull. Amer. Phys. Soc.*, **8**, 39 (1963).

Bilger, H., Baldinger, E. and Czaja, W., Ionisation von Silicon-Rückstosskernen in Silicon-Zähldioden Bestrahlung mit Neutronen von 3, 0 bis 3, 9 Mev., *Helv. Phys. Acta.*, **36**, 405 (1963).

Blankenship, J. L., and Mruk, W. F., Evidence for a Fano factor less than 1 in silicon diode radiation detectors. *Bull. Amer. Phys. Soc.*, **9**, 49 (1964).

Bøgh, E., Davies, J. A. and Nielsen, K. O., Experimental evidence for the extinction of (p, γ) yields in single crystals. *Physics Letters*, **12**, 129 (1964).

Bussolati, C., Fiorentini, A. and Fabri, G., Energy for electron-hole pair generation in silicon by electrons and alpha particles. *Phys. Rev.*, **136A**, 1756, (1964).

Czaja, W., Zur theorie der arbeit pro electron-loch-paar in halbleitern de IV gruppe. *Helv. Phys. Acta*, **34**, 760 (1961).

Chynoweth, A. G. and McKay, K. G., Threshold energy for electron-hole pair-production by electrons in silicon. *Phys. Rev.*, **108**, 29 (1957).

Chynoweth, A. G., Ionization rates for electrons and holes in silicon. *Phys. Rev.*, **109**, 1537 (1958).

Chynoweth, A. G., Energy required for electron-hole pair formation in silicon. *National Academy of Science National Research Council Publication* **871**, 95, (1961).

Dearnaley, G., The channelling of ions through silicon detectors. *I.E.E.E. Trans. Nucl. Sci.*, **NS-11**, No. 3, 249 (1964).

Dearnaley, G. and Sattler, A. R., Channelling of ions through single-crystal silicon lattices. *Bull. Amer. Phys. Soc.*, **9**, 656 (1964).

Erginsoy, C., Wegner, H. E. and Gibson, W. M., Anisotropic energy loss of light particles of MeV energies in thin silicon single crystals. *Phys. Rev. Letters*, **13**, 530 (1964).

Ewing, R. I., Charge production in silicon surface-barrier counters by helium ions. *Bull. Amer. Phys. Soc.*, **8**, 296 (1963).

Finke, G. and Lantz, G., Zur stoszionisation in germanium-einkristallen im temperaturbereich von $4.2°$ K bis $10°$ K. *Z. Naturforsch.*, 12a, 223 (1957).

Hodgkinson, R. J., Impact ionization threshold in semiconductors. *Proc. Phys. Soc.*, A82, 1010 (1963).

Koch, L. and Messier, J., Measurement of the mean ionization energy in silicon for alpha and beta particles using N-I-P junctions. *Comptes Rendus*, **252**, 74 (1961).

Lindhard, J. and Nielsen, V., Nuclear collisions and ionization fluctuations in charged particle detectors. *Physics Letters*, **2**, 209 (1962).
Lindhard, J., Motion of swift charged particles, as influenced by strings of atoms in crystals. *Physics Letters*, **12**, 126 (1964).

McIntyre, R. J., A note on the method of determining ionization coefficients for electrons and holes in silicon. *J. Electronics and Control*, **9**, 229 (1960).
McKay, K. G., Electron-hole production in germanium by alpha particles. *Phys. Rev.*, **84**, 829 (1951).
McKay, K. G. and McAfee, K. B., Electron multiplication in silicon and germanium. *Phys. Rev.*, **91**, 1079 (1953).

Ritter, R. C. and Porterfield, C. D., Low-energy nuclear reaction recoils in solid-state detectors. *Bull. Amer. Phys. Soc.*, **9**, 67 (1964).

Tauc, J., Electron impact ionization in semiconductors. *J. Phys. Chem. Solids*, **8**, 219 (1959).

Patskevich, V. M., Vavilov, V. S. and Smirnov, L. S., Energy of ionization in silicon crystals by electrons. *Soviet Phys. JETP*, **6**, 619 (English). *Zh. Eksper. Teoret. Fiz.*, **33**, 804 (1957) (Russian).

Sattler, A. R., Ionization in silicon from monoenergetic neutron bombardment below 1 MeV. *Bull. Amer. Phys. Soc.*, **9**, 668 (1964).

Sattler, A. R. and Silbert, M. G., Ionization by energetic silicon atoms within a silicon lattice. *Bull. Amer. Phys. Soc.*, **9**, 655 (1964).

Schiffer, J. P. and Holland, R. E., Channelling of 3.6 MeV protons through a single crystal of silicon. *Bull. Amer. Phys. Soc.*, **10**, 54 (1965).

Schweinler, H. C., Energy loss of moving charged particles in a valence or ionic crystal. *National Academy of Science National Research Council Publication* **871**, 91 (1961).

Vavilov, V. S., Kolomenskaya, T. I., Vintovkin, S. I., and Chukichev, M. V., On the generation of non-equilibrium carriers by fast electrons in silicon. *Prib. Tekhn. Eksper.*, Sept–Oct. 1964, No. 5, 79.

Vavilov, V. S., On photo-ionization by fast electrons in germanium and silicon. *J. Phys. Chem. Solids*, **8**, 223 (1959).

Vavilov, V. S., Radiation ionization processes in germanium and silicon crystals. *Soviet Physics Uspekhi*, **4**, 761 (1962).

Wegner, H. E., The energy loss by charged particles in silicon as a function of track orientation. *I.E.E.E. Trans. Nucl. Sci.*, **NS-12**, No. 1 (1965).

Crystal and conduction counters

Batty, C. J., Griffiths, R. J. and Gibbons, P.E., Some results using bulk ionization semiconductor detectors. *Nucl. Instr. & Methods*, **17**, 125 (1962).

Blumenfeld, H. and Pandolfi, F. P., Preparation and performance of a minimum-ionizing particle detector. *I.E.E.E. Trans. Nucl. Sci.*, **NS-12**, No. 1, (1965).

Bull, C. S. and Flowers, B. H., Preliminary report on crystal counters. *A.E.R.E. N/R 125* (1947).

Champion, F. C., Solid conduction counters. *Prog. in Nuclear Phys.*, **3**, 159 (1953).

Champion, F. C., Symposium on solid state conductivity. II. Recent experiments with crystal counters. *Phys. in Med. Biol.*, **4**, 334 (1960).

Chynoweth, A. G., Conductivity crystal counters. *Am. J. Phys.*, **20**, 218 (1952).

Davis, W. D., Silicon crystal counters. *J. Appl. Phys.*, **29**, 231 (1958).

Garlick, G. F. J., Symposium on solid state conductivity. I, Radiation-induced conductivity. *Phys. in Med. Biol.*, **4**, 325 (1960).

Gibbons, P. E. and Northrop, D. C., Semiconductor counters II. Experiment. *Proc. Phys. Soc.*, **80**, 276 (1962).

Gibbons, P. E. and Northrop, D. C., A silicon gamma ray spectrometer. *Nature*, **188**, 803 (1960).

Golovin, B. M. and Osipenko, B. P., Homogeneous crystal counters of nuclear radiations. *Pribory i Tekhnika Eksperimenta*, **6**, 5 (1961).

Griffiths, R. J., Batty, C. J., Gibbons, P. E. and Northrop, D. C., Preliminary experiments with a solid-state ionization chamber. *Nuclear Electronics*, **I**, 497 (1962).

Harding, W. R., Hilsum, C., Moncaster, M. E., Northrop, D. C. and Simpson, O., Gallium arsenide for gamma ray spectroscopy. *Nature*, **187**, 405 (1960).

Hofstadter, R., Milton, J. C. D. and Ridgeway, S. L., Behaviour of silver chloride crystal counters. *Phys. Rev.*, **72**, 977 (1947).

Hofstadter, R., Crystal counters. Part I. *Nucleonics*, **4**, 2 (1949). Part II. *Nucleonics*, **4**, 29 (1949).

Hofstadter, R., Crystal counters. *Proc. I.R.E.*, **38**, 726 (1950).

McKay, K. G., The crystal conduction counter. *Phys. Today*, **6**, 10 (1953).

Marinov, M., Semiconductors as detectors of nuclear radiation. *Tekhnika*, **10**, 27 (1961).

Northrop, D. C. and Simpson, O., Semiconductor counters. I, Theory. *Proc. Phys. Soc.*, **80**, 262 (1962).

Ryvkin, S. M., On the mechanism of pulse formation in semiconducting crystalline counters. *Dokl. Akad. Nauk S.S.S.R.*, **106**, 250 (1956).

Ryvkin, S. M., Bogomazov, A. P., *et al.*, Semiconducting device for gamma-ray detection. *Zh. Tekh. Fiz.*, **27**, 1601 (1957) (in Russian). *Soviet J. Tech. Phys.*, **2**, 7 (1957) (in English).

Ryvkin, S. M., Mechanism of pulse formation in semiconducting crystal counters. *Soviet J. Tech. Phys.*, **1**, 2580 (1957) (English). *Zh. Tekh. Fiz.*, **26**, 2667 (1956) (Russian).

Ryvkin, S. M., The so-called 'secondary' and 'through' photocurrent in semiconductors. *Soviet J. Tech. Phys.*, **1**, 2357 (English). *Zh. Tekh. Fiz.*, **26**, 2439 (1956) (Russian).

Simpson, O., Silicon and gallium arsenide conduction counters. *Proc. Symp. on Nucl. Instr.*, 75 (Heywood & Co., 1962).

Taylor, K. N. R., The operation of crystal counters with non-uniform electric field distribution. *Brit. J. Appl. Phys.*, **13**, 242 (1962).

Van Heerden, P. J., *The Crystal Counter*. N. V. Noordhollandsche Uitgevers Maatschappij, Amsterdam (1945).

Van Heerden, P. J., The crystal counter for beta and gamma rays, Parts I and II. *Physica*, **16**, 505 (1950).

Van Heerden, P. J., Copper-doped germanium as a model for high-resistivity photoconductors. *Phys. Rev.*, **108**, 230 (1957).

Van Putten, J. D. and Vander Velde, J. C., Solid state detector for penetrating and minimum ionizing particles. *Bull. Am. Phys. Soc.*, **5**, 197 (1960).

Van Putten, J. D. and Vander Velde, J. C., Homogeneous solid state ionization detector. *I.R.E. Trans. Nucl. Sci.*, NS-8 *No.* 1, **124** (1961).

Vitovsky, N. A., Maleev, P. I. and Ryvkin, S. M., The mechanism of pulse formation in crystalline counters and the formation of a 'through conducting channel'. *Zh. Tekh. Fiz.*, **28**, 460 (1958).

Weis, C. G., Vetter, A. F., John, G. and Spialter, L., Organo-silicon compounds for radiation detection. *Trans. Amer. Nucl. Soc.*, **4**, 23 (1961).

Yamakawa, K. A., Silver bromide crystal counters. *Phys. Rev.*, **82**, 522 (1951).

Cadmium sulphide counters

Borisov, M. and Marinov, M., A study of the possibilities of using cadmium sulphide crystal counters. *Nuclear Electronics*, **I**, 363 (1962).

Borisov, M. and Marinov, M., Crystal counters of cadmium sulphide with a high-frequency electric field. *Compt. Rend. Acad. Bulgare Sci.*, **11**, 169 (1958).

Broser, I. and Warminsky, R., Modifications produced by alpha particle irradiations in CdS crystals. *Z. Naturforsch.*, **6a**, 85 (1951).

Clayton, C. G., Detection of gamma radiation by induced conductivity. *A.E.R.E.* Report *R-3289* (1960).

Gerthsen, C. and Kolb, W., The 'differential ionization' by radiation in CdS crystals. *Z. Naturforsch.*, **8a**, 315 (1953).

Henry, B. and Cole, H., Single crystal CdS as soft X-ray detector. *Rev. Sci. Instr.*, **30**, 90 (1959).
Hollander, Jr., L. E., Preparation of high-sensitivity cadmium sulphide cells for gamma-ray detection. *Rev. Sci. Instr.*, **28**, 322 (1957).

Kallman, H. and Warminsky, R., On the amplification effect of the electrical conduction of a cadmium sulphide crystal for irradiation with alpha particles, electrons and gamma rays. *Ann. Physik*, **4**, 69 (1948).
Klick, C. C., Peake, H. J., Cole, P. T., Rabin, H. and Lambe, J. J., Simple fall-out meter uses CdS. *Nucleonics*, **13**, 48 (1955).
Konozenko, I. D. and Ust'yanov, V. I., Crystalline CdS gamma-radiation receivers. *Soviet Phys.-Solid State*, **1**, 81 (1959).
Konozenko, I. D. and Ust'yanov, V. I., Production of large cadmium sulphide monocrystals for gamma field dosimetry. *Ukrain. Fiz. Zh.*, **5**, 606 (1960).
Kolb, W., On the differential conductivity-excitation of CdS crystals by alpha particles. *Ann. Physik*, **14**, 397 (1954).

Marinov, M. and Vodenicarov, H., Counting efficiency of thin CdS crystals used as channel conductors. *C.R. Acad. Bulg. Sci.*, **12**, 509 (1959).
Mills, D. L., Price, W. J., Reynolds, D. C., and Lehmann, W. L., CdS as a solid-state radiation detector. *Bull. Amer. Phys. Soc.*, **7**, 542 (1963).
Moos, W. S. and Spongberg, F., CdS-crystal probes are convenient for dosimetry in body cavities. *Nucleonics*, **13**, 88 (1955).

Powderly, J. E., Bean, K. E. and Medcalf, W. E., Research on growing of cadmium sulfide crystals for dosimeter purposes. *Final Contract Report*, Eagle Picher Research Labs., Miami, Oklahoma (1958).

Rabson, T. A., A small, linear wide range nuclear radiation detector. *Nucl. Instr. & Methods*, **16**, 37 (1962).

Schaal, A., Investigations on the applicability of cadmium sulfide crystals to dosage determinations in the X and gamma ray range. *Strahlentherapie*, **94**, 393 (1954).

Van Heerden, P. J., Primary photocurrent in CdS. *Phys. Rev.*, **106**, 468 (1957).

Diamond counters

Champion, F. C., Some physical consequences of elementary defects in diamonds. *Proc. Roy. Soc.*, **A234**, 541 (1956).

Champion, F. C., Electrical counting properties of diamonds. *Proc. Phys., Soc.* **B65**, 465 (1952).

Cotty, W. F., Diamond, a practical radiation counter. *J. Brit. I.R.E.*, **16**, 329 (1956).

Freeman, G. P. and Van der Velden, H. A., Some aspects of the counting properties of diamond. *Physica*, **17**, 565 (1951).

Freeman, G. P. and Van der Velden, H. A., Differences between counting and non-counting diamonds, Parts I and II. *Physica*, **18**, 1 and 9 (1952).

Ralph, J. E., Some scintillation characteristics of diamond under alpha particle bombardment. *Proc. Phys. Soc.*, **A73**, 233 (1959).

Taylor, K. W., Particle counting behaviour of diamond conduction counters at field strengths up to 200 kV cm^{-1}. *Proc. Phys. Soc.*, **A69**, 593 (1956).

Trott, N. G., Variations in the beta particle counting properties of diamond. *Proc. Roy. Soc.*, **A220**, 498 (1953).

Germanium counters

Airapetyants, A. V. and Ryvkin, S. M., The characteristics and mechanism of operation of germanium *p-n* alpha counters. *Soviet J. Tech. Phys.*, **2**, 79 (1957) (English). *Zh. Tekh. Fiz.*, **27**, 95 (1957) (Russian).

Airapetyants, A. V., Kogan, A. V., Reinov, N. M., Ryvkin, S. M. and Sokolov, I. A., On the use of germanium *n-p* alpha ray counters at low temperatures. *Soviet J. Tech. Phys.*, **2**, 1482 1482 (1957) (English). *Zh. Tekh. Fiz.*, **27**, 1599 (1957) (Russian).

Alferov, Zh. I., Konovalenko, B. M., Ryvkin, S. M., Tuchkevich, V. M. and Uvarov, A. I., Plane germanium photodiodes. *Zh. Tekh. Fiz.*, **25**, 11 (1955).

Konovalenko, B. M., Ryvkin, S. M. and Tuchkevich, V. M., The sensitivity of germanium photodiodes to X-ray irradiation. *Zh. Tekh. Fiz.*, **25**, 18 (1955).

McKay, K. G., A germanium alpha counter. *Phys. Rev.*, **76**, 1537 (1949).

McKenzie, J. M. and Bromley, D. A., Gold-germanium junctions as particle spectrometers. *Proceedings of the Sixth Tripartite Instrumentation Conference* (held at Chalk River, Ontario, April 20-24, 1959). Part 5: Radiation detectors.

McKenzie, J. M. and Bromley, D. A., Gold-germanium junctions as particle spectrometers. *Proc. Inst. Elec. Eng.*, **106**, 731 (1959).

Mayer, J. W. and Gossick, B. R., Use of gold germanium broad area barriers as alpha particle spectrometers. *Rev. Sci. Instr.*, **27**, 407 (1956).

Orman, C., Fan, H. Y., Goldsmith, G. J. and Lark-Horovitz, K., Germanium *p-n* barriers as counters. *Phys. Rev.*, **78**, 646 (1950).

Pantchechnikoff, J. I., A large area germanium photocell. *Rev. Sci. Instr.*, **24**, 135 (1952).

Ryvkin, S. M., On the question of the mechanism of germanium photodiode action. *Zh. Tekh. Fiz.*, **25**, 21 (1955).

Simon, E., Gold-germanium surface barriers. *Ph.D. Thesis*, Purdue University (1955).

Vul, B. M., Vavilov, V. S., Smirnov, L. S., Galkin, G. N., Patskevich, V. M. and Spitsyn, A. V., The conversion of the energy of beta particles to electron energy in germanium crystals with *p-n* junctions. *Kernenergie*, **1**, 279 (1958) (in German). *Atomnaya Energ.*, **2**, 533 (1957) (in Russian).

Walter, F. J., Dabbs, J. W. T., Roberts, L. D. and Wright, H. W., A study of germanium surface barrier counters. *Oak Ridge National Laboratory Report*, CF-58-11-99 (1958).

Walter, F. J., Dabbs, J. W. T. and Roberts, L. D., Large area germanium surface-barrier counters. *Oak Ridge National Laboratory Report*, ORNL 2877 (1960).

Walter, F. J., Dabbs, J. W. T. and Roberts, L. D., Large area germanium surface-barrier counters. *Rev. Sci. Instr.*, **31**, 756 (1960).

Junction counters—General

Alvager, T. and Hansen, N. J., Doping of crystals by ion bombardment to produce solid state detectors. *Rev. Sci. Instr.*, **33**, 567 (1962).

Amsel, G., Baruch, P. and Smulkowski, O., Heavy particles detected with n-p silicon junction. *Compt. Rend.*, **250**, 1468 (1960).

Amsel, G., Baruch, P. and Smulkowski, O., High resolution study of nuclear reactions by p-n junction detectors. *I.R.E. Trans. Nucl. Sci.*, **NS-8**, No. 1, 21 (1961).

Amsel, G., Experiments with n-p junction detectors. *National Academy of Science National Research Council Publication* **871**, 35 (1961).

Amsel, G., Oxide-stabilized surface barrier detectors. *Rev. Sci. Instr.*, **32**, 1253 (1961).

Ananiades, C. S. and Dewdney, J. W., Transistor alpha-particle detector. *Am. J. Phys.*, **29**, 329 (1961).

Åstrom, B., Recent work on instrumentation for nuclear pulse height spectroscopy. *Nuclear Electronics*, **I**, 535 (1962).

Axtmann, R. C. and Kedem, D., Non-linear response of silicon detectors to fission-fragment energy. *Bull. Amer. Phys. Soc.*, **10**, 13 (1965) and *Nucl. Instr. & Methods*, **32**, 70 (1965).

Baily, N. A. and Mayer, J. W., p-n junction semiconductor radiation detector for use with beta and gamma ray emitting isotopes. *Bull. Am. Phys. Soc.*, **6**, 107 (1961).

Baily, N. A., Grainger, R. J., Kramer, G. L., Mayer, J. W., Simon, G. and Wiggins, J. S., Physical parameters affecting performance of p-n junction detectors. *Hughes Nuclear Electronics Lab. Report* (1961).

Baldinger, E., Czaja, W. and Farooqi, A. N., p-n junctions as solid body ionization chambers. *Helv. Phys. Acta*, **33**, 551 (1960).

Baldinger, E., Czaja, W. and Gutmann, J., Temperature effects in silicon p-n junction detectors. *Proc. Symp. on Nucl. Instr.* Harwell, Heywood & Co. (1962).

Bilaniuk, O. M., Marsh, B. B., Hamann, A. K. and Heurtley, J. C., An array of solid state counters with delay line pulse sorting. *Nucl. Instr. & Methods*, **14**, 63 (1962).

Bilaniuk, O. M., Semiconductor particle detectors. *Scientific American*, **207**, 78 (1962).

Binder, D. and Kramer, G., Response of p-n silicon junction detectors to high-intensity X-rays and pulsed bremsstrahlung. *Bull. Am. Phys. Soc.*, **7**, 52 (1962).

Blamires, N. G., Combination of a scintillator and a semiconductor photodiode for nuclear particle detection. *Nucl. Instr. & Methods*, **24**, 441 (1963).

Blanc, D., Semiconductor particle detectors. *Nucleus*, **376** (1960).

Blankenship, J. L., Silicon surface barrier spectrometers. *Proc. of the Sixth Tripartite Instrumentation Conf.*, 75 (1959).

Blankenship, J. L., Borkowski, C. J., Semiconductor surface-barrier counters of improved energy resolution. *Bull. Am. Phys. Soc.*, **5**, 38 (1960).

Blankenship, J. L. and Borkowski, C. J., Silicon surface-barrier nuclear particle spectrometer. *I.R.E. Trans. Nucl. Sci.*, **NS-7**, No. 2–3, 190 (1960).

Blankenship, J. L., Surface barrier detectors. *National Academy of Science National Research Council Publication* **871**, 43 (1961).

Blankenship, J. L. and Borkowski, C. J., Performance of silicon surface barrier detectors with charge sensitive amplifiers. *I.R.E. Trans. Nucl. Sci.*, **NS-8**, No. 1, 17 (1961).

Blankenship, J. L., Borkowski, C. J. and Fox, R. J., Silicon surface barrier nuclear particle detectors. *Nuclear Electronics*, **I**, 379 (1962).

Bok, J. and Noel, J. P., Surface barrier diode for the detection of nuclear particles. *Nucl. Instr. & Methods*, **13**, 206 (1961).

Bomal, R., Detection of nuclear particles by means of semiconductors. *Bull. Inform. Sci. et Tech.* (Paris), 2 (1959).

Bomal, R., Koch, L., Van Dong, N. and Schneider, Utilization of semiconductors as detectors of nuclear radiation. *Bull. Inform. Sci. et Tech.* (Paris), 137 (1959).

Bredel, V. V., Mikheev, V. L. and Polikanov, S. M., Silicon detectors of heavy charged particles. *Instrum. eksper. tekh.*, 1085 (1962).

Brown, G. M., Clark, A. F., *et al.*, Principles of *p-n* junction detectors. *Amer. J. Phys.*, **31**, 19 (1963).

Brown, W. L., Introduction to semiconductor particle detectors. *I.R.E. Trans. Nucl. Sci.*, **NS-8**, No. 1, 2 (1961).

Brown, W. L., Properties of space charge regions. *National Academy of Science National Research Council Publication* **871**, 9 (1961).

Buck, T. M., Wheatley, G. H. and Rodgers, J. W., Silicon *p-n* junction radiation detectors for the Telstar satellite. *I.E.E.E. Trans. Nucl. Sci.*, **NS-11**, No. 3, 294 (1964).

Chwaszczewska, J. and Chwaszczewski, S., Semiconductor particle detectors. *Nukleonika*, **6**, 635 (1961).

Chwaszczewska, J., Roman, J., Szwaj, Z and Urbanowicz, Z., Large-area high-resolution semiconductor alpha spectrometer. *Inst. of Nucl. Research, Warsaw.* Report **CLOR/IBJ-II-25** (1963).

Cindro, N., A possible method for distinguishing charged particles with semiconductor detectors. *Nucl. Instr. & Methods*, **13**, 99 (1961).

Coche, A., Détecteurs de rayonnements nucléaires à barrière de surface. *Mem. Soc. Roy. Sci. de Liège*, X, No. 2, 23 (1964).

Coche, A. and Siffert, P., Construction and study of the properties of surface barrier detectors of heavy particles. *J. Phys. Radium*, **22**, 162 (1961).

Colard, J. and Gal, J., Calibration of solid state *p-n* detectors with alpha and heavy high-energy particles. *Nucl. Instr. & Methods*, **16**, 195 (1962).

Crawford, G. I., Semiconductors as radiation detectors. *Nuclear Power*, **4**, 84 (1959).

Czulius, W., Engler, H. D. and Kuckuck, H., Halbleiter Sperr-schichtzähler. *Ergebnisse der Exakten Naturwissenschaften*, **34**, 235 (1962).

Dabbs, J. W. T. and Walter, F. J., Pulse rise times in semiconductor particle detectors. *Bull. Am. Phys. Soc.*, **6**, 456 (1961).

Dearnaley, G. and Whitehead, A. B., Surface barrier charged-particle detectors. *A.E.R.E. R.3278* (1960).

Dearnaley, G. and Whitehead, A. B., The solid-state surface barrier charged particle detector. *A.E.R.E. R.3437*, 35 (1960).

Dearnaley, G., Characteristics of surface barrier detectors. *National Academy of Science National Research Council Publication* **871**, 49 (1961).

Dearnaley, G. and Whitehead, A. B., How Harwell makes surface-barrier detectors. *Nucleonics*, **19**, 72 (1961).

Dearnaley, G. and Whitehead, A. B., The semiconductor surface barrier for nuclear particle detection. *Nucl. Instr. & Methods*, **12**, 205 (1961).

Dearnaley, G., Semiconductor Nuclear Radiation Detectors. *J. Brit. I.R.E.*, **24**, 153 (1962).

Dearnaley, G., Semiconductor counters. *Progress in Nuclear Physics*, **9**, ed. Frisch, O. R. (Pergamon Press, 1963).

Dodge, W. R., Domen, S. R., Hirshfield, A. T., and Hoppes, D. D., The anomaly in the response of semiconductor detectors at low temperatures. *I.E.E.E. Trans. Nucl. Sci.*, **NS-11**, No. 3, 238 (1964) and **NS-12**, No. 1, (1965).

Donovan, P. F., Paint-on particle detectors (Recipe No. 2). *National Academy of Science National Research Council Publication* **871**, 268 (1961).

Dunmur, I., George, G., Gunnersen, E. M. and Hitchcock, A., Properties of solid state detectors. *Nucl. Electronics*, **I**, 501 (1962).

Engler, H. D., The individual detection of beta particles with germanium and silicon surface diodes. *Z. Naturforsch.*, **15a**, 82 (1960).

Engler, H. D., Alloyed silicon diodes as particle counters. *Nukleonik*, **2**, 215 (1960).

Fabri, G., Prospects of semiconductor radiation detectors. *Energia Nucleare* (Milan), **8**, 337 (1961).

Fox, R. J. and Borkowski, C. J., Silicon surface barrier detectors with high reverse breakdown voltages. *I.R.E. Trans. Nucl. Sci.*, **NS-9**, No. 3, 213 (1962).

Friedland, S. S. and Keywell, F., Semiconductor devices as charged particle detectors and energy spectrometers. *Proc. 2nd Conf. on Nucl. Radiation Effects on Semiconductor Devices, Materials & Circuits*, 123 (1959).

Friedland, S. S., Mayer, J. W., Denney, J. M. and Keywell, F., Room temperature operated *p-n* junctions as charged particle detectors. *Rev. Sci. Instr.*, **31**, 74 (1960).

Friedland, S. S., Mayer, J. W. and Wiggins, J. S., Tiny semiconductor is fast, linear detector. *Nucleonics*, **18**, 54 (1960).

Gibbons, P. E., Metal-semiconductor contacts for solid state radiation detectors. *Nucl. Instr. & Methods*, **29**, 289 (1964).

Gibson, W. M., Oxide edge protection. *National Academy of Science National Research Council Publication* **871**, 232 (1961).

Gonchar, V. Y., Zalyubovskii, I. I., Zubritskii, L. A., Titov, Y. I. and Chursin, G. P., Semiconductor spectrometer for charged particles. *Bull. Acad. Sci. U.S.S.R.–Physical Series*, **28**, No. 1, 102 (1964).

Gordon, G. E., Kilian, G. W., Larsh, A. E. and Sikkeland, T., Silicon *p-n* junctions as charged-particle detectors. University of California, Lawrence Radiation Laboratory, Berkeley, California *UCRL-9052* (1960).

Goulding, F. S., A survey of the applications and limitations of various types of detectors in radiation energy measurement. *I.E.E.E. Trans. Nucl. Sci.*, **NS-11**, No. 3, 177 (1964).

Grainger, R. J., Mayer, J. W., Wiggins, J. S. and Friedland, S. S., Further characteristics of the solid-state ionization chamber. *Bull. Am. Phys. Soc.*, **5**, 265 (1960).

Grainger, R. J., Mayer, J. W. and Oliver, J. W., Temperature behaviour of *p-n* junction detectors. *I.R.E. Trans. Nucl. Sci.*, **NS-8**, No. 1, 116 (1961).

Halbert, M. L. and Blankenship, J. L., Response of semiconductor surface-barrier counters to nitrogen ions and alpha particles. *Nucl. Instr. & Methods*, **8**, 106 (1960).

Halbert, M. L., Surface-barrier counters for nuclear reaction studies. *Nuclear Electronics*, **I**, 403 (1962).

Hansen, N. J., Encapsulated surface barrier particle detectors. *I.R.E. Trans. Nucl. Sci.*, **NS-9**, No. 3, 217 (1962).

Hansen, N. J., Solid state charged particle detectors. *Prog. in Nucl. Energy*, Series IX, **4**, 1 (1964).

Hansen, W. L. and Goulding, F. S., Oxide-passivated silicon *p-n* junction particle detectors. *Nucl. Instr. & Methods*, **29**, 345 (1964).

Hanzlik, J., Silicon-based semiconductor detectors. *Jaderna Energie*, **8**, 366 (1962).

Hemmendinger, A., Silbert, M. G. and Moat, A., Transient response of solid state detectors. *I.E.E.E. Trans. Nucl. Sci.*, **NS-12**, No. 1, (1965).

Hofker, W. K., The reverse current of silicon barrier detectors. *Mem. Soc. Roy. Sci. de Liège*, **X**, No. 2, 53 (1964).

Huml, K., Exploitation of the *p-n* junction of semiconductors for detection of ionizing radiation. *Pokroky mat. fys. a astron.*, No. 4, 424, (1960).

Huth, G. C., Trice, J. B. and McKinney, R. A., Internal pulse amplification in silicon *p-n* junction radiation detection junctions *Rev. Sci., Instr.*, **35**, 1220 (1964).

Huth, G. C., Trice, J. B., Shannon, J. A and McKinney, R. A., Internal pulse amplification in high-field silicon radiation detectors. *I.E.E.E. Trans. Nucl. Sci.*, **NS-12**, No. 1, (1965).

Jackson, R. W., Semiconductor junction alpha detectors. *Phys. in Canada*, **15**, 21 (1959).

Jackson, R. W., Webb, P. P., Williams, R. L., Improvements in encapsulated silicon junction alpha detectors. *I.R.E. Trans. Nucl. Sci.*, **NS-8**, No. 1, 29 (1961).

Kessel, W., Radiation detectors using crystal diodes. *Electronische Rundschau*, **16**, 147 (1962).

Klema, E. D., Preparation of high-resistivity silicon surface-barrier detectors for use at large reverse-bias voltages. *Nucl. Instr. & Methods*, **26**, 205 (1964).

Klema, E. D., Preparation, characteristics and applications of high-voltage silicon surface-barrier detectors. *I.E.E.E. Trans. Nucl. Sci.*, **NS-12**, No. 1, (1965).

Koch, L., Aspects actuels de la détection par semiconducteurs. *Mem. Soc. Roy. Sci. de Liège*, X, No. 2, 11 (1964).

Koch, L., Messier, J. and Valin, J., N-I-P silicon junction detectors. *I.R.E. Trans. Nucl. Sci.*, NS-8, No. 1, 43 (1961).

Kowalski, L. and Radvanyi, P., Barrier semiconductor junctions as nuclear radiation detectors. *Postepy Fizyki*, 13, 463 (1962).

Lauterjung, K. H., Pokar, J., Schimmer, B. and Staudner, R., Surface-barrier detectors for position and energy determination. *Max-Planck-Institute Report 1962/V/10* (Heidelberg, 1962).

Ludwig, E. J., Gibson, W. M. and Hood, J., Utilization of web silicon for position-sensitive detectors. *I.E.E.E. Trans. Nucl. Sci.*, NS-12, No. 1, (1965).

McKenzie, J. M. and Bromley, D. A., Room temperature semiconductor particle spectrometer. *Bull. Am. Phys. Soc.*, 4, 422 (1959).

McKenzie, J. M. and Waugh, J. B. S., Silicon junctions as particle spectrometers. *I.R.E. Trans. Nucl. Sci.*, NS-7, No. 2-3, 195 (1960)

McKenzie, J. M. and Ewan, G. T., Semiconductor electron detectors. *I.R.E. Trans. Nucl. Sci.*, NS-8, No. 1, 50 (1961).

Mann, H. M., Haslett, J. W. and Lietz, G. P., Pulse rise time for charged particles in p-n junctions. *I.R.E. Trans. Nucl. Sci.*, NS-8, No. 1, 151 (1961).

Mann, H. M. and Managan, W. W., Detection of minimum ionizing particles in silicon p-n junctions. *Rev. Sci. Instr.*, 31, 908 (1960).

Mann, H. M. and Sherman, I. S., Determination of transient response of semiconductor detectors by use of a nano second-pulse electron accelerator. *I.E.E.E. Trans. Nucl. Sci.*, NS-11, No. 3, 270 (1964).

Mann, H. M. and Janarek, F. J., B^{10} diffused junctions in n-type silicon. *I.R.E. Trans. Nucl. Sci.*, NS-9, No. 3, 200 (1962).

Martin, F. W., King, W. J. and Harrison, S., Junction counters produced by ion implantation doping. *I.E.E.E. Trans. Nucl. Sci.*, NS-11, 280 (1964).

Maxwell, J. R. and Parkinson, W. C., Solid state detector for nuclear spectroscopy. *Bull. Am. Phys. Soc.*, 7, 276 (1962).

Mayer, J. W., Performance of Ge and Si surface-barrier diodes as alpha particle spectrometers. *J. Appl. Phys.*, 30, 1937 (1959).

Mayer, J. W., The development of the junction detector. *I.R.E. Trans. Nucl. Sci.*, NS-7, No. 2-3, 178 (1960).

Mayer, J. W., Pulse formation in semiconductor detectors. *National Academy of Science National Research Council Publication* 871, 1 (1961).

Mayer, J. W., Semiconductor detectors: Have they improved? *Nucleonics*, **20**, 60 (1962).

Mayer, J. W., The 'state-of-the-art' in nuclear particle detectors. *I.R.E. Trans. Nucl. Sci.*, **NS-9**, No. 3, 124 (1962).

Mayer, J. W., Grainger, R. J., Oliver, J. W., Wiggins, J. S. and Friedland, S. S., Performance of large-area *p-n* junction particle spectrometers. *Bull. Am. Phys. Soc.*, **5**, 355 (1960).

Mednikov, A. K., and Babushkin, A. A., Silicon surface-barrier alpha-detectors. *Prib. Tekhn. Eksper.*, May–June 1964, No. 3, 55.

Mednikov, A. K., Stroikin, N. I. and Babushkin, A. A., 'Window' in a semiconductor spectrometer of charged particles. *Prib. Tekhn. Eksper.*, Sept–Oct. 1964, No. 5, 87.

Messier, J. and Valin, J. Influence of the presence of a PP+ junction on the bahaviour of an *NP* junction particle detector. *Nucl. Instr. & Methods*, **14**, 307 (1962).

Messier, J., le Coroller, Y. and Merlo Flores, J., Thick junctions made with nuclear-compensated silicon. *I.E.E.E. Trans. Nucl. Sci.*, **NS-11**, No. 3, 276 (1964).

Miller, G. L., Diffused junction detectors. *National Academy of Science National Research Council Publication* **871**, 19 (1961).

Miller, G. L. and Gibson, W. M., Charge collection in semiconductor radiation detectors. *Nuclear Electronics*, **I**, 477 (1962).

Miller, G. L., Gibson, W. M. and Donovan, P. F., Semiconductor particle detectors. *Annual Reviews of Nuclear Science*, **12**, 189, (1962).

Miller, G. L., Brown, W. L., Donovan, P. F. and Mackintosh I. M., Silicon *p-n* junction radiation detectors. *I.R.E. Trans Nucl. Sci.*, **NS-7**, No. 2-3, 185 (1960).

Murphy, J. F., Solid state neutron detectors. *U.C.R.L. Report 6505*, Lawrence Radiation Lab., Livermore (1961).

Nordberg, E., Gold-silicon surface barrier counters. *Bull. Am. Phys. Soc.*, **4** (1959).

Quaranta, A. A., Martini, M., Ottaviani, G. and Zanarini, G., Some considerations on charge collection time in solid state detectors. *Nucl. Instr. & Methods.*, **29**, 173 (1964).

Raymo, C. T., Mayer, J. W., Wiggins, J. S. and Friedland, S. S., Performance of *p-n* junction particle detectors under gamma irradiation. *Bull. Am. Phys. Soc.*, **5**, 354 (1960).

Raymo, C. T. and Mayer, J. W., Transient response of *p-n* junction detectors. *I.R.E. Trans. Nucl. Sci.*, **NS-8**, No. 1, 157 (1961).

Rosenzweig, W., Silicon solar cells as versatile radiation dosimeters. *Rev. Sci. Instr.*, **33**, 379 (1962).

Rougeot, H., Coche, A. and Siffert, P., Détecteurs de rayonnements nucléaires à barrière de surface à réponse rapide. *Mem. Soc. Roy. Sci. de Liège*, X, No. 2, 119 (1964).

Ryvkin, S. M., Maslov, L. V., Matveev, O. A., Strokan, N. B. and Tarkhin, D. V., Silicon counters for nuclear spectrometry. *Atomnaya Energ.*, **11**, 861 (1962).

Salzberg, B. and Siegel, K., Semiconductor p-n junction radiation counter. *Proc. I.R.E.*, **46**, 1536 (1958).

Schmitt, H. W., Neiler, J. H., Walter, F. J. and Silva, R. J., Response of silicon surface-barrier detectors to fission fragments. *O.R.N.L. 3268*, 94 (1962).

Sharpe, J., Semiconductor radiation detectors. *Electronics Weekly*, No. 92, 21 (1962).

Siffert, P., Laustriat, G. and Coche, A., Rectifying Process in surface barrier detectors. *I.E.E.E. Trans. Nucl. Sci.*, **NS-11**, No. 3, 244 (1964).

Siffert, P. and Coche, A. New Results concerning the rectifying process in surface-barrier counters. *I.E.E.E. Trans. Nucl. Sci.*, **NS-12**, No. 1, (1965).

Stolyarova, E. L., Semiconductor detectors of nuclear radiation. *Uspekhi Fiz. Nauk.*, **81**, 641 (1963), English translation in *Sov. Phys. Uspekhi*, **6**, 872 (1964).

Strokan, N. B., An investigation of characteristics that determine the energy resolution of silicon n-p nuclear particle counters. *Instr. and Exper. Tech.*, Sept. 1964, No. 1, 92.

Tove, P. A. and Falk, K., Transit time of charge carriers in the semiconductor ionization chamber. *Nucl. Instr. & Methods*, **12**, 278 (1961).

Tove, P. A. and Falk, K., Pulse formation and transit time of charge carriers in semiconductor junction detectors. *Nucl. Instr. & Methods*, **29**, 66 (1964).

Trousil, Z. and Skrivankova, M., The two-barrier detector. *Czech. J. Physics*, **12**, 534 (1962).

Vallois, G., Étude des propriétés d'un détecteur à plusieurs jonctions jointives. *Mem. Soc. Roy. Sci. de Liège*, X, No. 2, 105 (1964).

Van der Does de Bye, J. A. W., Signal-to-noise ratio of a p-n junction radiation counter. *Philips Research Rep.*, **16**, 85 (1961).

Van Putten, J. D. and Vander Velde, J. C., Solid-state detector for penetrating and minimum ionizing particles. *Bull. Am. Phys. Soc.*, **5** (1960).

Walter, F. J., Multiplication in the fission fragment pulse height response of silicon surface barriers. *I.E.E.E. Trans. Nucl. Sci.*, **NS-11**, No. 3, 232 (1964).

Walter, F. J., Dabbs, J. W. T. and Roberts, L. D., Resolution, stability and noise in Si nuclear particle detectors. *Bull. Am. Phys. Soc.*, **6**, 456 (1961).

Walter, F. J., Moak, C. D., Neiler, J. H., Schmitt, H. W., Gibson, W. M. and Thomas, T. D., Response of silicon detectors to high-energy bromine and iodine ions. *Bull. Amer. Phys. Soc.*, **8**, 39, (1963).

Walter, F. J., Dabbs, J. W. T. and Roberts, L. D., Semiconductor particle counters at low temperatures. *I.R.E. Trans. Nucl. Sci.*, **NS-8**, No. 1, 79 (1961).

Walter, F. J., Dabbs, J. W. T. and Roberts, L. D., Behaviour of semiconductor nuclear particle detectors. *Nuclear Electronics*, **I**, 391 (1962).

Wang Tsen-yea, Sidorov, A. I., Sidorova, L. P. and Simonova, L. I., Method of obtaining silicon spectrometric detectors having a wide area of the sensitive layer. *Prib. Tekhn. Eksper.*, July–August 1964, No. 4, 84.

Webb, P. P., Williams, R. L. and Jackson, R. W., An encapsulated silicon junction alpha particle detector. *I.R.E. Trans. Nucl. Sci.*, **NS-7**, No. 2-3, 199 (1960).

Wegner, H. E., Britt, H. C. and Shlaer, W. J., Semiconductor detector response to fission fragments. *Bull. Am. Phys. Soc.*, **7**, 36 (1962).

Weiss, W. L., Evaluation and vacuum stability tests of silicon radiation detectors. *I.E.E.E. Trans. on Nucl. Sci.*, **NS-10**, No. 1, 202 (1963).

White, F. A., Semiconductor electron multiplier. *National Academy of Science National Research Council Publication* **871**, 177 (1961).

White, F. A. and Sheffield, J. C., Silicon junctions detect positive ions. *Electronics*, **34**, 74 (1961).

Williams, R. L., Encapsulated detectors. *National Academy of Science National Research Council Publication* **871**, 28 (1961).

Williams, R. L. and Webb, P. P., Transistor form of nuclear particle detector. *I.R.E. Trans. Nucl. Sci.*, **NS-8**, No. 1, 35 (1961).

Williams, R. L. and Webb, P. P., The window thickness of diffused junction detectors. *I.R.E. Trans Nucl. Sci.*, **NS-9**, No. 3, 160 (1962).

Williams, R. L. and Webb, R. P., Silicon junction nuclear particle detectors. *R.C.A. Review*, **23**, 29 (1962).

Yavin, A. I., Detection of alpha particles with commercially available transistors. *Rev. Sci. Instr.*, **31**, 351 (1960).

Ziemba, F. P., Pelt, G., Ryan, G., Wang, L. and Alexander, R., Properties of an $n^+ i p^+$ semiconductor detector. *I.R.E. Trans. Nucl. Sci.*, **NS-9**, No. 3, 155 (1962).

Zubritskii, L. A., Chursin, G. P., Gonchar, V. Y. and Zalyubovskii, I. I., Surface barrier counters with a shielding electrode. *Bull. Acad. Sci. U.S.S.R.–Physical Series*, **28**, No. 1, 105 (1964).

Zubritskii, L. A., Popov, A. I., Sorokin, P. V. and Samoilov, V. F., Semiconducting spectrometers for charged particles. *Nuclear Electronics*, **I**, 591 (1962).

Thin dE/dx counters

Andrews, P. T., Thin silicon surface barrier counters. *Proc. Symp. on Nucl. Instr.*, Harwell (1961) (Heywood & Co., 1962).

Elliott, J. H. and Pehl, R. H., Thin semiconductor transmission-counter system for nuclear particle detection. *Rev. Sci. Instr.*, **33**, 713 (1962).

Fox, R. J., Procedure for dE/dx silicon surface-barrier diodes. *National Academy of Science National Research Council Publication* **871**, 270 (1961).

George, K. A. and Dell, G. F., Solid-state detectors as dE/dx counters. *Bull. Amer. Phys. Soc.*, **6**, 93 (1961).

Heinrich, J. T. and Braid, T. H., Solid-state counters for dE/dx and total energy measurement at cyclotron energies. *Bull. Am. Phys. Soc.*, **6**, 46 (1961).

Inskeep, C. N., Eidson, W. W. and LaSalle, R. A., Considerations in the development and use of very thin diffused-junction counters suitable for $\Delta E/\Delta X$ detection. *I.R.E. Trans. Nucl. Sci.*, **NS-9**, No. 3, 167 (1962).

Madden, T. C., and Gibson, W. M., Uniform and stable dE/dx p-n junction particle detectors. *I.E.E.E. Trans. Nucl. Sci.*, **NS-11**, No. 3, 254 (1964).

Mollenauer, J. F., Wagner, S. and Miller, G. L., Silicon surface barrier $\Delta E/\Delta x$ detectors for nuclear reaction studies. *Brookhaven National Laboratory Report B.N.L. 737* (T-266).

Phelps, C. G., Silicon wafers for dE/dx detectors. *National Academy of Science National Research Council Publication* 871, 273 (1961).

Wegner, H. E., dE/dx-E Semiconductor detector systems. *National Academy of Science National Research Council Publication* 871, 74 (1961).

Lithium-drifted detectors

Baily, N. A., Grainger, R. J. and Mayer, J. W., Capabilities of lithium-drifted p-i-n junction detectors when used for gamma-ray spectroscopy. *Rev. Sci. Instr.*, 32, 865 (1961).

Benveniste, J., Booth, R. and Mitchell, A. C., Observations on the response of lithium-drifted detector to protons. University of California, Lawrence Radiation Laboratory, *U.C.R.L. 6441* (1961).

Blankenship, J. L. and Borkowski, C. J., Improved techniques for producing p^{+}-I-N^{+} diode detectors. *I.R.E. Trans. Nucl. Sci.*, NS-9, No. 3, 181 (1962).

Blankenship, J. L. and Borkowski, C. J., The use of lithium-drifted diodes in beta and gamma spectroscopy. *Rev. Sci. Instr.*, 33, 778 (1962).

Carter, J. R. Jr. and Swalin, R. A., On the kinetics and mechanism of the precipitation of lithium from germanium. *J. Appl. Phys.*, 31, 1191 (1960).

Chasman, C. and Allen, J., Large active volume, thin entry window, semiconductor radiation detectors. *Nucl. Instr. & Methods*, 24, 253 (1963).

Chasman, C. and Ristinen, R. A., A cryostat for semiconductor gamma-ray detectors. *Brookhaven National Laboratory*, Report BNL-8692 (1964).

Dearnaley, G. and Lewis, J. C., A lithium-drifted silicon surface-barrier detector for nuclear radiations. *Nucl. Instr. & Methods*, 25, 237 (1964).

Delyser, H., Ziemba, F. P. and van Antwerp, W. R., A lithium-drifted germanium surface-barrier detector *I.E.E.E. Trans. Nucl. Sci.*, NS-12, No. 1, (1965).

Elliott, J. H., Thick junction radiation detectors made by ion drift. *Nucl. Instr. & Methods*, **12**, 60 (1961).

Elliott, J. H., Experimental results with a lithium-drifted silicon diode radiation detector. *Bull. Am. Phys. Soc.*, **5**, 501 (1960).

Freck, D. V. and Wakefield, J., Gamma ray spectrum obtained with a lithium-drifted *p-i-n* junction in germanium. *Nature*, **193**, 669 (1962).

Garin, A., Détecteur dopés au lithium. *Mem. Soc. Roy. Sci. de Liège*, **X**, No. 2, 67 (1964).

Goulding, F. S. and Hansen, W. L., An automatic lithium drifting apparatus for silicon and germanium detectors. *I.E.E.E. Trans. Nucl. Sci.*, **NS-11**, No. 3, 286 (1964).

Gibbons, P. E., On the design of a silicon junction radiation detector made by ion drift. *Nucl. Instr. & Methods*, **16**, 284 (1962).

Grégoire, G., Heughebaert, J., Lemaître, G., Oostens, J. and van Gerven, L., Performance of a *p-i-n* type semiconductor detector at low temperatures. *Nucl. Instr. & Methods*, **28**, 346 (1946).

Hansen, W. L. and Jarrett, B. V., Techniques for the fabrication of lithium-drifted germanium gamma detectors. University of California, *Lawrence Radiation Laboratory*. Report no. **UCRL-11859** (1964).

Heughebaert, J., Lemaître, G., Oostens, J., and van Gerven, L. Étude du comportement à basse température d'une jonction au silicium compensée au lithium. *Mem. Soc. Roy. Sci. de Liège*, **X**, No. 2, 303 (1964)'

Kashy, E. and Rickey, M. E., Preparation of germanium detectors. *Rev. Sci. Instr.*, **35**, 1364 (1964).

Koch, L. and Messier, J., N.I.P. junctions used as particle detectors: spectrometry of high-energy ionizing particles and detection of X-rays. *Comptes Rendus*, **251**, 2912 (1960).

Koch, L., Messier, J. and Valin, J., NIP structures in silicon as detectors of nuclear radiation. *National Academy of Science National Research Council Publication* **871**, 52 (1961).

Lehrer, F. A. and Reiss, H., Details of ion drift in an *n-p* junction. *J. Appl. Phys.*, **33**, 2353 (1962).

Llacer, J., Study of surface effects in thick lithium-drifted silicon radiation detectors. *I.E.E.E. Trans. Nucl. Sci.*, **NS-11**, No. 3, 221 (1964).

McIntyre, R. J., Anomalous capacitance effect in lithium-drifted germanium diodes: theory. *Bull. Amer. Phys. Soc.*, **10**, 124 (1965).

Mann, H. M., Haslett, J. W. and Janarek, F. J., Lithium-drifted *p-i-n* junction detectors. *I.R.E. Trans. Nucl. Sci.*, **NS-9**, No. 4, 43 (1962).

Mann, H. M. and Janarek, F. J., Effect of forward-voltage ion-drift on the operation of lithium-drifted silicon junction detectors. *Nucl. Instr. & Methods*, **17**, 71 (1962).

Mayer, J. W., Characteristics of *p-i-n* junctions produced by ion-drift techniques in silicon. *J. Appl. Phys.*, **33**, 2894 (1962).

Mayer, J. W., Baily, N. A. and Dunlap, H. L., Characteristics of ion-drifted *p-i-n* junction particle detectors. *Nucl. Electronics*, **I**, 567 (1962).

Miller, G. L., Pate, B.D. and Wagner, S., Production of thick semiconductor radiation detectors by lithium drifting. *I.E.E.E. Trans. on Nucl. Sci.*, **NS-10**, No. 1, 220 (1963).

Monteith, L. K., Correlation of *I-V* characteristic with noise for ion drifted *p-i-n* junction particle detectors. *Rev. Sci. Instr.*, **35**, 388 (1964).

Norgate, G., and McIntyre, R. J., Stabilization of lithium-drifted radiation detectors. *I.E.E.E. Trans. Nucl. Sci.*, **NS-11**, No. 3, 291 (1964).

Palms, J. M. and Greenwood, A. H., Thermoelectric control apparatus for the fabrication of thick lithium-drifted germanium detectors. *Bull. Amer. Phys. Soc.* **10**, 124 (1965).

Pell, E. M., Solubility of lithium in silicon. *J. Phys. Chem. Solids*, **3**, 77 (1957).

Effect of Li-B ion pairing on Li$^+$ ion drift in Si. *J. Appl. Phys.*, **31**, 1675 (1960).

Ion drift in an *n-p* junction. *J. Appl. Phys.*, **31**, 291 (1960).

Diffusion of Li in Si at high T and the isotope effect. *Phys. Rev.*, **119**, 1014 (1960).

The ion drift process. *National Academy of Science National Research Council Publication* **871**, 136 (1961).

Diffusion rate of Li in Si at low temperatures. *Phys. Rev.*, **119**, 1222 (1961).

Study of Li-O interaction in Si by ion drift. *J. Appl. Phys.*, **32**, 1048 (1961).

Pell, E. M. and Ham, F. S., Recombination kinetics for thermally dissociated Li-B ion pairs in Si. *J. Appl. Phys.*, **32**, 1052 (1961).

Siffert, P., Coche, A. and Rougeot, H., Détection de rayonnements nucléaires à l'aide de compteurs compensés au lithium sans fenêtre d'entrée. *Mem. Soc. Roy. Sci. de Liège*, X, No. 2, 95 (1964).

Tavendale, A. J. and Ewan, G. T., A high-resolution lithium-drifted germanium gamma-ray spectrometer. *Nucl. Instr. & Methods*, **25**, 185 (1963).

Wang, L., Zatzick, M. R. and Ziemba, F. P. A lithium-drifted silicon surface-barrier detector with guard ring. *I.E.E.E. Trans. Nucl. Sci.* NS-11, No. 1, 314 (1964).

West, H. L., Burns, F. P., Wang, L. and Ziemba, F. P., Lithium ion drift semiconductor detector as a beta ray spectrometer. *Rev. Sci. Instr.*, **33**, 380 (1962).

Applications of lithium-drifted germanium detectors

Alexander, T. K., Pearson, J. D., Litherland, A. E. and Broude, C., Pulse-shape discrimination on the gamma-ray pulses from F^{19} ($d, n\gamma$) Ne^{20} observed with a lithium-drifted germanium gamma-ray spectrometer. *Phys. Rev. Letters*, **13**, 86 (1964).

Alexander, T. K. and Allen, K. W., Recoil method of measuring lifetimes of excited nuclear states using high-resolution Ge(Li) detectors. *Bull. Amer. Phys. Soc.*, **10**, 118 (1965).

Bemis, C. E. Jr., and Gordon, G. E., Decay of 37-min. Sb^{130}. *Bull. Amer. Phys. Soc.*, **10**, 82 (1965).

Bornemeier, D. D., Potnis, V. R., Ellsworth, L. D. and Mandeville C. E., Radioactive decay of Te^{129}. *Bull. Amer. Phys. Soc.*, **10**, 82 (1965).

Boyd, H. W., Johnson, N. R., Eichler, E., and Hamilton, J. H., Precision measurements of Cs^{132} gamma-rays. *Bull. Amer. Phys. Soc.*, **10**, 82 (1965).

Brown, R. A. and Ewan, G. T., Study of the decay of Cs^{134} with a Ge(Li) gamma-ray spectrometer. *Bull. Amer. Phys. Soc.*, **10**, 82 (1965).

Chasman, C., Jones, K. W. and Ristinen, R. A., Energy levels of Sc^{49} from the Ca^{49} (p, n) Sc^{49} reaction. *Bull. Amer. Phys. Soc.*, **10**, 26 (1965).

Chilosi, G., O'Kelley, G. D. and Eichler, E., Low-energy states in Sc^{49} populated in the decay of Ca^{49}. *Bull. Amer. Phys. Soc.*, **10**, 92 (1965).

Easley, W., Huntzicker, J., Matthias, E., Rosenblum, S. S. and Shirley, D. A., Nuclear Zeeman effect in Ir[193]. *Bull. Amer. Phys Soc.*, **9**, 435 (1964).

Eichler, E., Johnson, N. R., and Chilosi, G., Decay of Ru[94]. *Bull. Amer. Phys. Soc.*, **10**, 81 (1965).

Evans, J. S. and Naumann, R. A., Decay of Pd[100]. *Bull. Amer. Phys. Soc.*, **10**, 81 (1965).

Ewan, G. T. and Tavendale, A. J., Application of high-resolution lithium-drifted germanium gamma-ray spectrometers to high-energy gamma rays. *Nucl. Instr. & Methods*, **26**, 183 (1964).

Ewan, G. T. and Tavendale, A. J., High resolution studies of gamma-ray spectra using lithium-drifted germanium gamma-ray spectrometers. *Can. J. Phys.*, **42**, 2286 (1964).

Holland, R. E., Lynch, F. J. and Mann, H. M., Partial M2 lifetime of the $d_{3/2}$ hole state of Ca[43]. *Bull. Amer. Phys. Soc.*, **10**, 119 (1965).

Julian, G. M. and Jha, S., Decay of La[132]. *Bull. Amer. Phys. Soc.*, **10**, 82 (1965).

Julian, G. M. and Jha, S., Low-lying levels in Ba[134]. *Bull. Amer. Phys. Soc.*, **9**, 663 (1964).

Kaye, G. and Graham, R. L., Decay of Lu[171] and Lu[172]. *Bull. Amer. Phys. Soc.*, **9**, 498 (1964).

Kettelle, B. H., Brosi, A. R. and van Hise, J. R., Discovery of 13.5 min. Pr[136]. *Bull. Amer. Phys. Soc.*, **10**, 83 (1965).

Lidofsky, L. J., Mo, L., Lee, Y. K. and Wu, C. S., Lifetimes of low-lying excited states in Al[27]. *Bull. Amer. Phys. Soc.*, **10**, 119 (1965).

Litherland, A. E., Alexander, T. K. and Broude, C. Gamma-ray transitions in N[15] and O[15]. *Bull. Amer. Phys. Soc.*, **10**, 37, (1965).

Mo, L., Hsu, F. and Wu, C. S., Energy Levels of Kr[82]. *Bull. Amer. Phys. Soc.*, **10**, 81 (1965).

Motz, H. T., Jurney, E. T. and Ford, W. T., Thermal-neutron capture gamma-ray spectrum from U[238] (n, γ) U[239]. *Bull. Amer. Phys. Soc.*, **9**, 664 (1964).

Namenson, A. and Smither, R. K., Intercalibration of (n, γ) and gamma spectra following beta decay through the use of a bent-crystal spectrometer and a Ge diode assembly. *Bull. Amer. Phys. Soc.*, **10**, 54 (1965).

Nieschmidt, E. B., Mandeville, C. E. and Ellsworth, L. D., Radiations of Br^{82} and Cd^{115m}. *Bull. Amer. Phys. Soc.*, **10**, 129 (1965).

Pearson, J. D., Alexander, T. K., Broude, C., Litherland, A. E., Kuehner, J. A. and Almqvist, E., Comparison between the F^{19} + d and C^{12} + C^{12} reactions leading to levels in Ne^{20}. *Bull. Amer. Phys. Soc.*, **10**, 37 (1965).

Ristinen, R. A., Chasman, C. and Jones, K. W., Charged particle and gamma-ray spectra from fast-neutron bombardment of a lithium-drifted germanium gamma-ray detector. *Bull. Amer. Phys. Soc.*, **10**, 36 (1965).

Shirley, D. A. and Rosenblum, S. S., High-resolution gamma-ray spectroscopy of Ho^{166m}. *Bull. Amer. Phys. Soc.*, **9**, 498 (1964).

Slaughter, G. G. and Harvey, J. A., Gamma-ray spectrum from the capture of thermal neutrons in bismuth. *Bull. Amer. Phys. Soc.*, **9**, 664 (1964).

Smither, R. K. and Namenson, A., Combination of a bent-crystal spectrometer and a germanium diode for high-resolution gamma-ray studies. *Bull. Amer. Phys. Soc.*, **10**, 54 (1965).

Stone, N. J., Frankel, R. B. and Shirley, D. A., Gamma-ray spectroscopy using Ge(Li) counters. *Bull. Amer. Phys. Soc.*, **9**, 486 (1964).

Tavendale, A. J., Semiconductor lithium-ion drifted diodes as high-resolution gamma-ray pair spectrometers. *I.E.E.E. Trans. Nucl. Sci.*, **NS-11**, No. 3, 191 (1964).

Tavendale, A. J., Large germanium lithium-drifted p-i-n diodes for gamma-ray spectroscopy. *I.E.E.E. Trans. Nucl. Sci.*, **NS-12**, No. 1, (1965).

Wetzel, K. J., Wasson, O. A. and Bockelman, C. K., Gamma-rays from neutron capture in gold. *Bull. Amer. Phys. Soc.*, **10**, 13 (1965).

White, D. H. and Saunders, B. G., Gamma emission following neutron capture in As^{75}. *Bull. Amer. Phys. Soc.*, **10**, 13 (1965).

Silicon carbide

Canepa, P. C., Malinaric, P., Campbell, R. B. and Ostroski, J., High temperature nuclear particle detector. *I.E.E.E. Trans. Nucl. Sci.*, **NS-11**, No. 3, 262 (1964).

Heerschap, M. and de Coninck, R., Change of I-V characteristics of SiC diodes upon reactor irradiation. *Nucl. Electronics*, **I**, 513 (1962).

O'Connor, J. R. and Smiltens, J. (eds.), Silicon carbide, a high temperature semiconductor. *Proceedings of the conference on silicon carbide*, Boston, Massachusetts, April 2–3, 1959, 538 (Pergamon Press, 1960).

Weisman, J., Loving, J. J., Chang, H. C., Campbell, R. and Babcock, R. Progress reports on the development of a miniature neutron detector. *Westinghouse Electric Corp. reports WCAP* 1874, 1929, 1989, 2653 (1962).

Applications of silicon junction counters

Aiginger, H., Ein Compton-Spektrometer mit einem Halbleiter-Sperrschichtzähler. *Atomkernenergie*, **9**, 355, (1964).

Aitken, J. H. and Dixon, W. R., Studies of the (n, a) and (n, p) reactions in Si^{28} at 14 MeV by a coincidence method. *Physics Letters*, **2**, 152 (1962).

Ajdačić, V. S., Kurepa, M. and Lalović, B., Semiconductor measures fluxes in operating core. *Nucleonics*, **20**, 47 (1962).

Ajdačić, V. S., Azuma, R. E. and Fleming, W. H., Measuring in-core neutron fluxes with semiconductors. *Nucleonics.* **21**, 60 (1963).

Ajdačić, V. S., Lalović, B. I. and Petrović, B. P., Measurement of fast neutron spectra inside reactors with a Li^6 semi-conductor counter spectrometer. *Inst. of Nucl. Sciences 'Boris Kidrich'*, Vinča, Belgrade, report no. **IBK-20**.

Aleksandrowicz, J. and Bartenbach, M., Germanium dosimeter for evaluation of fast neutron distribution in the reactor core. *Selected topics in radiation dosimetry*, 639 (1961) (I.A.E.A., Vienna).

Alkhazov, D. G., Energy resolution of silicon p-n detectors in recording heavy ions. *Izvestiya Akad. Nauk SSSR, Seriya Fizsicheskaya*, **26**, 1506 (1962).

Allemand, R., Ensemble de mesure pour spectrométrie alpha. *Mem. Soc. Roy. Sci. de Liège*, X, No. 2, 201 (1964).

Alsmiller, F. S., The distribution in energy of alpha-triton pairs resulting from neutron bombardment of lithium fluoride. *Oak Ridge National Laboratory Report O.R.N.L. 3016* (1960).

Amsel, G. and Smulkowski, O., High resolution spectroscopy using p-n junctions, applied to the study of nuclear reactions: O^{18} $(d, a)N^{16}$ reaction. *Compt. rend.*, **251**, 950 (1960).

Andersson-Lindström, G., Durch 14 MeV-Neutronen ausgelöste (n, α) Reaktionen in Si^{28} und Si^{29}. Z. für Naturforschung, 17, 238 (1962).

Andersson-Lindström, G., Betz, G., Mausberg, W. and Rössle, E. Measurements of Si (n, p) and (n, α) reactions in the neutron energy range from 5.2 to 9 MeV. Mem. Soc. Roy. Sci. de Liège, X, No. 2, 265 (1964).

Anderson, H. L., Alpha particle thickness gauge using a solid state detector. Nucl. Instr. & Methods, 12, 111 (1961).

Babcock, R. V., Davis, R. E., Ruby, S. L., Sun, K. H. and Wolley, E. D., Coated semiconductor is tiny neutron detector. Nucleonics, 17, 116 (1959).

Baum, J. J., The development of a fast neutron spectrometer using silicon surface barrier diodes. General Electric Co. Report APEK-639 (1961).

Beech, A. McG., Parry, J. K. and Urquhart, D. F., A two-crystal coincidence gamma-ray spectrometer using a solid-state detector. Nucl. Instr. & Methods, 27, 169 (1964).

Beets, C., Colle, Ph., Deckers, H., Gierts, G. and de Leeuw, S., Examen des possibilités des methodes directes en analyse spectrale des neutrons intermédiaires et rapides. Mem. Soc. Roy. Sci. de Liège, X, No. 2, 317 (1964).

Berényi, D. and Fényes, T., Silicon junction detector in a magnetic beta-ray spectrometer. Nucl. Instr. & Methods, 27, 122 (1964).

Bertolini, G., Cappellani, F., Fantechi, R. and Restelli, G., Correction des spectres beta obtenus par détecteurs à barrière de surface pour la résolution et la rétrodiffusion. Mem. Soc. Roy. Sci. de Liège, X, No. 2, 255 (1964), and Nucl. Instr. and Methods 27, 281 (1964).

Bizzeti, P. G., Bizzeti-Sona, A. M., et al., Cross-section fluctuations in the Si (γ, p) reaction at 17.6 MeV. Il Nuovo Cimento, 26, 1412 (1962).

Blanc, D., Cambou, F., Devillers, D., Rème, H. and Vedrenne, G., Reaction Si^{28} (n, α) Mg^{25} for 14·6 MeV neutrons. Il Nuovo Cimento, 23, 1140 (1962).

Blinov, V. A., Karamyan, S. A., Matveev, O. A., Nemelov, Y. A. and Selitskii, Y.A., On some peculiarities of measuring the energy spectra of alpha particles and fission fragments with semiconductor detectors. Atomnaya Energ., 13, 476 (1962).

Bok, J. and Schuttler, R., Use of semiconductor devices for the detection and dosimetry of nuclear particles. Onde Electrique, 41, 364 (1961).

Bok, J., de Cosnac, B., Noel, J. P., and Schuttler, R., Spectrometre a neutrons rapides a lithium 6 et diodes du silicium. *Nucl. Electronics*, I, 451 (1962).

Bonner, T. W., Mainsbridge, B. and Rabson, T. A., (n, p) and (n, a) reactions in Si^{28}. *Bull. Am. Phys. Soc.*, **6**, 440 (1961).

Braid, T. and Heinrich, J., Solid state detectors for measurement of dE/dx and total energy in nuclear reactions at cyclotron energies. *Nuclear Electronics*, I, 447 (1962).

Bromley, D. A., Semiconductor detectors in nuclear physics. *National Academy of Science National Research Council Publication* **871**, 61 (1961).

Bromley, D. A., Semiconductor detectors in nuclear physics. *I.R.E. Trans. Nucl. Sci.*, NS-9, No. 3, 135 (1962).

Brownell, G. L., Medical applications. *National Academy of Science National Research Council Publication* **871**, 86 (1961).

Burns, F. P., Starnes, K., and Alexander, R., Design and response of semiconductor detectors to high-intensity transient gamma pulses. *UCRL–13041* (1962).

Cassen, B., Crough, R. and Gass, H., Initial development of a semiconductor fast neutron dosimeter. *Nucleonics*, **13**, 58 (1955).

Cathey, L., Low level alpha counting with solid state detectors. *I.R.E. Trans. Nucl. Sci.*, NS-8, No. 2, 10 (1961).

Cathey, L. and Jenkins, W. J., The operation of solid-state alpha counters in chemical process streams. *I.R.E. Trans. Nucl. Sci.*, NS-9, No. 3, 193 (1962).

Cedarlund, R., Horn, A. and Scolnick, M., Solid-state detector for monitoring 14 MeV neutron production. *Nucl. Instr. & Methods*, **13**, 305 (1961).

Cerny, J., Pehl, R. H., Rivet, E. and Harvey, B. G., Investigation of isobaric-spin conservation in the O^{16} (d, a) N^{14} reaction using a high resolution semiconductor E-dE/dx system. *Physics Letters*, **7**, 67 (1963).

Chetham-Strode, A., Tarrant, J. R. and Silva, R. J., The application of silicon detectors to alpha particle spectroscopy. *I.R.E. Trans. Nucl. Sci.*, NS-8, No. 1, 59 (1961).

Colli, L., Facchini, U., Iori, I., Marcazzan, G. M., Milazzo, M. and Tonolini, F., Fluctuations in the cross-section of Si^{28} (n, a) Mg^{25} reaction with fast neutrons. *Physics Letters*, I, 120 (1962).

Colli, L., Iori, I., Marcazzan, M. G. and Milazzo, M., Ericson fluctuations in the Si^{28} (n, a) Mg^{25} reaction. *Physics Letters*, **2**, 12 (1962).

Crawford, G. W., Cosmic radiation measurement problems. *National Academy of Science National Research Council Publication* **871**, 57 (1961).

Czekajewski, J., Tove, P. A. and Grabowski, Z., A solid-state spectrometer for measuring the distribution of charged particles in aurorae. *Nucl. Instr. & Methods*, **26**, 66 (1964).

Davies, L. W., Semiconductor junctions as positional indicators of radiation. *Proc. Inst. Radio Engrs. Austral.*, **22**, 180 (1961).

Dearnaley, G., Ferguson, A. T. G. and Morrison, G. C., Semiconductor fast neutron detectors. *I.R.E. Trans. Nucl. Sci.*, **NS-9**, No. 3, 174 (1962).

Dearnaley, G., Counter techniques for the study of neutron induced reactions. *Prog. in Fast Neutron Physics*, p. 173. ed. Phillips, G. C., Marion, J. B. and Risser, J. R. (Univ. of Chicago Press, 1963).

Depraz, J., Duborgel, B., Grenier, G. and Salin, R., Use of silicon junction detectors for measuring the neutron flux in *D-D* and *D-T* reactions. *J. de Phys. et le Rad.*, **23**, 390 (1962).

Deruytter, A., Large gold-silicon surface-barrier detectors for fission experiments. *Mem. Soc. Roy. Sci. de Liège*, **X**, No. 2, 83 (1964).

Deruytter, A., Pulse-height defect of semiconductor detectors for fission fragments. *Mem. Soc. Roy. Sci. de Liège*, **X**, No. 2, 231 (1964).

Deuchars, W. M. and Lawrence, G. P., Interaction of 14 MeV neutrons with a silicon semiconductor nuclear particle detector. *Nature* (London), **391**, 995 (1961).

Donovan, P. F., Miller, G. L. and Foreman, B. M., Application of thick-depletion-layer silicon *p-n* junctions to proportional detection of gamma radiation and penetrating nuclear particles. *Bull. Am. Phys. Soc.*, **5**, 355 (1960).

Endt, P. M., The use of silicon detectors in the investigation of (p, a) and (p, p) reactions. *Mem. Soc. Roy. Sci. de Liège*, **X**, No. 2, 245 (1964).

Ewing, R. I., Response of silicon surface barrier detectors to hydrogen ions of energies 25 to 250 keV. *I.R.E. Trans. Nucl. Sci.*, **NS-9**, No. 3, 207 (1962).

Facchini, U., Marcazzan, M. G., Merzari, F. and Tonolini, F., (n, a) reactions in heavy elements. *Physics Letters*, **I**, 6 (1962).

Figuera, A. S. and Milone, C., A proton recoil fast-neutron spectro-meter with solid state detectors. *Nucl. Instr. & Methods*, **27**, 339 (1964).

Fox, R. J. and Borkowski, C. J., Use of guard-ring silicon surface-barrier detectors in beta spectrometry. *Rev. Sci. Instrum.*, **33**, 757 (1962).

Friedland, S. S., Ziemba, F. P., Olson, R. M. and Delyser, H., Application of nuclear semiconductor detectors for proton spectrometry in space applications. *I.R.E. Trans. Nucl. Sci.*, NS-9, No. 3, 391 (1962).

Friedland, S. S., Katzenstein, H. S. and Ziemba, F. P., Advances in semiconductor detectors for charged particle space spectro-metry,. *I.E.E.E. Trans. Nucl. Sci.*, NS-10, No. 1, 190 (1963).

Furr, A. K. and Runyon, R. S., A fast-neutron spectrometer for reactor flux measurements. *Nucl. Instr. & Methods*, **27**, 292 (1964).

Furr, A. K., and Runyon, R. S., Study of the fast-neutron energy distribution in a reactor spectrum with a recoil-proton detector. *Bull. Amer. Phys. Soc.*, **8**, 379 (1963).

Gibson, W. M., Studies of the kinetic energies of fission fragments with solid-state detectors. *Bull. Am. Phys. Soc.*, **7**, 37 (1962).

Gibson, W. M., Thomas, T. D. and Miller, G. L., Measurement of mass and energy of fragments from spontaneous fission of Cf^{252} using solid-state detectors. *Bull. Am. Phys. Soc.*, **6**, 376 (1961).

Gierts, G., Analyse spectrale des neutrons par la réaction Li^6 (n, t) He^4 dans le domaine situé en dessous de 500 keV. *Mem. Soc. Roy. Sci. de Liège*, X, No. 2, 351 (1964).

Goulding, F. S., Landis, D. A., Cerny, J., and Pehl, R. H., A new particle identifier technique. *I.E.E.E. Trans. Nucl. Sci.*, NS-11, No. 3, 388 (1964).

Gremmelmaier, R., Irradiation of p-n junctions with gamma rays; a method for measuring diffusion lengths. *Proc. I.R.E.*, **46**, 1045 (1958).

Gremmelmaier, R. and Welker, H., Detection of neutrons with an indium phosphide p-n junction. *Z. Naturforsch.*, 11a, 420 (1956).

Guldbrandsen, T. and Madsen, C. B., Radiation dosimetry by means of semiconductors. *Acta Radiol.*, **58**, 226 (1962).

Hay, H. J. and Lawrence, L. G., The use of a semiconductor counter to study the endothermic reaction C^{13} (p, α) B^{10}. *Austr. J. of Sci.*, **25**, No. 3, 77 (1962).

Hertz, C. H. and Gremmelmaier, R., Miniature semiconductor dose rate meter. *Acta Radiol.*, **54**, 69 (1960).

Hick, H., Rumpold, K. and Weinzierl, P., A high-resolution Compton spectrometer using a semiconductor detector. *Nucl. Instr. & Methods*, **24**, 327 (1963).

James, G. D., The fission cross-section of Pu^{241} between 3 eV and 20 eV. *Proc. Symp. on Neutron Time of Flight methods*, Saclay, July, 1961 E.A.N.D.C. (1961).

Jones, A. R., Uses of semiconductor detectors in health-physics monitoring. *Nucleonics*, **18**, 86 (1960).

Jones, A. R. The measurement of gamma dose with silicon junction counters. *I.R.E. Trans. Nucl. Sci.*, NS-9, No. 5, 17 (1962).

Joyner, W. T., Schmitt, H. W., Neiler, J. H. and Silva, R. J., Energy spectra of correlated fragment pairs from the spontaneous fission of Cf^{252}. *I.R.E. Trans. Nucl. Sci.*, NS-8, 54 (1961).

Kazarinov, N. M., Matveev, O. A., Povkin, C. M., Soloviev, C. M., Strokan, N. B., and Tarkhin, D. V., Use of semiconductor spectrometric counters to measure the energies of fission fragments. *Atomnaya Energiya*, **12**, 153 (1962).

Klein, C. A. and Staub, W. D., A semiconductor device for fast- and slow-neutron dosimetry. *Proc. Inst. Elec. Eng.*, **106**, 735 (1959).

Koch, L., Messier, J. and Kerns, Q., Nuclear method of measurement of diffusion length in p-n junctions. *I.R.E. Trans. Nucl. Sci.*, NS-8, No. 1, 83 (1961).

Koch, L., Messier, J. and Valin, J., Operating principles and properties of N-I-P semiconductor detectors for the detection of relativistic particles. *Nuclear Electronics*, **I**, 465 (1962).

Kocharov, G. E. and Starbunov, Yu. N., Concerning simultaneous measurement of particle energy and emission angle by means of solid-state detectors. *Bull. Acad. Sci. U.S.S.R.-Phys. Series*, English translation, **27**, No. 7, 922 (1963).

Koerts, L. A. C., The determination of angular distributions in one experiment with two solid state detectors. *Nucl. Instr. & Methods*, **26**, 123 (1964).

Kohler, T. R., Semiconductor X-ray detectors. *National Academy of Science National Research Council Publication* **871**, 193 (1961).

Konijn, J. and Lauber, A., Cross section measurements of the Ni^{58} (n, p) and Si^{29} (n, a) reactions in the energy range 2.2 to 3.8 MeV, *Nucl. Phys.*, **48**, 191 (1963).

Konopleva, R. F. and Novikov, S. R., Measuring the relative fast-neutron flux distribution in the VVR-M reactor with semi-conductor detecting elements. *Atomnaya Energiya*, **11**, 1199 (1962).

Kushniruk, V. F., Ryndina, E. Z., Solov'ev, S. M. and Chuburkova, I. I., The use of large area semiconductor detectors in alpha spectrometry. *Atomnaya Energiya*, **15**, No. 4, 324 (1963). English translation in *Soviet Atomic Energy*, **15**, No. 4, 1047 (1963).

Larsh, A. E., Gordon, G. E. and Sikkeland, T., Use of silicon *p-n* junction detectors in studies of nuclear reactions induced by heavy ions. *Rev. Sci. Instr.*, **31**, 1114 (1960).

Lemaître, J. G., Détecteur annulaire pour spectrométrie à 180 degrés. *Mem. Soc. Roy. Sci. de Liège*, **X**, No. 2, 307 (1964).

Lieber, A., The design of a scattering chamber for solid state detectors. *Nucl. Instr. & Methods*, **26**, 51 (1964).

Love, T. A. and Murray, R. B., Fast neutron spectroscopy with dual detectors. *National Academy of Science National Research Council Publication* **871**, 196 (1961).

Love, T. A. and Murray, R. B., The use of surface barrier diodes for fast neutron spectroscopy. *I.R.E. Trans. Nuclear Sci.*, **NS-8**, No. 1, 91 (1961).

Love, T. A., Murray, R. B., Manning, J. J. and Todd, H. A., A silicon surface-barrier fast-neutron spectrometer. *Nuclear Electronics*, **I**, 415 (1962).

McKenzie, J. M. and Bromley, D. A., Observation of charged particle reaction products. *Phys. Rev. Letters*, **2**, 303 (1959).

Mainsbridge, B., Bonner, T. W., and Rabson, T. A., The disintegration of silicon by fast neutrons. *Nucl. Phys.*, **48**, 83 (1963).

Marcazzan, M. G., Merzari, F. and Tonolini, F., Application of silicon semiconductor detectors to measurements on mono-energetic neutron beams. *I.R.E. Trans. Nucl. Sci.*, **NS-9**, No. 3, 234 (1962).

Maslova, L. V., Possibilities of using silicon counters in nuclear research. *Izvestiya Akad. Nauk SSSR, Seriya Fizsicheskaya*, **26**, 1498 (1962).

Melkonian, E., Fission measurements with surface barrier solid-state ionization chambers. *A.E.R.E. R-3524* (1960).

Miller, G. L., Foreman, B. M., Yuan, L. C. L., Donovan, P. F. and Gibson, W. M., Application of solid-state detectors to high-energy physics. *I.R.E. Trans. Nucl. Sci.*, **NS-8**, No. 1, 73 (1961).

Moncaster, M. E., Northrop, D. C. and Raines, J. A., A semi-conductor gamma ray monitor. *Nucl. Instr. & Methods*, **22**, 157 (1963).

Moritz, J., Measurements with a Li⁶F sandwich spectrometer at the reactor station, Geesthacht. *Mem. Soc. Roy. Sci. de Liège*, **X**, No. 2, 311 (1964).

Oostens, J., Collins, G. and Menes, J., Utilisation des junctions dopées au silicium en physique des hautes énergies. *Mem. Soc. Roy. Sci. de Liège*, **X**, No. 2, 293 (1964).

Otto, D. L., Horwitz, N. H., Kurtzman, R. S. and Hofstrom, J. E., Radioactive I¹³¹ and P³² as aids in the diagnosis of lesions of the stomach. *Amer. J. of Roentgenology, Radium Therapy and Nuclear Medicine*, **91**, 784 (1964).

Parker, J. B., White, P. H. and Webster, R. J., The interpretation of recoil proton sprectra. *Nucl. Instr. & Methods*, **23**, 61 (1963).

Patterson, J. H., Turkevich, A. L. and Franzgrote, E., Chemical analysis of surfaces using alpha-particles. *Journ. Geophys. Research (to be published*, 1965).

Pieper, G. F., Bostrom, C. O., Zmuda, A. J. and O'Brien, B. J., Detection of solar and van Allen belt protons by Injun satellite in July, 1961. *Bull. Am. Phys. Soc.*, **7**, 62 (1962).

Pisarevskii, A. N. and Soshin, L. D., Use of p-n junctions for recording nuclear radiations. *Pribory i Tekhnika Eksperimenta*, **6**, 14 (1961).

Potenza, R. and Rubbino, A., Fast neutron spectrometer. *Nucl. Instr. & Methods*, **25**, 77 (1963).

Potenza, R., Ricamo, R. and Rubbino, A. (n, α) and (n, p) reactions in silicon at neutron energies up to 5.5 MeV. *Nucl. Phys.*, **41**, 298 (1963).

Potenza, R. and Rubbino, A., Spectrometers for fast neutrons from nuclear reactions and from collimated beams. *Nucl. Instr. & Methods*, **26**, 93 (1964).

Rapaport, J. and González. L. Angular distribution for the S³² (n, α) Si²⁹ ground-state reaction. *Bull. Amer. Phys. Soc.*, **10**, 11 (1965).

Rechenmann, R. V. and de Swart, J. G., Mise au point et premières applications d'un ensemble de détection à semiconducters destiné aux recherches biologiques et médicales. *Mem. Soc. Roy. Sci. de Liège*, **X**, No. 2, 357 (1964).

Rössle, E. and Mausberg, W., A solid state detector telescope. *Mem. Soc. Roy. Sci. de Liège*, **X**, No. 2, 277 (1964).

Sakai, E., Semiconductor counter and its applications for neutron measurement. *Nuclear Electronics*, **I**, 551 (1962).

Scharf, K. and Sparrow, J. H., Steady-state response of silicon radiation detector cells to X-rays. *Bull. Amer. Phys. Soc.*, 9, 216 (1964).

Scheer, J. A., Schlüpmann, K. and Triantafyllidis, F., Die Energiespektren der alpha-teilchen aus Kernphoto-processen an Ti, Ni, Cu, Nb. *Nucl. Phys.*, 56, 113 (1964).

Scheer, J. A., Schlüpmann, K. and Triantafyllidis, F., Photoprotons from O^{16} measured with a solid state detector telescope. *Physics Letters*, 7, 269 (1963).

Sen, S. K., The performance of a gold-silicon surface barrier diode as a beta-ray detector. *Nucl. Instr. & Methods*, 27, 74 (1964).

Sheen, E. M., Alpha monitor with solid-state detector. *Nucl. Instr. & Methods*, 17, 140 (1962).

Stanton, L. and Lightfoot, D. A., Junction diode semiconductors for X- and gamma ray dosage measurement. *Radiology*, 78, 633 (1962).

Steinberg, R., Semiconductor fission probe. *Nucleonics*, 18, 85 (1960).

Steinberg, R., A technique for increasing the sensitivity of a solid-state fission probe. *National Aeronautics and Space Administration, TN-D-1054* (1961).

Sun, C. R., Gold-doped silicon detectors for the control of bubble chamber photography. *I.R.E. Trans. Nucl. Sci.*, NS-9, No. 3, 211 (1962).

Takaki, R., Perkins, M. and Tuzzolino, A., A gold-silicon surface-barrier proton range telescope. *I.R.E. Trans. Nucl. Sci.*, NS-8, No. 1, 64 (1961).

Tepper, L., Miller, G. L. and Kycia, T., A beam profile indicator with solid state detectors. *I.E.E.E. Trans. Nucl. Sci.*, NS-11, No. 3, 431 (1964).

Tove, P. A., and Jonasson, L. G., A method of measuring ultra-short nuclear lifetimes using particle time to energy conversion with a h.f. voltage and energy selection by solid state detectors. *Nucl. Instr. & Methods*, 27, 45 (1964).

Trice, J. B., Shannon, J. A. and Huth, G. C., The use of the Si (n, α) and (n, p) reactions in a semiconductor diode for measuring neutron spectra. *I.E.E.E. Trans. Nucl. Sci.*, NS-12, No. 1, (1965).

Ullrich, H., The reactions Si^{28} (γ, p) Al^{27} and Si^{28} (γ, α) Mg^{24}. *Physics Letters*, 12, 114 (1964).

Walter, F. J., Dabbs, J. W. T. and Roberts, L. D., Fission fragment counting with germanium n-p junction counters. *Bull. Am. Phys. Soc.*, 3, 181 (1958).

Walter, F. J., Neiler, J. H., Silva, R. J. and Schmitt, H. W., Fission fragment correlation experiments. *O.R.N.L. 3268*, 54 (1962).

Wegner, H. E., Semiconductor detector systems (dE/dx and E) for the detection and mass identification of protons, deuterons, tritons, He^3 and α-particles in the 10-30 MeV region. *Nuclear Electronics*, I, 427 (1962).

Wegner, H. E., Semiconductor and gas ion-chamber detection system for the mass identification of 10 to 30 MeV particles. *Rev. Sci. Instrum.*, 33, 271 (1962).

West, H. L. Jr., Mann, L. G. and Bloom, S. D., Some electron spectra in the radiation belts in the fall of 1962. *University of California Radiation Laboratory*, Report **UCRL-7659** (1964).

West, H. L., Bloom, S. D., Mann, L. G., Friedland, S. S., Olson, R. M. and Ziemba, F. P., Beta ray spectrometer for space physics experiments utilizing an array of semiconductor detectors. *Bull. Am. Phys. Soc.*, 6, 362 (1961).

West, H. L., Mann, L. G. and Bloom, S. D., Observations of the electron spectrum from 80 to 1258 keV on Discoverers 29 and 31. *Bull. Am. Phys. Soc.*, 7, 62 (1962).

White, P. H., A semiconductor proton recoil telescope for neutron spectra and flux determination. *Mem. Soc. Roy. Sci. de Liège*, X, No. 2, 341 (1964).

Williams, C. W., Kiker, W. E. and Schmitt, H. W., Correlated energy and time-of-flight measurements of fission fragments with semiconductor detectors: system design and performance. *Rev. Sci. Instr.*, 35, 1116 (1964).

Wolke, R. L. and Sodd, V. J., Recoil counting with surface barrier semiconductors. *Nucl. Instr. & Methods*, 25, 357 (1964).

Yuan, L. C. L., Miller, G. L. and Wagner, S. Investigations on Li-drift solid-state detectors for high-energy particle detection. *Proc. Conf. on Instr. for High Energy Physics*, CERN (1962).

Instrumentation

Ammerlaan, C. A. J., Shaping of p-i-n detector pulses by RC networks. *Mem. Soc. Roy. Sci. de Liège*, X, No. 2, 211 (1964).

Arecchi, R. T., Cavalleri, G., Gatti, E. and Svelto, V., Signal to noise ratio and resolving time in pulse amplifiers. *National*

Academy of Science National Research Council Publication **871**, 226 (1961).

Beskrovnyi, I. M., Transistor amplifier for use with semiconductor alpha-particle detectors. *Bull. Acad. Sci. U.S.S.R.-Phys. Series*, English translation, **27**, No. 7, 936 (1963).

Blalock, T. V., A low-noise charge-sensitive pre-amplifier with a field-effect transistor in the input stage. *I.E.E.E. Trans. Nucl. Sci.*, **NS-11**, No. 3, 365 (1964).

Blankenship, J. L., Design of low-noise vacuum-tube pulse amplifiers for semiconductor radiation detector spectrometry. *I.E.E.E. Trans. Nucl. Sci.*, **NS-11**, No. 3, 373 (1964).

Chaminade, R. and Falcoz, A., L'électronique associée aux détecteurs à jonction dans les expériences au cyclotron de Saclay. *Mem. Soc. Roy. Sci. de Liège*, X, No. 2, 155 (1964).

Chase, R. L., Parametric amplification of radiation detector signals. *National Academy of Science National Research Council Publication* **871**, 221 (1961).

Chase, R. L., Higinbotham, W. A. and Miller, G. L., Amplifiers for use with *p-n* junction radiation detectors. *I.R.E. Trans. Nucl. Sci.*, **NS-8**, No. 1, 147 (1961).

Corbé, G., Pré-amplificateur à transistors utilisés au laboratoire de physique nucléaire d'Orsay avec les détecteurs à jonction au silicium. *Mem. Soc. Roy. Sci. de Liège*, X, No. 2, 221 (1964).

Cottini, C., Gatti, E., Giannelli, G. and Rossi, G., Minimum noise preamplifier for fast ionization chambers. *Il Nuovo Cimento*, **3**, 473 (1956).

Emmer, T. L., Low noise transistor amplifiers for solid state detectors. *I.R.E. Trans. Nucl. Sci.*, **NS-8**, No. 1, 140 (1961).

Emmer, T. L., Nuclear instrumentation for scintillation and semiconductor spectroscopy. *I.R.E. Trans. Nucl. Sci.*, **NS-9**, No. 3, 305 (1962).

Fabri, G., Gatti, E. and Svelto, V., Spectrum expander for semiconductor detector spectroscopy. *Nucl. Instr. & Methods*, **15**, 237 (1962).

Fairstein, E., Preamplifier configurations and noise. *National Academy of Science National Research Council Publication* **871**, 210 (1961).

Fairstein, E., Considerations in the design of pulse amplifiers for use with solid-state radiation detectors. *I.R.E. Trans. Nucl. Sci.*, **NS-8**, No. 1, 129 (1961).

Funsten, H., Pulse shape discrimination in p-n junction detectors. *I.R.E. Trans. Nucl. Sci.*, NS-9, No. 3, 190 (1962).

Gemmell, D. S., Particle discrimination by time-of-flight methods. *I.E.E.E. Trans. Nucl. Sci.*, NS-11, No. 3, 409 (1964).

Gere, E. A. and Miller, G. L., A high speed analog pulse divider. *I.E.E.E. Trans. Nucl. Sci.*, NS-11, No. 3, 382 (1964).

Goodman, C. D. and Ball, J. B., A system for detecting and processing energy spectra for several types of charged particles simultaneously. *Proc. Symp. on Nucl. Instr.*, Harwell, 1961, 163 (Heywood & Co., 1962).

Gorodetzky, S., Port, M. and Graff, J., Préamplificateur linéaire a faible bruit pour detecteurs à jonction. *Nucl. Instr. & Methods*, 15, 183 (1962).

Goulding, F. S. and Hansen, W. L., Leakage current in semiconductor junction radiation detectors and its influence on energy-resolution characteristics. *Nucl. Instr. & Methods*, 12, 249 (1961).

Hahn, J. and Mayer, R. O., A low noise high gain-bandwidth charge sensitive preamplifier. *I.R.E. Trans. Nucl. Sci.*, NS-9, No. 4, 20 (1962).

Hansen, W. L. and Goulding, F. S., Leakage, noise, guard rings and resolution in detectors. *National Academy of Science National Research Council Publication* 871, 202 (1961).

Hansen, W. L. and Goulding, F. S. Electrical limitations to energy resolution in semiconductor particle detectors. *Nuclear Electronics*, I, 583 (1962).

Jonasson, L. G., Low noise solid state amplifiers for semi-conductor detectors. *Nucl. Instr. & Methods*, 26, 104 (1964).

Langemann, H. L. and Meyer, O., Ein Rauscharmer ladungsempfindlicher Vorverstärker für Halbleiterdetektoren. *Nucl. Instr. & Methods*, 30, 135 (1965).

Moritz, J. and Tauffenbach, H. J., A low-noise charge-sensitive preamplifier for semiconductor particle detectors. *Atomkern Energie*, 7, 330 (1962).

Radeka, V., Fast analogue multiplier with field-effect transistors. *I.E.E.E. Trans. Nucl. Sci.*, NS-11, No. 1, 302 (1964).

Radeka, V., The field-effect transistor—its characteristics and applications. *I.E.E.E. Trans. Nucl. Sci.*, NS-11, No. 3, 358 (1964).

Sona, A. and Svelto, V., A transistor preamplifier for semi-conductor detectors. *Energia Nucleare*, 9, 694 (1962).

Takeda, S., Ein neuer Vorverstärker für Halbleiterdetektoren. *Nucl. Instr. & Methods*, 27, 269 (1964).

Tauffenbach, H., Characteristics of the electronic equipment used with semiconductor detectors at the reactor station, Geesthacht. *Mem. Soc. Roy. Sci. de Liège*, X, No. 2, 285 (1964).

Tsukuda, M. and Fairstein, E., The effect of pulse shaping on the S/N ratio of pulse amplifiers for use with solid-state radiation detectors. *I.R.E. Trans. Nucl. Sci.*, NS-9, No. 4, 63 (1962).

Tsukuda, M., A simple pulse voltage dividing circuit and its application to the fission fragments study. *Nucl. Instr. & Methods*, 25, 265 (1964).

Wahl, H., A fast coincidence pre-amplifier for solid state radiation detectors. *Nucl. Instr. & Methods*, 25, 247 (1964).

Williams, C. W., and Biggerstaff, J. A., Sub-nanosecond timing with semiconductor detectors. *Nucl. Instr. & Methods*, 25, 370 (1964).

Williams, C. W., Schmitt, H. W., Walter, F. J. and Neiler, J. H., Instrumentation for fission-fragment energy correlation experiments, *Nucl. Instr. & Methods*, 29, 205 (1964).

Radiation damage

Ascoli, A., Asdente, M. and Germagnoli, E., On the atomic displacements produced by α particles in germanium. *Il Nuovo Cimento*, 5, 1145 (1957).

Backenstoss, G., Braunersreuther, E. and Goebel, K., Radiation damage of semiconductors by protons. *CERN-62-5*. CERN (Jan., 1962).

Baranov, I. A., Radiation damage in silicon surface-barriers irradiated by 5.5 MeV alpha-particles. *Instr. and Exper. Tech.*, Nov. 1964, No. 2, 377

Bubàkovà, R. and Szmid, Z., Proton bombardment damage in silicon. *Physica Status Solidi*, 8, No. 1, 105 (1965).

Carter, J. R. Jr., Study of energy levels in high-energy proton damaged silicon. *I.E.E.E. Trans. Nucl. Sci.*, NS-11, No. 1, 290 (1964).

Chukichev, M. V. and Vavilov, V. S., Generation of lattice defects in silicon crystals as a result of thermal neutron irradiation in a nuclear reactor. *Soviet Phys.—Solid State*, 3, 1103, (1961).

Coleman, J. A. and Rodgers, J. W., Radiation damage in lithium-drifted p-i-n junctions. *I.E.E.E. Trans. Nucl. Sci.*, **NS-11**, No. 3, 213 (1964).

Dearnaley, G., Radiation damage by charged particles in silicon junction detectors. *I.E.E.E. Trans. Nucl. Sci.*, **NS-10**, No. 1, 106 (1963).

George, G. G. and Gunnersen, E. M., Irradiation damage effects in silicon surface-barrier counters. *Nucl. Instr. & Methods*, **25**, 253 (1964).

Mann, H. M. and Yntema, J. L., Heavy particle radiation damage effects in lithium-drifted silicon detectors. *I.E.E.E. Trans. Nucl. Sci.*, **NS-11**, No. 3, 201 (1964).

Messenger, G. C. and Spratt, J. P., The effects of neutron irradiation on germanium and silicon. *Proc. I.R.E.*, **46**, 1038 (1958).

Miller, W., Bemig, K. and Salzberg, B., Note on the reduction of carrier lifetime in p-n junction diodes by electron bombardment. *J. Appl. Phys.*, **27**, 1524 (1956).

Schulman, R. G., Hole trapping in germanium bombarded by high energy electrons. *Phys. Rev.*, **102**, 1451 (1956).

Schuttler, R., Comportement des détecteurs solides dans un flux de rayonnements. *Mem. Soc. Roy. Sci. de Liège*, X, No. 2, 127 (1964).

Scott, R. E., Radiation effects of protons and electrons in silicon diffused-junction detectors. *I.E.E.E. Trans. Nucl. Sci.*, **NS-11**, No. 3, 206 (1964).

Tanaka, T. and Inuishi, Y., Hall effect measurement of radiation damage and annealing in silicon. *Journ. Phys. Soc. Japan*, **19**. 167 (1964).

Van Lint, V. A. J., Wikner, E. G. and Miller, P. H., Jr., High-energy electron irradiation of semiconductors. *Proc. International Conf. on semiconductor physics*, Prague, 1960, p. 306 (Academic Press, 1961).

Vavilov, V. S., Smirnova, I. V. *et al.*, Interaction of lithium ions. introduced into silicon, with radiation defects of the structure. *Soviet Phys.—Solid State*, **4**, 830 (1962).

Vitovskii, N. A., Lukirskii, D. P., *et al.*, Energy spectrum of defects produced in silicon by irradiation with electrons. *Soviet Phys.—Solid State*, **4**, 840 (1962).

See also the references following Chapter 10 on this topic.

AUTHOR INDEX

Page numbers in italics indicate references in the Bibliography

SUBJECT INDEX

RETURN TO: PHYSICS LIBRARY
351 LeConte Hall   510-642-3122

LOAN PERIOD 1 1-MONTH	2	3
4	5	6

ALL BOOKS MAY BE RECALLED AFTER 7 DAYS.
Renewable by telephone.

DUE AS STAMPED BELOW.

FEB 0 3 2005		
NOV 28 2011		